The Fossil Origins of Man

By

HALSEY W. MILLER, Ph.D.

Professor of Geography
Southern Illinois University, Edwardsville

SECOND EDITION

Published By
STIPES PUBLISHING COMPANY
Champaign, Illinois

DEDICATED TO THE MEMORY OF GEORGE F. STERNBERG

TABLE OF CONTENTS

INTRODUCTION

Purpose

This book is intended for use as a non-prerequisite primary or supplementary textual introduction to the fossil record and human evolution, as indicated in the table of contents. Furthermore the text is designed for use in a one-quarter or one-semester course to fulfill the general education requirements of non-science majors, and for use in courses designed for Earth Science Education majors.

The relevancy of evolution and paleontology to man's biologic development and history are stressed. The probable future of man with respect to natural phenomena over which man may or may not be able to exert control is also discussed.

Scope

The historical development of paleontology, and the conflict of Earth Science with religion is discussed. Evolution of the Universe and Solar System is traced into chemical evolution, through the origin of life and into biological evolution. The evolution of life is traced from the earliest-known Precambrian life forms into the evolution of man and the other vertebrates.

The evolution of Homo sapiens and the origin, distribution, and evolution of the living races of man are examined in the light of known animal distribution patterns and the hominoid fossil record. The evolution and distribution of fossil men seemingly diverges from Matthew's classical concept of an evolution caused distribution pattern in some significant details. Human behavior is considered to be partially derived from genetic causes, partially a response to environment, and partially determined by unknown, but possible ontogenetic influences. The future of man is at best enigmatic, but could be considerably alleviated by man's own efforts, stemming from recognition of his behavioral shortcomings and attempting to change the historic trend of human relationships.

Acknowledgements

I am indebted to Professor Dean Marlow, and Dr. Dorothy Gore of Southern Illinois University, Dr. David Jensen formerly of the University of Colorado Medical Center, Denver, and Mr. Robert T. Davison of Winston-Salem, North Carolina, for reading and commenting upon the text. Miss Judy Stein prepared the drawings and Professor Myrl Walker, Director of the Sternberg Memorial Museum supplied several photographs and specimens that I photographed. Mr. Joseph Marak of the Miami University Museum of Geology (Ohio) loaned me many specimens of invertebrate fossils that I photographed and Dr. George Distler, formerly a graduate student at Miami University kindly supplied me with some photographs of brachiopods. Dr. Ralph Wyckoff of the University of Arizona sent me a photograph of a virus and Dr. Horace G. Richards of the Philadelphia Academy of Natural Sciences sent me photographs of the Natchez Man pelvis. I am also indebted to Dr. Donald Nash of Colorado State University for photographs of human genes, and to Stephen Babcock and Kent Bratton for preparation of some other diagrams.

I stress that the content, main concepts and conclusions presented in the text are mine and the reviewers and editors are not responsible for any conclusions or inaccuracies incorporated in the text.

Chapter I

GEOLOGIC TIME

The Geologic Time Scale

Geologists characterize elapsed geologic time (Figure 1) by separating time into arbitrarily defined intervals known as eras and periods. The intervals are of unequal time span and are defined by fossil content, and not in terms of years. The Precambrian Period encompasses approximately the first 4.1 billion years of Earth history, and extends from the formation of the Earth until the first appearance of abundant, shell-bearing animal life that is found fossilized in the oldest Paleozoic rocks.

The Paleozoic (ancient life) Era was next, lasted nearly 250 million years, and was characterized largely by archaic life forms that lived in the sea. The Mesozoic (middle-life) Era succeeded the Paleozoic Era, and lasted about 160 million years and is usually referred to as the "Age of Reptiles". The Mesozoic was in turn followed by the Cenozoic (recent-life) Era, or "Age of Mammals", that extends from approximately 65 million years ago to include the present time.

The eras are subdivided into shorter time intervals known as periods and the rocks that were deposited during the temporal extent of a period are referred to as a system. For example, the rocks that comprise the Cambrian System were deposited during the time interval known as the Cambrian Period. The term Cambrian is flexible, but the concept of a period being an elapsed time interval, and the idea of the term, system, being applied only to rocks, is inflexible.

The rock systems were arbitrarily defined and named at different times during a 100 year span, in different places by different people. Growth of our knowledge and identification of the geologic time scale was neither orderly nor sequential, nor are the systems composed of equally thick rock sections or the periods composed of equally long time intervals. All the systemic boundaries, except those of the Cambrian, were originally defined upon changes in fossil content of the rocks and the periods are therefore biologically defined time units.

The Period Names

The semantic origins of the systemic names, the years and authors of the initial definition and publication of each is as follows.

Cambrian: derived from <u>Cambria</u>, the Latin name for Wales, and first applied to rocks exposed in and near Wales by Adam Sedgwick in 1835.

Ordovician: derived from <u>Ordovices</u>, an ancient Celtic tribe that inhabited a portion of Britain. The term was proposed by Charles Lapworth in 1879.

Silurian: derived from <u>Silures</u>, another ancient Celtic tribe that lived in part of Britain. The term was proposed by Roderick Murchison in 1835.

Devonian: named for Devonshire in England, and was proposed jointly by Murchison and Sedgwick in 1837.

Mississippian: named by Alexander Winchell in 1870 for the upper Mississippi River Valley where rocks of that age are exposed.

Pennsylvanian: derived from the State of Pennsylvania, where rocks of that age are well exposed. The name was proposed by H. S. Williams in 1891.

MAJOR DIVISIONS OF GEOLOGIC TIME			
Era	System or Period	Epoch	Began about Million years ago
Cenozoic	Quaternary	Recent	Last 5,000 years
Cenozoic	Quaternary	Pleistocene	3
Cenozoic	Tertiary	Pliocene	7
Cenozoic	Tertiary	Miocene	28
Cenozoic	Tertiary	Oligocene	40
Cenozoic	Tertiary	Eocene	55
Cenozoic	Tertiary	Paleocene	65
Mesozoic	Cretaceous		135
Mesozoic	Jurassic		190
Mesozoic	Triassic		225
Paleozoic	Permian		275
Paleozoic	Carboniferous system — Pennsylvanian		325
Paleozoic	Carboniferous system — Mississippian		345
Paleozoic	Devonian		395
Paleozoic	Silurian		430
Paleozoic	Ordovician		500
Paleozoic	Cambrian		560
Proterozoic	Precambrian		4,800

Figure 1. Geologic Time Chart.

Permian: named after the ancient kingdom of Permia, now part of Russia, by R. I. Murchison in 1841.

Triassic: named for the three-fold (triad) development of rocks of that age (basal sandstone, middle limestone, and upper sandstone) in Germany by Friedrich von Alberti in 1834.

Jurassic: named for the Jura Mountains of Switzerland by Alexandre von Humboldt in 1795.

Cretaceous: derived from the Latin word Creta, meaning chalk, in that chalk is an abundantly occurring rock type in the Cretaceous System. The system was named by J. J. d'Omalius d'Halloy in 1822, and was first applied to rocks exposed in the Paris Basin.

Tertiary: this is the oldest generally used periodic term and was proposed by Giovanni Arduino in 1760 for fossiliferous sedimentary rocks overlying the Secondary Mountains (and rocks) in Italy.

Quaternary: was first proposed by Paul Desnoyers in 1829, to include those rocks overlying the Tertiary System.

Eocene, Miocene and Pliocene were proposed as subdivisions of the Tertiary by Charles Lyell in 1833, and were based on the percentages of species yet living that occurred within the molluscan faunas found in the rocks. The terms are etymologically derived as follows: Eocene = dawn of the recent, Miocene = less recent, and Pliocene = more recent.

Pleistocene: (most-recent) was proposed by Lyell in 1839 as a term to characterize the upper portion of the Pliocene epoch, after that epoch had been divided into two portions.

Paleocene: (ancient-recent) proposed by W. P. Schimper in 1874, as a new name for the lower portion of Lyell's Eocene, following subdivision of the Eocene epoch.

Oligocene: (slightly-recent) proposed in 1854 by Heinrich von Beyrich, for rocks located between those of Eocene and Miocene ages.

The epochs of the Tertiary were first proposed as systems, but are generally regarded now as being epochs (lesser subdivisions) of the Tertiary System.

The periods are subdivided into epochs and the epochs in turn are further subdivided, in accord with the following scheme:

TIME DIVISIONS	TIME-STRATIGRAPHIC TERMS*
Era (composed of two or more periods)	No equivalent
Period	System
Epoch	Series
Age	Stage
No equivalent	Zone

*Based upon fossils that are used to define zones, a stage then, consists of certain zones and a series of certain stages, etc.

The majority of the subdivisions are not of general interest to us and are therefore not discussed.

Formation

A term generally used to characterize specific rock beds by geologists is "formation", a name that may be applied to any rock-unit that has mappable boundaries. Most formations have a rather uniform lithology, and many have been shown to be depositionally genetic units. Fossils are not used to define formations, nor does the concept of time enter into their definition. The concept of time can not be used because some formations were continuously deposited by seas gradually encroaching across land masses, and the basal portions (at least) of those formations are of decreasing age along the direction of the sea's advance. This is analogous to a machine paving a road as it moves along. The last section of road deposited is the youngest.

Formations are given names based on local geographic features, such as Morrison Formation (after the town of Morrison) or the Denver Formation. Some formation names have the term for the dominant lithologic type replacing the word formation, such as Niobrara Chalk, Graneros Shale, or Dakota Sandstone.

Correlation

After a system has been described and the boundaries of its type (initially described) section have been defined, rocks of the same age and belonging within the defined boundaries of that system may be identified elsewhere. This is done by making a study of the fossils of the first named area, the type section, and comparing them with fossils found elsewhere to identify similar or identical faunas that are presumed to be synchronous. Faunas and floras consisting of the same species or closely related species if shown to be from rocks of equivalent stratigraphic "age" are said to be correlative or to correlate.

Correlations are made on temporal bases, and can be accomplished by one or more methods:

I.   "Absolute" Correlations
   a.   Radioactive decay sequence age determinations
   b.   Tree rings
   c.   Varves

II.   Relative Correlations
   a.   Fossils
   b.   Continuity of beds
   c.   Physical criteria
   d.   Bentonite beds, ash falls

Absolute correlations are made in terms of years, for example, if the age of an igneous intrusion in Arizona is found by radioactive age determination methods to be 76,000,000 years old, and a similar intrusion in Nevada is determined to have occurred at the same time, those intrusions correlate, and both occurred during the Late Cretaceous Period in that Cretaceous time began about 140 million years ago, and ended about 65 million years ago.

The initials B.P., are used after carbon 14 "absolute" age dates and indicate the number of years ago (Before Present) that the dated event occurred. Geochronologists have agreed to regard 1950 as "the present", however, determinations of "absolute" dates involve a margin of error (caused by sample contamination, inherent inaccuracies in chemical analysis, etc.) far in excess of the elapsed time between 1950 and today, so there is no appreciable loss of accuracy by using 1950 as "the present". Because of the margin of error, "absolute" dates are not really absolute, and the term is encompassed with quotation marks.

Additional inaccuracies of carbon 14 age determinations have recently been confirmed. Apparently the sun's putput of cosmic radiation, and the subsequent production of carbon 14 in the Earth's upper atmosphere, have not been static. Age determinations of 5,000 to 6,000 B.P. are very likely 1,000 years older, although those dates to year 1 are accurate, and those of 4.000 B.P. should be corrected to 4,500 B.P. Furthermore carbon 14 age determinations prior to 8,000 B.P. may actually be younger than the determined date.

Other absolute age determinations may be obtained by counting annually incremented layers, such as tree growth rings or some distinctively layered lake sediments, especially those known as varves that are deposited in lakes located near the terminus of melting glaciers. Studies of growth rings in bristle cone pine trees have locally extended the usefulness of tree ring chronology back to 10,200 B.P.

Relative correlations are based on the synchronous occurrence of events, deposition of rocks, or the geographically widespread distribution of organisms that lived at the same time. However, the ages of the events, in terms of years, involved in relative correlations are unknown. Although geologists can equate many events and rock beds that occurred or formed in the geologic past rather accurately, they cannot precisely determine when they happened in terms of years before the present.

The use of fossils in making relative correlations is based upon the fact that plants and animals have evolved with the passage of time, and some relative correlations have been based on the stage of an organism's evolutionary development, and others have been established by the geographically widespread occurrence of a characteristic species that is confined to rocks that were deposited during a short time interval.

Other means of making relative correlations include determining if the rock beds being studied can be traced laterally and seen to grade into each other or into the type section. The use of physical criteria is perhaps less accurate than the other methods, the criteria that are usually applied in correlating rock units of formational rank during geologic mapping, consist of factors such as thickness of the rock bed, color, weathering characteristics, and lithology.

The Index Fossil Concept

The concept of faunal and floral correlations, when first introduced, was based on the premise of a fauna and flora having a world-wide, or nearly world-wide distribution. If this were so, rocks of the same age would have the same faunal and floral content, even in the most distant regions. With further geologic exploration, it became obvious that an entire fossil fauna was not distributed over extreme distances; usually few or no species can be found in common for probably contemporaneous rock beds separated by thousands of miles. However, the species that are most widely distributed would serve as indices, that is index or guide fossils to indicate that the rock beds containing them were deposited at approximately the same time. An index fossil may be defined as a fossil plant or animal with a wide geographic distribution and restricted geologic time range, which can be used to identify or give a relative date to the rocks in which it was found. Beyond the geographic range of a particular guide fossil correlation can be made through use of a second guide fossil where its geographic range overlaps that of the first one.

The index fossil concept works well with many groups of animals and plants; however, it is not infallible, in that many organisms do not make good time indices because of a marked affinity for a certain environment that enables them to continue to live in geographically isolated areas, after they have seemingly become extinct elsewhere, or have become extirpated from much of their former geographic distribution.

Modern Index Fossils

As a general statement, species are more abundant in the tropics so that there, one could theoretically easily capture specimens of 100 different species of insects but only a relatively few members of each species. Toward the arctic the number of species diminishes, however the individuals comprising the population of each species become more numerous, so that it would be much easier to capture 100 individuals of each species than to capture a large number of specimens belonging to many discrete species. Accompanying the equatorial to arctic decline in numbers of species is a change in the fauna and flora (life zones) that is associated with each climate zone. These life zones or biomes are based on the animal and plant communities present and range from (1) the tundra, a treeless region inhabited by caribou, musk oxen, and Eskimos; (2) coniferous forests, with spruce and pine trees and an accompanying fauna of elk, moose, brown bears, and lynx; (3) deciduous forests, with oak, maple and beech trees associated with raccoons, white-tailed deer, and grey squirrels; (4) grassland areas (laterally equivalent to the deciduous forests, but in drier or semi-arid areas) are characterized by tall and short grasses, sagebrush, coyotes, jack rabbits, badgers, prairie owls, and antelope; (5) desert regions, are also laterally equivalent, but even drier regions (arid) characterized by cacti, ocotillo, peccaries, desert mule deer and gila monsters; to (6) the tropical rain-forests that consist of broad-leaved, non-deciduous trees, such as plantains, bananas, and rubber plants, and are inhabited by a fauna of monkeys (locally apes or prosimians), tapirs, crocodilians, and large constrictor snakes.

This has in general led to a north-south stratification of faunas, so that wide-ranging index fossils suitable for correlations are seemingly absent.

Dall and Harris in 1892 discussed the distribution of shelled molluscs along the eastern coast of North America, and recorded:

Greenland	180 species
Gulf of Maine	277 species
Carolina Coast	305 species
Florida (west)	681 species
Panama	517 species
Total	1960 species

This graphically shows the increase in numbers of species toward the tropics, the Panamanian fauna probably seeming to be lesser in variety because it had not been as well studied as the more easily reached and studied fauna from the west coast of Florida. Furthermore, Dall and Harris recorded 1,772 different species, with an overlap of less than 200 species among the various regions. Few (if any) of the species overlapped more than two of the the widely separated areas. This study tended to show that modern seas lacked easily preserved molluscan index fossils.

As an additional complication the Earth can be divided into zoogeographic realms that are characterized by a distinctive flora and fauna even though they may be located at equivalent latitudes and have identical climates. The realms are presumably created by barriers to animal and plant distribution, for example north-south trending land masses would block east-west migration of tropical and temperate marine faunas and floras. Wide deep-sea areas would block migration of land animals and some shallow water-dwelling marine forms. Climate, as we have discussed, also forms an effective barrier. The Australian Realm is characterized by gum trees, archaic conifers, monotremes, a wide variety of marsupials and the dubious distinction of having the world's highest ratio of poisonous to nonpoisonous snake species. In general it is essentially a late Mesozoic fauna. The Ethiopian Realm (Africa) is characterized by a fauna reminiscent of the Pleistocene, composed of elephants, rhinos, horses (zebras), apes, hippos, many primitive artiodactyls and large carnivorous cats. The Neotropical Realm (South America) is characterized by remnants of an early Cenozoic fauna (many marsupials), as well as monkeys that are unrelated to Old World forms, llamas, sloths, tapirs, capybaras, and alligators (including the caiman). Other realms are the Palearctic (European), Nearctic (North American), and the Oriental (Asian). These last three realms are distinctive in many respects but also closely allied in that many species are in common, especially across the temperate zone. For example wolves (Canis lupus), red foxes (Vulpes vulpes), reindeer and caribou, (Rangifer taurandus), brown bears (Ursus arctos), some weasels, the wolverine (Gulo gulo), and the lynx (Felis lynx), are species in common across the three areas.

Correlations between North America, Europe, and Asia could readily be made by means of fossil remains of those mammals. The main problem seems to be a lack of species with a broad north-south distribution, and a wide east-west distribution in the southern hemisphere.

Widely ranging mammals with a north-south distribution pattern include the puma (Felis concolor) that lives today in a range extending from Tierra del Fuego in South America to southern British Columbia in Canada, and the fur seal (Callorhinus ursinus) that ranges southward from the Pribilof Islands to northeastern Asia and California.

A useful sequence of index fossils with overlapping geographic ranges could be derived from a study of seals. The South American fur seal ranges from the South Atlantic Ocean (Falkland Islands) up the west coast of South America to the Galapagoes Islands. There its range is overlapped by that of the California sea lion (Zalophus californianus) that ranges from the Galapagoes Islands to North America and the Sea of Japan. Further correlations may then be based upon the presence of the Australian sea lion (Neophoca cinerea) that ranges from Japan to southern Australia, and the common seal that ranges from northeastern Asia across northern Europe to North America. Thus a nearly world-wide correlation chart could be formulated on a patch-work basis.

Similar index species would include migratory birds, the swallow (Hirundo rustica) that ranges from Great Britain to the Union of South Africa, and many storks with a similar range. Many shore birds migrate annually from the Arctic tundra to southern areas, some as far as the temperate zones of the southern hemisphere. Perhaps the most widely distributed sea birds (gulls and petrels) as well as the albatross would be useful index fossils.

Many sharks (Hexanchus sp.; the great white shark, Carcharodon rondeleti; and the whale shark, Rhinodon typus) range widely across the Atlantic, Indian, and Pacific Oceans and into temperate regions. Similarly some whales, especially the killer whale (Orcinus orca), have world-wide distributions from the Antarctic to Arctic Seas. Similar ranges are occupied by the sperm whale (Physeter catodon) and the right whale (Eubalaena sp.). These marine species would make excellent index fossils.

The dugong (Dugong dugon) ranges from eastern Africa, through the Red Sea, Indian Ocean, along the southern coast of Asia to Australia. The closely related manatees (Trichechus spp.) range from the west coast of Africa to South and North America. This geographic distribution as well as those of the whales could be used to temporally link or correlate the rocks of the southern and northern hemispheres.

The distribution of the wild boar (Sus scrofa) from Europe, in Africa south to the Sudan, across Asia, to Sumatra, Ceylon, Java, Formosa, and Japan, and its recent introduction to North America by man, make it one of the most widely distributed mammals, and a potential index fossil of high value. However the most widely distributed modern animal is man (Homo sapiens) and it is his bones and artifacts ("Coke" bottles through discarded automobiles) that may form the most widespread and lasting index for identification of Recent rocks.

Geologic Time Perspective

If we were able to condense the last 4.6 billion years of geologic time into one year, our story would begin on January 1st, the oldest known life (bacteria-like forms) would appear about mid-April, the oldest known shell-bearing sea fossils (brachiopods) would show up about November 1st, the first trilobites and shell-bearing marine organisms would become numerous on November 18th, the first vertebrates (primitive fishes) would appear on November 25th, the first land vertebrates (amphibians) would evolve on December 4th, the first reptiles would appear about December 6th, the first dinosaur would evolve about December 14th, the first mammals late the 15th, the earliest recognizable hominids (man-like apes) on December 30th, with more man-like forms (australopithecines) appearing around four hours before midnight on the 31st. Modern man (Homo sapiens) would appear about one hour before midnight, and Columbus would rediscover the New World about three seconds before midnight.

HISTORY OF PALEONTOLOGY

Classical Observations and Theories

Observations of nature and the Earth in classical time were largely characterized by a lack of application of scientific methodology and the nearly complete absence of empirical data. The classical period ended about 500 A.D., and was characterized by great advances in philosophic and humanistic thought. Despite the great advances in those fields, science was mainly confined to baseless hypotheses, random observations, and was intimately intermixed with philosophy and religion. No attempt was made by the Greeks or Romans to separate the disciplines of science and philosophy. Nevertheless, the Greeks were able to understand and use some geologic principles in that silver miners at Laurium followed along faults and successfully relocated the displaced mineralized veins.

The ancient Greeks were the first people to make written references to fossils, and to interpret them as remains of prehistoric animals and plants. In the year 500 B.C. Xanthos of Sardis noticed that sea shells could be found in rocks far from the present seashore, and Xanthos explained this by saying that the sea had been present in those areas at some time in the past. This afforded a direct and logical explanation of their occurrence, an interpretation that many great philosophers and scientists of the future were unable to accept. For example, Aristotle (383-332 B.C.) wrote that fishes lived motionless within the Earth and were found in excavations. Aristotle did not realize the meaning or true nature of fossils. This was extremely unfortunate because Aristotle's works were accepted by medieval scholars as an explanation for many natural phenomena second only to the Bible.

It is rather odd that pious Christian scholars, who supposedly despised all things pagan and non-Christian accepted the explanations of the pagan scientist and philosopher Aristotle. Concepts written hundreds of years before the medieval scholars were born were taken up by them, and adhered to as though the concepts were a portion of their own religious dogma.

The idea that fossils were remains of once living sea or land animals and plants was very slow to regain acceptance. One of Aristotle's pupils, Theophrastus, said that the motionless fishes found within the Earth developed from fish spawn that had been left on the surface of the earth and covered over and buried before hatching, or that some fishes had wandered from rivers and swum along underground passages and had gotten far inside the Earth and laid their eggs. Theophrastus' statements were the beginning of the idea that fossils grew inside the Earth and that some occult powers caused them to form; or, perhaps, seeds were carried from the Earth's surface by percolating waters to deep within the Earth's stony framework.

Middle Ages and Dark Ages

The Dark Ages extended from 500 A.D. to 1100 A.D. and the Middle Ages from 1100 A.D. to 1540 A.D.

The chapter of Genesis in the Bible states that the lands and seas were divided before animals were created, and thus gave rise to the concept of a static world; when this was combined with Aristotle's ideas, the consequence was to delay the recognition of fossils and the occurrence of geological phenomena and geologically caused changes upon the Earth for a great many years.

Fossils continued to be considered stones, curiosities, or things that grew within rocks. Some people even thought that fossils had been formed by plastic forces related to the Devil, or by effects resulting from the motions of the stars, planets, sun and moon, and a few fossils were said to have been caused by thunderbolts that struck the earth. When large mammalian fossils were found they were interpreted in accordance with the Scriptures and were usually referred to as the bones of antediluvian giants.

The Renaissance

The birth of geology as a science began shortly after 1540 with the beginning of the scientific Renaissance, which had been sparked by the publication of several books. The Belgian physician, Andreas Vesalius, published his "De Humani Corporis Fabrica" (Structure of the Human Body) in 1543, the same year that the Polish astronomer Copernicus published "De Revolutionibus Orbium Caelestium" (The motions of celestial spheres).

Vesalius, as a youth, developed an interest in dissecting and studying portions of the local vertebrate fauna, and in so doing acquired a technical skill in dissection that far exceeded the accepted standard of his time. Vesalius attended medical school in Paris, and recognized that the then prevalent teaching methods were inadequate. The professor sat on a dais and read from Galen's 1,300 year old text, Administrationes anatomica (Anatomical Procedures) in a droning monotone. The assistant professors stood on a lower level and indicated to barber-surgeons when and where to make the demonstrative dissections. Vesalius showed that the barber-surgeons were unskilled and clumsy, and carried out his own meticulous dissections; this led to his independent investigations, the first important contribution to anatomy in over a thousand years.

Eventually, Vesalius began teaching at the University of Padua, and in 1543, at the age of 29, he published his text that ended the thousand year-long intellectual stalemate during which no scientific advances in the study of human anatomy had been made, and during which Galen's ancient text had been slavishly adhered to.

The gross anatomy of the human body was well established by Vesalius' studies, a truly monumental step forward in human knowledge. Later in life, Vesalius was forced to recant his teachings by some church authorities, but was not given the usual treatment provided most intellectual nonconformists by Christians, i.e., execution. Actually, the latter portion of Vesalius' life is apparently unknown, different versions have him either disappearing on a pilgrimage to the Holy Land or being murdered.

The Polish astronomer-churchman, Nikolaus Kopernik or Copernicus, in a similar master stroke demonstrated that the earth orbited around the sun and helped phase out the concept of a Ptolemaic Universe. Perhaps Copernicus was fortunate in dying the year his book was published, as probably only his demise saved him from the wrathful revenge of his fellow churchmen. Legend has it that a copy of the book, fresh from the press, was given to Copernicus as he was dying. Martin Luther remarked, "Der Narr will die ganz Kunst Astronomiae umkehren" (the fool will upset the entire science of astronomy). For the record, Copernicus did, but he is not generally considered to be a fool. Father Inchofer further added his comment that:

> "The opinion of the earth's motion is of all heresies the most abominable, the most pernicious, the most scandalous; the immovability of the earth is thrice sacred. Argument against immortality of the soul, the existence of God, and the incarnation should be tolerated sooner than an argument to prove that the earth moves."

Copernicus' own Roman Catholic Church placed his book on the Index of Prohibited Books, where it remained until 1835.

Geology began with the publication by the German geologist, Agricola, of "De Natura Fossilium" (1546) and "De Re Metallica" (1556). Agricola is called the "father of mineralogy" for his books were the first in which ores, minerals, and ore-deposit finding were discussed as a scientific endeavor. The term "fossil", as used in Agricola's time, meant anything, whether organic remains, ores or minerals, dug up from within the Earth. As a great many scientists of his time had done, Agricola wrote (his books) in Latin and translated his name from Georg Bauer (Bauer is German for farmer) to Georgius Agricola (Agricola is Latin for farmer). Perhaps Agricola escaped the tribulations afforded Vesalius and Copernicus in that the money-making potential of this applied science, then as even today, was more appreciated and tolerated.

In the late 15th and early 16th centuries, the Italian artist-engineer-scientist, Leonardo da Vinci (1452-1519), before Agricola had written his books, made a series of remarkably astute geological observations which he recorded in his private notebooks. He wrote of finding seashells within the Earth in excavations for canals and roadways and recognized that those shells were remains of once living marine animals and that the sea had formerly been present in those areas. Da Vinci did not publish any of this information and it was revealed many years after his death when his coded writings were interpreted in the later 1800's.

The Early Development of Paleontology and Geology in Europe

In 1669 Nicholas Steno (1638-1686) published the idea that fossils were remains of animals that had been washed about and covered over by sediments deposited during the Noachian or Biblical Flood. Martin Lister, one of Steno's contemporaries, reported to a meeting of the Royal Society of London that the fossil shells from English rock quarries were not remains of animals at all, and Lister had probably read Steno's book. Apparently the problem was that Steno's ideas were only acceptable if people were willing to believe that the Noachian Flood had been universal, but before this was possible, they had to be educated away from acceptance of Aristotle's opinion that a universal flood could not have occurred. An amazing paradox! Pious Christians rejecting a portion of Genesis because of a pagan scientist's statements!

Even early in the eighteenth century the true nature of fossils was still not recognized by all scientists. However, in 1726 Johann Scheuchzer described a fossil from Oligocene lake beds in Switzerland, that he correctly recognized as the remains of an animal that had lived in the past: He badly misinterpreted his fossil as he actually had found the bones of a large salamander, which he described under name Homo diluvii testis. The bones were believed by Scheuchzer to be the remains of one of the antediluvian men who drowned in the Noachian Flood and the name "Homo diluvii testis" means "man who witnessed the flood." Even this was progress, for earlier in his career, Scheuchzer had denied the possibility of an organic origin for any fossils.

Giovanni Arduino (1714-1795) did geologic field work in the mountains and the Po River Valley of northern Italy, and published his first book in 1759. In that year, he also expounded his ideas of stratigraphy and the Earth's formation in letters to a friend. He distinguished four portions of the Earth's crust, each expressed as mountains, and each type of mountain characterized by its own rock type. Rock varieties were synonymous with the mountains they constituted in Arduino's concept of the Earth, and this synonymy of consolidated rocks and mountains stayed in geologic thought for a long time.

Arduino classed mountains into four main groups:

1. Primary Mountains: Crystalline rocks containing metallic ore deposits.

2. Secondary Mountains: Bedded limestones with abundant "petrified organic remains from the sea".

3. Tertiary Mountains: Gravel, sand, clay, etc., with marine fossils. Volcanic rocks were also included here.

4. Alluvium: Loose materials washed from the mountains by streams.

Two contemporaries of Arduino, Johann Gottlob Lehmann and Johann Christian Fuchsel, each independently discovered that the Earth's crust was built up of layers. The rock layers were composed of three distinct main rock types, and one rock type was characteristic of each of the three different types of mountain ranges.

Lehmann's report was published in German in 1756 and ascribed the deposition of all rocks to the Noachian Flood.

Fuchsel's report was published in Latin (1762), and it was more advanced with respect to usage of some essentially modern concepts, but lesser known. Fuchsel was able to draw geologic cross-sections properly and he believed the rocks to have been deposited by processes that were still in operation. He ignored the story of the Biblical Flood, without attempting to deny the story. The Principle of Uniformitarianism was presented in Fuchsel's book, the idea that the processes that formed all rocks were still in operation, and that all geologic processes operating today also had functioned in the past, long before Hutton and Lyell popularized the idea. Unfortunately, these rather advanced ideas of Fuchsel were ignored, and the elaborate hypotheses of Werner rose up.

Abraham Gottlob Werner (1750-1817) believed that all rocks comprising the Earth's crust had been deposited from a universal ocean. He believed that they had precipitated out in a sequence concordant with their specific gravities, the heavier rocks first, the lighter rocks last. Thus, Werner accounted for the crustal rock sequence consisting of heavy crystalline rocks at the base, overlain by lighter, consolidated sediments, with the supposedly lightest rocks of all, unconsolidated sediments, at the top. Werner's rock classification system was little different from the earlier one proposed by Lehmann, however, Werner did not believe that his universal ocean had been the Noachian Flood.

After the Earth was created, according to Werner, it was covered by a universal sea, and all the substances that were to form the rocks were dissolved in this sea and were precipitated out in order of their specific gravity. Following deposition of the rocks, the sea disappeared through a hole into the interior of the Earth.

The first rocks precipitated from Werner's universal sea were crystalline igneous and metamorphic rocks. Rocks were still considered to be synonymous with mountain ranges by Werner and he called the first precipitated rocks the primitive mountains, "Urgebirge" or "Uranfangliche Gebirge". After the dense, primitive rocks had precipitated, a series of less dense, and layered, consolidated sediments was formed. These rocks Werner called "Flötzgebirge" (stratified rocks).

The next sequence was the "Vulkanische Gebirge" (volcanic rocks), composed of ash falls and other volcanic rocks. The uppermost sequence was the Aufgeschwemmte Gebirge (alluvium), a series of loose, largely unlayered alluvial rocks located in valleys. As Werner travelled and saw more stratigraphic sequences, he modified his system so as to include new discoveries. About 1796 Werner introduced the subdivision Übergangsgebirge (transitional rocks) between the Urgebirge and Flötzebirge, and the Volcanic Rocks were referred to the top of the Aufgeschwemmte Gebirge.

Werner believed that only the alluvium (Aufgeschwemmte Gebirge) had been put down during the Noachian Flood; all of the other rocks had precipitated from the primordial sea, thus when the supposed Noachian Flood occurred, it loosened and moved fragments of the previously formed rocks, and this material became the unconsolidated sedimentary rocks of an obviously more recent origin in the valleys.

Werner interpreted vein deposits in rocks as having been formed by "fillings" precipitated from the sea into cracks in the sea floor. Werner believed that folded or tilted beds had been deposited in the positions they occupied. He did not account for any changes after the rocks had been deposited, as all rocks were laid down exactly in the form and position in which they were found later.

One of Werner's most important contributions was to introduce the concept of making careful field observations. However his adherence to preconceived answers determined before he had examined all of the evidence delayed development of knowledge within the science of geology as much as 50 years.

Werner recognized the existence of volcanoes, but thought they were of little importance, and he ascribed the source of volcanic heat and lavas to burning coal beds melting rocks locally in the subsurface. According to the Wernerian concept, the Earth consisted of a hollow sphere, containing the bulk of the ancient universal sea, thus there was no room for plutonism, or a hot interior of the planet containing magma. The volcanic basalts Werner found within the geologic rock column were explained by him as having formed by precipitation from his universal sea. It was the controversy over the origin of basalts that exposed the flaws incorporated into Werner's system.

The Emergence of Modern Concepts

Today, we call the Wernerian system the Neptunist concept, and opposing the Neptunist concepts were the Plutonists who were led by James Hutton (1726-1797). Hutton had been trained as a physician, but he turned to farming and then later in his life he became a geologist. In 1785 Hutton published a paper detailing his theory of the Earth's structure with a concept of sediment formation similar to that accepted today; and furthermore, he realized that rocks could be metamorphosed by heat and pressure, and that diastrophic changes such as mountain building and faulting occurred in the Earth's crust, that magma was intruded from great depths within the Earth into overlying rocks and was similarly extruded out upon the surface of the Earth as lava.

Hutton had traveled quite widely and visited several portions of Europe, and he made many very accurate field observations. In his travels he became aware of active volcanoes and their associated basalt flows. Hutton saw all of these processes as a never ending cycle; everything that occurred in the past could occur again and all of the geologic processes operating upon the Earth today had also operated in the past.

Werner had worked entirely in Germany and should have limited his theories to his observations, but he did not and that was his major mistake. It is a failing of man, to attempt to construct inflexible universal schemes or explanations before all the facts are gathered.

Breakdown of the dominance of Werner's system began when some of his former students examined volcanoes in central France. These were recently extinct volcanoes, and the students saw clearly that basaltic lava flows had originated from them. Therefore, if some basalts were igneous, all basalt could not have been a marine precipitate as required by Werner's hypothesis, and the flaws in his explanation became increasingly apparent.

Hutton's paper was rather difficult to read and consequently had little general appeal to scientists and the public. It wasn't until 1802 that John Playfair rewrote Hutton's ideas in a book called "Illustrations of the Huttonian Theory of the Earth". Then the concept of the Doctrine of Uniformitarianism became widely known and the groundwork of historical geology was firmly established. The decline of Neptunism accelerated after the publication of this book, and by 1830 there were only a few die-hard Wernerians left.

In 1752 Jean Guettard published his concept that rocks formed bands of layers and that these bands could be traced laterally and mapped. Guettard also recognized that fossils were remains of once living animals, and he laid the groundwork which resulted in acceptance of William Smith's (1769-1839) idea that rocks and their fossil faunas were laterally persistent. That is specific fossils were a characteristic of only those beds that contained them.

William Smith was largely uneducated, employed as a civil engineer, and travelled widely through Great Britain during the course of his work. This was an ideal situation for Smith. He collected fossils as a hobby, and thus could indulge in collecting during working hours. Smith's conclusion of using fossils for geologic correlation was reached in 1791 and it is the most important single concept we have today in stratigraphy and paleontology. Smith, unfortunately, did not publish this concept, as apparently he failed to see its importance. Not until 1799 did he distribute it in a manuscript form to some of his friends. They urged him to publish, but he delayed. In 1813, one of Smith's friends, Reverend Townsend, published the concept of correlation in a small book, giving Smith full credit for the idea. In 1815, Smith published a large geological map of Great Britain and finally in 1816 and 1817 he published books stating his Principle of Correlation or the Law of Faunal Succession. The books contained lists of the strata of England and Wales and the fossils contained within the strata.

Baron Georges Cuvier (1769-1832) and his collaborator Alex Brongniart (1770-1847) discovered the Law of Faunal Succession independently of William Smith. Cuvier began work as a French civil servant, then he began to do scientific investigations in entomology, next in comparative anatomy and eventually in 1798 began to work in vertebrate paleontology. Cuvier was the exact opposite of Smith, in that Cuvier was well educated, a Professor at the College de France, ambitious, interested in publishing his ideas, and had plenty of assistants and financial backing. One would expect a professional like Cuvier, rather than an amateur like Smith, to make important discoveries such as the Law of Faunal Succession. Cuvier worked mainly with the late Cretaceous and Tertiary vertebrate faunas of the Paris Basin in collaboration with the mining engineer Brongniart. Cuvier and Brongniart published a report of their discovery of the Law of Faunal Succession in 1811, although this was before William Smith's concepts were published, Smith discovered the idea first and deserves recognition. In addition, their investigative efforts did not overlap, for Smith based his concept upon observations of invertebrate fossils and Cuvier's work was based upon studies of vertebrate fossils, so that the two independently conducted studies complemented each other.

Cuvier was an outstanding scientist and one of the more famous men of his time, but he was a catastrophist and had no appreciation of the concept of biologic evolution. Cuvier believed a series of natural catastrophes had successively wiped out each of the floras and faunas that had lived during each of the various periods of the past. He further supposed that the distinct fauna and flora found in each successive rock layer had been specially created.

Cuvier's belief in catastrophism placed him at odds with his contemporary, Chevalier de Lamarck (1744-1829), who had a pre-Darwinian concept of evolution. Although Lamarck did not specify a mechanism for evolution, a century later Neo-Lamarckists implied that evolution was caused by inheritance of changes that took place during the animals life span; changes that are called somatic changes today. Examples of such somatic changes would include development of large muscles through exercises such as weight-lifting, the development of stunted or deformed bones through a lack of vitamins in one's diet, or dwarfed stature caused by a plant or animal living in an unfavorable environment. We know today such changes are not inheritable.

In 1830 Adam Sedgwick (1785-1873) began to investigate the sequence of sedimentary rocks in England and Wales known as the "graywacke". At the same time Roderick I. Murchison (1792-1871) a retired army officer, who had taken up the study of geology, began to investigate similar sediments in southern Wales. In 1835, Sedgwick completed the investigation of his sedimentary sequence, and named it the Cambrian System. Unfortunately, Sedgwick was a busy university teacher and lacked time to describe the rather few fossils that he found in the rocks. Murchison, unlike Sedgwick, studied the fossils he found and in 1835 he named the rock section he had examined the Silurian System. At first, Sedgwick and Murchison were friends, they worked together and began to organize the structurally jumbled mass of rock strata in England and Wales into a sequence of named systems, as in 1837 when they named the Devonian System. Then Murchison and Sedgwick began to re-investigate the two systems they had independently named at first and found an overlap. Some of the uppermost rocks of Sedgwick's Cambrian System were found to be equivalent to the lowermost rocks of Murchison's Silurian System. This started a squabble between the two men and they became bitter enemies, with their followers divided into two opposing camps, and an argument began that was not settled until 1879 when Lapworth resolved the problem. After a study of the fossils in the sections of sedimentary rocks in question, Lapworth decided that a new system, the Ordovician, should be created to include those beds of the uppermost Cambrian and lowermost Silurian Systems that had been claimed by both Murchison and Sedgwick for their systems.

One of the most outstanding geologists of the nineteenth century was Sir Charles Lyell (1797-1875). Although Lyell's father had been a naturalist, his son was trained to be a lawyer, but fortunately for science, Lyell became interested in geology. Sir Charles liked to travel and visited many parts of Europe and North America; partly as a result of his travels he was able to publish many authoritative books about geology. It was Lyell who put historical geology on a firm scientific basis with his pronouncement and application of the Doctrine of Uniformitarianism, the concept that all the geological processes that have operated in the past are still in operation today. Lyell's textbook "Principles of Geology" (1830-1833) popularized the Uniformitarian idea and helped phase out catastrophist theories. The influence of Lyell's ideas upon other workers in the field of geology was far reaching and pronounced.

When Charles Darwin (1809-1882) entered the University of Edinburgh in 1825, he attended some geology lectures (given by Professor Jameson). He wrote a letter home in which he stated that geology was the dullest of all of his subjects and resolved never to read a geology book or study the subject in any way whatsoever. It may be significant to note that Jameson was a die-hard Neptunist, and perhaps Darwin was shrewd enough to see through the Neptunian fallacies. Only a few years later though, after Darwin became acquainted with Lyell's text, he wrote rapturously of the joys of geology, and he continued this interest by making numerous perceptive geologic observations during his voyage on the Beagle. Darwin ascribed his interest entirely to Lyell's method of explaining geology by means of Uniformitarian Principles.

The Development of Paleontology and Geology in North America

Geologic studies were slow to develop in North America, as the colonies had been settled by religious fundamentalists to whom science, especially geology, was anathema. Answers to geologic questions were readily supplied from a seemingly inexhaustible store of fundamentalist misinformation. For example, when a tooth of a fossil elephant was discovered near Albany, New York, the tooth was submitted to Cotton Mather for his inspection and identification. The Reverend Mather weighed the tooth, assumed it was human, and since it was many times the weight and bulk of a modern human tooth, he concluded that it must have been the tooth of an ante-diluvian giant who drowned in the Noachian Flood. Similar teeth discovered at that time in the southeastern United States, were correctly identified by Negro slaves as elephant teeth. Apparently, formal education did not then, even as now, provide one with omniscence. One of the earlier, and more famous American fossil collectors was Thomas Jefferson, who had a large collection of fossil bones from Big Bone Lick in Kentucky. The claw of a large, and now extinct, ground sloth was named Megalonyx by Jefferson. When Jefferson became president, a room in the White House was set aside to house his fossil collection.

Serious geologic studies in North America began shortly after 1800 with the field work of William Maclure, who repeatedly traveled back and forth across the Appalachian Mountains from the northern part of the United States down to the Gulf Coast, at a time when most of the Appalachian area was without roads and permanent settlements. As a result of this field work Maclure published the first large scale geological map, with an accompanying text, of the eastern United States, in 1817 (based on Werner's system).

In the early 1800's there was no formal instruction in geology, or even much of any scientific education available in America. (College degrees were granted in law, ministry, or medicine, but not science). In 1805 Yale College began to offer education in science after they hired one of their recent graduates, Benjamin Silliman, to fill the newly established Chair of Natural Philosophy. In order to implement this, Silliman had to obtain a knowledge of science before he could begin teaching. After Silliman returned to Yale and began teaching, Yale College offered the first courses in geology given in North America.

The Eatonian decade was named for Amos Eaton and began in 1820, (Eaton, a graduate of Williams College, had been trained as a lawyer and practiced law until 1816 when he was forty years old.) At that time Eaton went to Yale College where he studied geology under Benjamin Silliman for one year, after which he returned to Williams College to give lectures on science.

In 1821 Eaton was employed by Steven Rensselaer to make a survey of Rensselaer County in New York. This appointment made Eaton the first professional geologist hired to make a geological survey, as all earlier geologic mapping and work had been done as a hobby. After Eaton completed the survey of Rensselaer County, he was hired to conduct a survey along the right of way of the proposed Erie Canal. In conjunction with the canal work, Eaton gave a series of lectures on geology to the New York legislature, and quite likely primed the legislature for development of the geological survey of New York in 1836. Later, Eaton wrote the first American geological textbook (one based on Wernerian concepts).

The decade of 1830 through 1840 was a period of founding of the first state-sponsored geological surveys. The surveys were set up on a temporary basis to determine the natural resources within the states, and in most of the states geology formed only one aspect of the survey, as topographic, botanical, and zoological studies were also included. In 1831 Massachusetts and Tennessee organized surveys and in 1835 New Jersey and Connecticut followed. In 1836 New York and Pennsylvania organized surveys as did several other states. The New York survey was a particularly important and large study.

James Hall began his career as a member of the first geological survey of New York. During the first year of the survey Hall was an assistant and in the second year of the survey, after one of the original members, Timothy Conrad, became despondent and quit, Hall was promoted to handling the geological investigations of the supposedly less-promising western portion of the state. Fortunately Hall's work became a major contribution to the final report of the survey. After the survey was concluded, the geologists were discharged and most of them joined other surveys. However, Hall was continued on salary and wrote an eight volume report on the paleontology of New York State that made Hall the dominant scientist of the New York Survey and eventually led to his becoming the chief geologist of several subsequent geological surveys in other states.

Discoveries of Vertebrate Fossils

The first dinosaur found in North America was dug from a marl pit near Haddonfield, New Jersey, and many of the bones were carried off as curiosities by the workmen. In 1858, Parker Foulke of the Philadelphia Academy of Natural Sciences located and reopened the pit and obtained much more skeletal material. Later many of the previously carted off bones were located and obtained for the Academy. The specimen was named Hadrosaurus by Dr. Joseph Leidy (1823-1891), of the Academy staff. Dr. Leidy is considered to be the "Father of American vertebrate paleontology."

Shortly before, and continuing once again after the Civil War, the federal government participated in a series of railroad and territorial surveys of the western United States. As a result of these geological surveys of the then largely unexplored western territories, many books and scientific articles describing the invertebrate fossils and stratigraphy were published by F. B. Meek independently or in collaboration with F. V. Hayden, as well as by other scientists.

Dr. Gideon Mantell (1790-1852), an English physician, described the first discovered dinosaur, Iguanodon, a large, bipedal, and herbivorous form, that was related to the duck-billed dinosaurs which evolved in the late Cretaceous. Actually, the first bone fragments were discovered by Mantell's wife in a rock garden, located in the yard of one of Mantell's patients.

The word "dinosaur" was not immediately applied to Mantell's reptile, for the word had not yet been coined and the concept of the former existence of a series of large reptiles had yet to develop.

Sir Richard Owen (1804-1892) began his career as a physician, but began to study fossil and living vertebrates to such an extent that he is known as the "Father of English Vertebrate Paleontology". Sir Richard invented the word "Dinosauria" ("terrible lizards"), as a taxonomic term to include Mantell's genus, Iguanodon, and several subsequently discovered large Mesozoic reptiles.

E. D. Cope (1840-1897) of the University of Pennsylvania and the Philadelphia Academy of Natural Sciences and O. C. Marsh (1831-1899) of Yale University studied many of the vertebrate fossils collected by the federal surveys and contributed much to our knowledge of the vertebrate paleontology of the western United States. Cope and Marsh began to collect and study vertebrate fossils at first as friends, then they organized their own collecting teams and studied specimens their teams collected or purchased and shipped to them. Eventually, in the race to get the most fossils, they became rivals and finally bitter enemies.

The First Fossil Men

The first skull of a readily recognizable fossil man was discovered in Neanderthal Cave near Dusseldorf, Germany, in 1856, but was not immediately widely recognized as being of great antiquity.

This was before Darwin's epochal book, The Descent of Man was published and the idea of extinct varieties of humans was neither widespread nor popular, so the skull was interpreted as that of an imbecile or that of a rather beetle-browed Russian soldier who had pursued Napoleon, by the German discoverers. This error of interpretation presumably received scant appreciation in Russia and elsewhere, and was only corrected after Darwin published, although many scientists continued to be doubtful of the skull's true nature until nearly 1900.

The Origin of Species was published by Charles Darwin in 1859 after many years of investigation and thought. The concept of biological evolution did not originate with this book; what Darwin did was to give such irrefutable proof to the concept of evolution, that informed, reasoning men could no longer doubt that evolution has and is occurring. Publication of The Origin of Species was followed by publication of Darwin's second book, The Descent of Man, and the two books provoked a controversy among the largely fundamentalist Victorians, that still is not yet resolved today. As Max Planck is supposed to have said, a new scientific truth does not triumph by convincing its opponents, but rather because its opponents die, and a new generation grows up that is familiar with it. Darwin's books provided the most significant contribution to biology and paleontology of the nineteenth century.

After 1890 the modern period of exploration and study of fossils began. Discoveries and studies of fossil men are one of the more interesting and significant developments of this era, and are discussed in the chapter on primate evolution.

The Conflict of Christianity with Paleontology

The authors of the chapter of Genesis in discussing the universe and origin of the Earth incorporated many contemporary interpretations of nature, so that parts of Genesis are based upon Babylonian or even earlier "science". Unfortunately, many people are apparently unaware of this, and have attempted to convert a book of religion into a book of science.

Among the ancient concepts incorporated into the Bible, is the idea of a flat Earth underlain by the sea, as mentioned in Genesis 7:11, Psalm 136:6, and Psalm 24:1-2, furthermore the heavens were considered to be constructed like a tent or upturned bowl over a flat Earth, as described in Genesis 1:6-8, Psalm 104:2, Job 37:18, and Isaiah 40:22. The authors of Genesis also considered the Earth to be stationary and that the sun, moon, and stars moved through the heavens only to illuminate the Earth, as stated in Genesis 1:14, Psalm 93:1, and Psalm 104:5. References to the nature of the universe were incidental to the authors' main purpose, and their contribution was intended to be for the advancement of religion, not the retardation of science. Fortunately, for most of us, those who insist upon a dogmatic acceptance of essentially a Babylonian scientific outlook, do not require acceptance of Babylonian medical practices.

The flat and stationary Earth concepts were upset by the discoveries and pronouncements of Copernicus and Galileo, to which the church has managed to adjust over the past few centuries. The more recent Doctrine of Biological Evolution has been only partially reconciled by many religions as not enough time has elapsed since Darwin's 1859 publication to allow for conservative minds to adjust. Actually, the creation story in Genesis consists of two conflicting stories written by different authors at different times. The older story, Genesis 2:4b-23, begins with "in the day that the Lord God made the Earth and the Heavens"............"watered the whole face of the ground".....""formed man of the dust of the ground" had man being made early in the sequence, with Eve being manufactured from a rib, and lacks any division into days. The second story in Genesis 1 and 2:1-4a has no rib sequence, is divided into days and has man being created last, plants were made on the 3rd day, then the sun, moon, and stars, with man being created on the 6th day, after the creation of the other animals.

The age of the Earth in terms of years is not mentioned in the Bible and the idea of a 6,000 year old Earth originated from 17th century European Anglicans. John Lightfoot, the Vice Chancellor of Cambridge, stated in 1642 that the Earth was created at 9:00 A.M. on September 17th. Later Lightfoot added that the year was 3928 B.C. In 1658, Archbishop Ussher of northern Ireland calculated the day of creation to have been October 22, 4004 B.C., by adding the time elapsed between given dates, the ages of the Patriarchs, and other time periods as stated in the Bible. Unfortunately, in 1701 Bishop Lloyd caused the date 4004 B.C. to be inserted as a footnote into the King James edition of the English Bible as the year of creation, and this has helped lead fundamentalists further astray.

THE OCCURENCE AND STUDY OF FOSSILS

Definition of Fossil

Fossils are the remains or traces of plants and animals that lived in the geologic past. I have purposely avoided using the term "prehistoric" in this definition because the term is ambiguous; records of history compiled by man did not start at a uniform time on a world-wide basis. For example, written history probably began in the Near East more than 4,000 years ago, but written history began in portions of North America less than 200 years ago. Areas of New Guinea and South America are still essentially "prehistoric".

The words "geologic past", are preferable to prehistoric, because we can define "geologic past" as preceding a synchronous, or nearly synchronous boundary. Some geologists regard as fossils those organic remains preserved before a time boundary of about 10,000 B.P., as determined by carbon 14 age determinations. Others would prefer to use a time boundary of 5,000 B.P. and would link the Pleistocene-Recent boundary to the melting of the last major ice sheets of Europe and North America and the beginning of the post-glacial "Thermal Maximum" or Hypsithermal, an interval of a warmer climate than that of the present.

Whether or not relatively recent organic remains are fossils is arbitrary, and depends upon what criterion is accepted to be the most recent limit of the "geologic past".

Processes of Fossilization

Fossilization is the process or processes by means of which plant or animal remains become preserved and entombed within sediments, and such remains, when we discover them, are called fossils. The word fossil is derived from the Latin word Fossa, meaning trench or ditch because fossilized remains were found in ancient and medieval times in excavations for roads and canals or in quarries.

When an animal or plant dies its remains normally lie on the surface of the ground and decay, oxidize, or are eaten by scavengers, so that the organic structures of the former organism become completely destroyed. This is usual situation, that which is made of the Earth's "dust" again returns to the state of "dust" and can not be identified as to its former morphology.

Only under exceptional conditions can organic remains become preserved, for shells and bones are easily dissolved away, oxidized, or even eaten. Obviously, one of these exceptional conditions is rapid burial, usually within sediments so that the remains do not lie on the surface of the ground exposed to hungry scavengers and destructive effects of weathering. Burial of fossils may be rapid and result in catastrophic deaths, such as has occurred in many fossilized forests, where the trees are found standing upright in growth position and their roots spread out into the underlying soil. The forests were destroyed by rapid ash falls or lava flows that overwhelmed and covered them. The ash or lava flows killed the trees, but their forms were preserved. Silica leached out of the ash or lava by downward migrating water, was redeposited either within the cellular structure of the wood, or else it replaced the cellulose of the wood, converting it into petrified wood. This is one example of fossilization and is called mineralization or petrification (Plate 1, Figure H). In a similar example, people seeking to escape poisonous gases and volcanic ash emitted by Monte Somma were overwhelmed by the wet, muddy ash fall of 79 A.D. in Pompeii. Their forms were preserved in that their outlines, including clothing form, made external molds in the ash, which hardened, and archaeologists are able today to fill the natural molds with plaster and obtain "death-casts" of individual Pompeians.

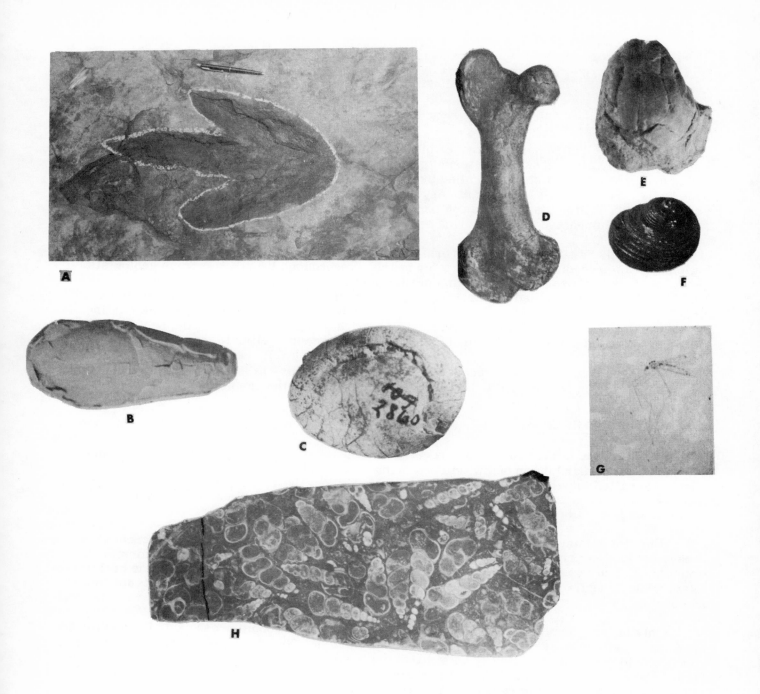

Plate 1. Preservation of fossils.

A.) Three-toed dinosaur footprint from the Triassic shales of the Connecticut Valley. Courtesy of L. Dean Marlow. B.) Fossilized egg of _Protoceratops_ (a horned dinosaur) from the Cretaceous of Outer Mongolia. Saint Louis Museum of Science and Natural History. C.) Fossilized egg of a bird from the western United States. Sternberg Memorial Museum. D.) Unaltered bone, femur of a Moa from late Pleistocene (or Recent) deposits of New Zealand. Sternberg Memorial Museum. E.) Cast of the interior of the skull "brain-cast") of a dog from Tertiary rocks of South Dakota. Southern Illinois University, Edwardsville. F.) Pyritized internal cast of a snail. Sternberg Memorial Museum. G.) Carbonized film of an insect from the Tertiary Florissant Shale of Colorado. Sternberg Memorial Museum. H.) Snails ("_Turritella_ agate") filled and replaced by silica. Sternberg Memorial Museum.

Unfortunately no fossil hominids have been found similarly preserved, although partial casts in the form of foot and hand prints have been found in caves and under lava flows.

Not all fossils are so spectacularly and rapidly covered over and preserved, as usually a local accumulation of sediments on the sea floor may cover some molluscs and the shells then become fossils without being altered structurally or mineralogically. Even eggshells have been preserved (Plate 1, Figures B, C). They merely lie within the sediments and become fossils by means of being sufficiently old. Vertebrate bones may, in a process similar to the formation of petrified wood, become fossilized by replacement, or more usually through pore filling by silica (petrification), or simply by being protected as original bone without any alteration or mineralization. (Plate 1, Figure D).

Excellently preserved and unaltered fossils are rare, as fossils occur more abundantly as casts or molds. (Plate 1, Figure E). A mold will form around a fossil shell that has been covered by sediments, and if the sediment is porous, ground water can seep through the rock and dissolve away the original material of the shell, leaving only its external impression, or mold, in the surrounding rock. Casts form as fillings of molds, or from fine-grained sediments that washed into the empty shell before it was buried. Some casts may be replaced by pyrite (Plate 1, Figure F). Fossil footprints, trackways and trails, and sitz (sit-down) marks, are incomplete external molds. (Plate 1, Figure A).

Frozen remains of nearly complete animals have been discovered in permafrost regions of Alaska and Siberia. The most famous specimen in the Beresovka Mammoth, found frozen in permafrost exposed along the Tunguska River in 1900. The Beresovka Mammoth was reputed to have been so well preserved that the meat was edible. There is confusion in various reports as to whether it was edible for the Russian discoverers, their sled dogs, local wolves, or possibly all three. Well preserved remains of Pleistocene mammals have also been recovered from "tar-pits" of Galicia (Russia) and La Brea (Figure 2) in California. No soft part remains were associated with the La Brea specimens, although some of the specimens from Galicia were partially "mummified."

Figure 2. La Brea in Los Angeles. The famed "tar-pits" from which bones of many Pleistocene animals have been recovered. The pits have refilled with tar from natural seeps subsequent to the original excavations, and life-sized models of ground sloths may be seen in the background.

Figure 3. Coprolites (fossil excrement) from the chalk beds of western Kansas. The spiral shape of the coprolites indicates that they may be shark excrement, as sharks (as well as some other fishes) have spiraled structures within their intestines. Courtesy of the Sternberg Memorial Museum.

Some fossils consist of carbonized films, as the original, hard-part lacking organic matter was distilled through loss of the volatile elements, so that only a thin layer of carbon remained. Plants and some shell-less or thin-shelled invertebrates may be preserved in this manner. (Plate 1, Figure G).

Rarely, insects are found preserved in amber or copalite, the fossilized saps or resins of trees that the insects lighted upon, adhered to, and were eventually covered over as more sap flowed down the tree.

Fossil excrement (Figure 3) is known as coprolites and occurs abundantly in some localities. Fossils provide direct evidence of past life, in that they are portions, or impressed replicas of portions, of an organism. Indirect, or non-fossil evidence of former life is supplied by gastroliths, the crop or gizzard stones of birds and reptiles, and by artifacts, tools or other objects manufactured by hominids.

The Study of Fossils

Fossils may be studied from either the taxonomic (evolutionary) or the stratigraphic point of view. The taxonomic study of fossils involves the discovery, classification, and identification of specimens. This is the classical approach to the study of fossils and of course is still carried on today.

The stratigraphic study of fossils began in 1790 when William Smith, an English civil engineer, discovered the Principal of Biological Correlation. Smith's astute observations led to the discovery that given species of fossils were found only in certain definite beds, and the presence of those given species could be used to recognize the same beds (or beds of the same age) in geographically isolated areas. This led to Oppel's zone concept (1856), and his statement that a flora and fauna were characteristic of a certain zone and would be found elsewhere in rocks of that age.

Thus paleontologists discovered that fossils could be used to distinguish different intervals of geologic time, one of the most important ideas ever expressed in geologic literature. It enabled geologists to define the Eras and Periods of geologic time, and their equivalent rock sequences, the Systems, and to correlate distant and previously unknown rock sections with the rocks of the type sections of the Systems. Geologists overextended use of the concept of lateral persistence of fauna and flora, as they neglected to account for faunal changes caused by environmental factors such as temperature and substrate variations. They even neglected to observe or account for the lateral changes in deposition of rock types, although lateral variation from beach sand to offshore mud is well known and obvious to modern stratigraphers. It is also obvious that plants and animals living today in different regions are not the same and that different rock types are being deposited in different areas, at the same time. The idea of facies changes or lateral rock and faunal variations, had to be rediscovered and became widely reapplied again in the 1930's.

There are two separate approaches through which geologists may study fossils from the stratigraphic viewpoint: one is to make correlations and the other is to interpret past ecology or environments of deposition.

Incompleteness of the Fossil Record

Paleontologists will never be able to discover a complete sequence of fossils illustrating evolution from the origin of life through development of Recent life forms. First of all, many organisms lack readily fossilized hard parts, and secondly, the rock record is incomplete. In general, probably more than 90% of all elapsed geologic time is not represented by preserved sediments. Sediments (even marine sediments) become extensively uplifted and exposed to erosion, and the older (Paleozoic) sedimentary records are far less complete than the younger (Cenozoic) sedimentary columns. This is especially true for non-marine rocks (sediments deposited on continental masses) where erosion is most prevalent, as those rocks become proportionately fewer in bulk when compared with the abundance of marine sediments in the older stratigraphic sections. The oldest definitely recognized non-marine rocks may be of Ordovician age, however, one can not be certain that all the known Precambrian rocks are non-marine because of a lack of fossils (the best criterion now available to determine ancient environments).

Apparently sediments are not deposited continuously and some gaps in the sedimentary record are the result of such non-deposition. Even a very slow rate (or intermittent periods of deposition separated by long time intervals) of sedimentation would not suffice to cover and preserve a complete fossil record of life forms that lived in the sea during that time. The shells of such potential fossils would lie exposed on the sea floor and dissolve into the sea-water or become worn or broken into a myriad of fragments by wave and current action.

Very likely many extensive areas of sedimentary rocks and their fossils have been destroyed by metamorphism and granitization. Sediments that become deeply buried are very likely to be so altered.

The completeness of the known fossil record becomes amazing, and not its incomplete-ness, when one considers the unusual conditions needed to preserve organic remains as fossils, as well as the unlikely probability of the fossiliferous rocks being perserved over long intervals of time.

Chapter IV

TAXONOMY

Linnaeus and Systema Naturae

Taxonomy is the science of identifying, classifying and naming plants and animals, and establishing their genetic or evolutionary relationships to other previously described plants and animals. This is one of man's major interests, for all human societies have named animals and we have more recently began to classify them in an evolutionarily arranged system.

Modern taxonomy began in 1759 when the Swedish biologist, Carl von Linné (Linnaeus) (1707-1778) published the tenth edition of his book of biological classification, Systema Naturae. The earlier editions, beginning with the first edition in 1735, had not been consistent, for Linnaeus either did not use generic names uniformly or did not properly describe the species listed in his book. The tenth edition was the first in which generic names and specific descriptions were properly used throughout the book; this is therefore designated as the beginning point of modern taxonomy. Scientific names published prior to 1758 (and the tenth edition) are invalid, even if generic names were used. Any scientific names published after 1758 that do not properly use generic names are also invalid.

Linnaeus divided the plant and animal kingdoms into major groups called phyla, each of which was divided into a series of progressively smaller groups. Each group having many features that distinguish it from all other groups.

The Classification Scheme

The biological classification scheme is dichotomously arranged or "branching". The Kingdom may be compared to a tree trunk with the phyla branching off the trunk as larger branches, and classes arise from the larger branches as smaller ones, and the orders and families are yet smaller branches. Finally, the twigs at the end of the branches are the genera, and the leaves and flowers are the species. Individuals would only be equivalent to the cells or protoplasm of the leaves or the flowers.

A man and a clam belong to the same kingdom, because of certain characteristics in common, but diverge enough to belong to different phyla. The phylum (the Chordata) to which man belongs, includes several classes among which are fish of several kinds, birds, reptiles, amphibians, and other mammals. Mammals, including man, are characterized by the presence of hair, warm bloodedness, and mammary glands. Man belongs to a mammalian order of monkey-like or ape-like forms. Other mammalian orders are characterized by the presence of an odd number of hooves (horses), or an even number of hooves, as in cattle, or flippers (whales), and so on.

The relationship of man to other primates is discussed in more detail in the chapter on primate evolution.

Group of Classification	Man	A fossil clam
Kingdom	Animalia-can locomote, no chlorophyll no cellulose	Animalia-can locomote, no chlorophyll, no cellulose
Phylum	Chordata-has backbone dorsal nerve cord, and gill slits (at least in embryo)	Mollusca-has a shell and mantle, no backbane
Class	Mammalia-has hair, milk glands, warm blooded, three inner ear bones	Pelecypoda-has hatchet-shaped foot
Order	Primatida-monkey-like and ape-like forms	Dysodonta-poorly developed hinge line
Family	Hominidae-great apes, pre-man, man	Pernidae-hinge composed of resilifers
Genus	Homo-man	Inoceramus ino=fibrous keramos=earthen vessel
Species	sapiens-a "wise" human	labiatus-labiate form of Inoceramus
Individual	John Doe, or you or I	specimen number 11384 of the University Museum

When an animal or plant is referred to by its scientific name, two words, consisting of a generic and a specific name must be used. The generic name is always capitalized and is placed first. The names are elements in the binomial (binominal) system and consist of names such as Homo sapiens Linné. Any biological scientist, no matter what his native language, will recognize this as the scientific name for man. The scientific "language" is largely made up of Latin and Latinized words. The generic name, Homo, is the Latin word for man, and the specific name sapiens is the Latin word for wise, a descriptive word for one of the attributes sometimes shown by man. These are words in a foreign language, and they are underlined in a typed text or manuscript so that the typesetter will italicize them. The underlining or italicizing serves to set them off from the rest of the text.

Without use of scientific names there would be confusion as to what animal is being referred to by some names in popular use. The name gopher may refer to either a south-eastern American tortoise or to a western American burrowing animal. The name elk may refer to either the North American Wapiti or the European "moose". The multiplicity of non-scientific names for Equus caballus; loshad, caballo, horse, Schimmel, Cheval and Pferd, among many others would be another source of confusion. Scientific names help to eliminate confusion when two or more animals have the same popular name, as well as the confusion resulting from the same animal having one or more names in each language.

Before the adoption of Linnaeus' system of taxonomy, scientific names were descriptive, of variable length, and lacked generic names that could link them to show close genetic relationships. For example, a pre-Linnaean name for a tree frog was Rana (arborea) pedibus fissus, unguibus fibrotundis, corpore laevi, pone angustato. This means literally, "Frog (tree-living), feet cleft, toes fibrous, body smooth, back narrowed posteriorly". A rather cumbersome though descriptive name. Another closely related frog could have been simply named Bufo, and with no generic name being used, a scientist not familiar with the species would not be able to determine the relationship between the two animals.

Species

Biologists define a species as a taxonomic group of morphologically similar plants or animals with an identical or nearly identical set of genes, so that the organisms, are capable, or potentially capable, of interbreeding and producing viable offspring. Species are difficult to define and many, especially in paleontology, are arbitrary units. The species concept was invented by scientists before knowledge of biologic evolution was popular and widespread, so that species were considered to be static. In nature, taxonomic units constantly change, and new groups evolve from older ones, obviously species are not morphologically or genetically sharply separated from their ancestors.

A subspecies is a geographically localized group of populations of a species that differ genetically, and therefore differ morphologically from other geographically localized population groups of the same species. It is usually easy to assign populations to a subspecies but individual variation is such that some individuals may not be readily identified as to subspecies. Interbreeding among subspecies with production of fertile young is possible and probable where subspecies are in contact. The term geographic race as applied to the various units of some animal species and perhaps to the major groups of Homo sapiens, is equivalent to the term subspecies.

Cultural differences, or cultural blocks that tend to prevent reproduction, such as cannabalism of potential interbreeding stock, or miscegnation taboos, are not relevant for specific separation so long as there is any genetic potential for production of fertile offspring. The origin of species is discussed in Chapter 7.

Obviously, all living men belong to the same species, Homo sapiens, and the species consists of several potentially interbreeding subspecies that produce overly fertile offspring; the subgroups historically have been called geographic races or morphologic subspecies.

The five living subspecies (Capoids, Australoids, Mongoloids, Caucasoids, and Negroids) of Homo sapiens consist of aggregates of populations, that historically have been largely geographically isolated. At the present time (and since 1500 at an ever accelerating rate) our geographically variable species has had various population groups become mobile, so that the historical restriction of each subspecies to a definite portion of the total range of the species is beginning to disappear, and this could lead to a reduction (but not total loss) of the subspecific morphologic differences, and a breakdown of the geographic isolation required to maintain that subspecific distinctiveness. For example, I have some morphologic characteristics (shovel-shaped incisor teeth, lack of wisdom teeth and a broad head) indicative of partial descent from Amerindians, and some other morphologic characteristics (blue eyes, and a relatively higher degree of hirsute adornment) that indicate partial descent from European ancestors.

Chapter V

ORIGIN OF THE EARTH

Relationship of Geology and Astronomy

Historical geology is the science of Earth history, and includes the study of changes that have occurred to the Earth during geologic time, including the evolution of life. Earth history begins with the formation of the planet at least 4.7 billion years ago.

Geologists read the record of past life and events in rocks and attempt to correlate interpretations so as to form a compilation of the former geography, biology and geologic processes that have modified the Earth during its existence. This is an attempt to form a continuous record of Earth history, and is really a synthesis of several branches of geology; no one man is capable of writing an authoritative summary of the entire Earth's history.

The rock sequence in any one locality is incomplete, because most (probably 90%) of elapsed geologic time is not represented by preserved rock sequences. The incompleteness of the rock record is caused by nondeposition of rocks, erosion of previously deposited rocks, and metamorphism or granitization of sediments, so the rock column at best is fragmentary and a complete or even nearly complete rock column could not be pieced together even if all the preserved rocks of different ages on Earth present today were used. Deciphering the history of the Earth is much like assembling a jigsaw puzzle with missing and damaged parts. In general, the older the rocks, the harder the task, as older rocks are more likely to have been eroded away or metamorphosed.

The Universe

The study of historical geology and the origin of the Earth overlaps into the realm of astronomy. The Earth is a very minor portion of the universe for it is one of nine relatively small planets that revolve around the sun, an "average" star with regard to size and type. Probably, other planetary systems exist, but they are too small to be seen by their reflected light and they do not glow. Even if planets orbited about the nearest star to our solar system, Alpha Centauri, a triple star 4.3 light years away, we could not observe them directly with our best telescopes, although we may detect their presence by other means. A light year is about six million million miles, the distance light can travel in a year.

Our sun and most of the other stars (Figure 4) we can see belong to our galactic system, a large spiral-shaped disc of stars and dust, with a diameter across the greatest width of its disc of approximately 80,000 light years. The sun is located about 26,000 light years away from the center of the galaxy, where the densest accumulation of stars has formed, and the sun is in motion within our galaxy toward the constellation Cygnus at a rate of approximately 150 miles per second. The center of our galaxy may be seen by looking from Earth toward the Milky Way and into that dense accumulation of stars, and the distribution of stars is more sparse if the observation is made through the galaxy at a divergent angle to that direction.

Our galaxy occupies only a small portion of space, and millions of other galaxies (Figure 5) can be detected. Hubble has estimated that there may be as many as a billion galaxies. One such galaxy, the spiral nebula in the constellation of Andromeda, may be seen by the unaided eye in the evening during late fall and winter. The nebula is a larger galaxy than ours and has a maximum diameter of 127,000 light years across the greatest width of its disc, like most galaxies, it is discoid in form with spirally distributed "arms".

Astronomers in examining light received from distant stars by means of telescopes, pass a portion of that light through prisms or gratings so as to examine the spectrum and determine the chemical composition of the source star. In doing so they noticed a displacement of lines of the spectrum (light waves) toward the red end of the spectrum relative to

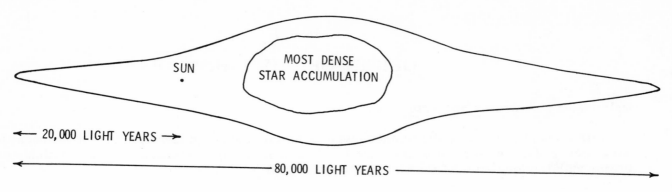

Figure 4. Cross-section of our galaxy.

Figure 5. An irregularly shaped galaxy known as the Orion Nebula. University of Kansas Observatory, photograph by author under direction of Dr. Henry Horak.

corresponding spectra made on earth. This displacement was found to be proportional to the distance of the stars from Earth, and the shift is assumed to be caused by a recession of the stars away from a central area in the universe. The farther away the systems are located from the presumed central area, the faster they seem to recede. The farthest away and fastest moving galaxy measured to date is in the constellation Hydra, a distance of approximately 720,000,000 light years, and that galaxy is receding at a rate of about 38,000 miles per second. Other rapidly receding objects are known as quasars and are rather small objects (a few light-days in diameter through their centers) that are very bright, and possess large, outer cores. They are faster moving, some seem to recede as fast as 153,000 miles per second, but their nature is poorly understood at present.

The universe seems to be exploding from a central area in which all matter had originally been accumulated. If this process of expansion were to be reversed or if we extrapolate the effect of such a reversal, we would find that about 12 billion years ago all matter in the universe would have been confined to a central area. This expanding universe concept is known as the Big Bang Theory.

Another theory proposed by Fred Hoyle, which Dr. Hoyle has since partially rescinded, is based on the assumption that matter is constantly being created from energy in intergalactic space and the universe is caused to expand as the matter occupies portions of space. There is no final answer as to whether or not the universe is expanding. Another concept of the structure of the universe is that it is "accordion-like" and expands and shrinks over an 82 billion year cycle. After each shrinking or collapse the universe is recreated, and begins to expand as the cycle continues.

Origin and Evolution of Stars

Space is not totally empty; and may contain as much as 1 milligram of matter to each ten cubic miles. Usually this matter is very sparsely distributed but locally it has built up into great clouds, some of which are luminous, and others are dark masses which may blot out light radiated by the stars located behind the clouds (as seen from Earth). In places these clouds seem to contract into small nebulae with masses equivalent to that of the sun. Perhaps the dust particles may be caused to accumulate by pressure exerted through impacts of light particles, and the dust particles (a maximum diameter of a few microns) begin to form aggregates. Eventually the aggregates become large enough to produce strong local gravitation and then condensation would proceed at a faster rate.

The nuclear reactions within stellar interiors require very high temperatures, of more than a million degrees Centigrade in order to occur. Temperatures of this magnitude are created on Earth only by thermonuclear explosions. Stellar radiation is caused by a complex nuclear reaction in which essentially four hydrogen atoms are converted by the nuclear fusion process into one helium atom with loss of 0.7% of the original mass involved. The lost mass is converted into energy. This reaction occurs according to Einstein's equation for nuclear reactions, $Energy = Mass \times C^2$ (where the constant C is the speed of light).

During their period of greatest radiation, stars gradually use up hydrogen and are extremely hot.

Stellar evolution (Figure 6) begins with contraction of interstellar dust clouds into globes, then the temperature of the globes rises as energy is produced by the contraction, and when the temperature reaches the proper level, nuclear fusion, the conversion of hydrogen to helium, takes place. Then the star becomes self-luminous, although it may still be surrounded by a cloud of unabsorbed dust. Stars similar to our sun follow a set evolutionary sequence, as shortly after contraction into globes takes place, they glow feebly with a dull, red light; then the hydrogen "fire" starts, and the stars become brighter, more stable, more luminous and are known as typical or main sequence stars. As the supply of hydrogen is used up, the stars begin to expand and become red giants. Next the stars' production of nuclear energy decreases, and they begin to collapse, possibly through an explosive outburst known as a "nova" and then become very dense pulsars (and may weigh more than 13 metric tons per cubic centimeter) and small, glow feebly, and are called white dwarfs. Recent studies indicate that collapsed stars may become so dense and have such a high gravitational attraction that light can not escape them. This theoretical remnant of a collapsed star is known as a "black-hole in space", as it is supposed that it would be a portion of space that would neither emit light nor permit light to pass through. Apparently the light emitting objects in space only have enough bulk to account for three percent of the mass of the universe. If this is so, then much of the matter in the universe is either in "black-holes in space" or is too far away to be detected.

Origin of the Solar System

There are two main theories, the collision (dynamic encounter) and nebular, that have been proposed to account for the origin of the solar system.

The collision hypothesis was described first, in 1749, by Georges de Buffon; his hypothesis was a collision of the sun and a comet disrupted a portion of the sun and splashed out matter that condensed and formed the planets. Later, the structure of comets became better understood, and astronomers realized that a disruptive collision with the sun was not possible as the comets not only lack enough mass, but are composed largely of frozen gases that would ablate away before striking the sun.

The collision idea was modified in 1900 and named the planetesimal hypothesis by the geologist T. C. Chamberlain and the astronomer F. R. Moulton. They assumed that if two stars approached and passed close by each other, large tidal bulges would be created within the stars that would result in bolts of matter being pulled away to form the nuclei of planets. Sir James Jeans and Harold Jeffreys further modified the collision idea into their tidal theory

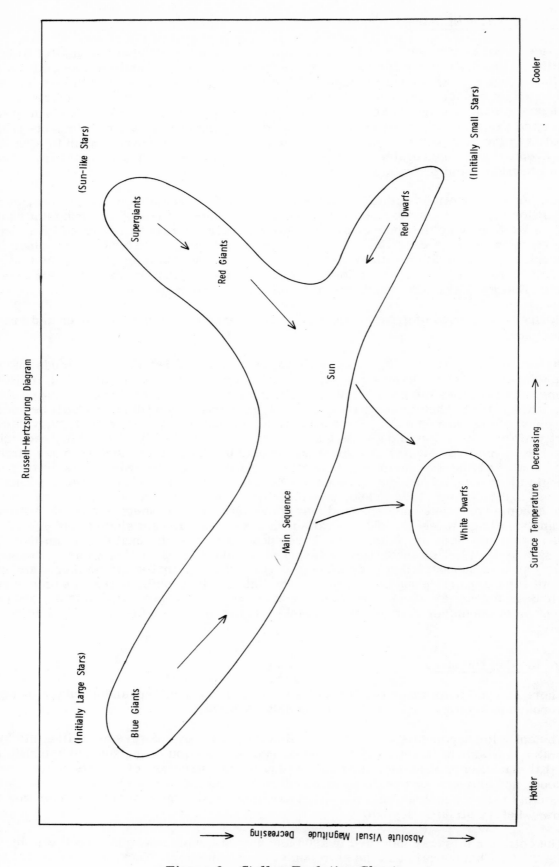

Figure 6. Stellar Evolution Chart.

so that instead of bolts of matter, there was a single filament that broke up into globules and the globules were given a rotational motion by gravitational pull of the receeding star.

The collision hypothesis was discarded in the late 1940's and astronomers have adopted a recently modified version of the nebular hypothesis that was first proposed by the German philosopher Immanuel Kant in 1755.

In 1796 the French mathematician Pierre de Laplace described how the solar system could have formed from a great cloud of hot gas, that cooled, contracted, and gave off concentric rings of matter because of centripetal force created by rotation of the mass. The rings were condensed into planets by gravitation, and the remaining gas consolidated in the center to form the sun. The planets sloughed off rings that formed satellites, and such rings were still around Saturn, according to Laplace. Laplace's hypothesis is similar to Kant's, but seemingly was independently arrived at by Laplace, for Laplace mentioned that only Buffon had previously attempted to account for the origin of the solar system. If the concepts of Laplace were correct, the sun should rotate more rapidly than it does, so the idea was largely ignored for many years.

The nebular hypothesis was modified and reintroduced by the German astronomer, Carl von Weiszäcker in 1944. Weiszäcker described how the planets formed from a cloud of dust particles in turbulent motion, and that gradually a systematic circulation pattern emerged from the random turbulence of the dust within the cloud. Collisions, resulting in pulverizing as well as adherence of particles occurred, and the systematic circulation pattern eventually resulted in accretion of solid planets at definite distances from the sun. Weiszäcker used mathematics to help prove his theory, and his concept of the nebular theory implies that the Earth and other planets formed in a cold state, and that all stars may go through a planet forming stage. G. P. Kuiper modified Weiszäcker's turbulence pattern, but kept the mechanism of accretion the same.

Other astronomers, such as Hannes Alfven, believe that all dust particles in space have electrical charges and it is this factor, not gravitational attraction or pressure applied by light particles, that causes motion and accumulation of interstellar dust particles into clouds. There is not much agreement on the details, but all astronomers seem to agree with the formation of the solar system from a turbulent dust cloud surrounding the sun, and that the planets were cold during infall of particles as the planets accumulated. If this theory is correct, nearly all stars would pass through a planet forming stage and there should be many planetary systems, unfortunately distant planets can not be detected readily with present day astronomical equipment. Nevertheless, recent studies indicate that star 61 Cygni has a non-luminous companion with a planet-like mass, about 17 times that of Jupiter, and other stars are also suspected to have planet-sized companions. Two satellites of about 0.7 and 1.12 times the mass of Jupiter have been detected near another star.

Pregeological Eras of the Earth

The sun may be six billion years old, and the Earth and rest of the solar system reached their present mass at least 4.5 to 4.8 billion years ago. Although we have not yet determined the age of any terrestrial rocks to be more than 3.98 billion years, we assume the Earth to be no less than 4.5 to 4.8 billion years old as radioactive age determinations of meteorites are of that order of magnitude. Meteorites are probably fragments of a planet that formed at the same time as the Earth, underwent differentiation into a core, mantle and crust, then disintegrated and formed the asteroids that are mostly located between Mars and Jupiter. Shortly after breaking up of the planet, the isolated masses of magma began to cool and then crystallized. Brian Mason has discussed the mineral suites that are characteristic of meteorites and has shown that they are compatible with an origin as small asteroid-sized bodies of approximately 80 kilometers diameter. After crystallization of the minerals, accumulation of radioactive decay products began, and our radioactive age determinations date the formation of the asteroids and not the planets. If asteroid formation occurred about 4.7 billion years ago, the Earth and the other planets are at least that old, and may well be much older.

Following accumulation of the bulk of the Earth there was a period of time when infall of dust and larger particles occurred at a much greater rate than at the present. The primaeval Earth formed through random accumulation of particles, and had a heterogeneously uniform composition from the center to the outer layer. This is not so today; the Earth (Figure 7) has

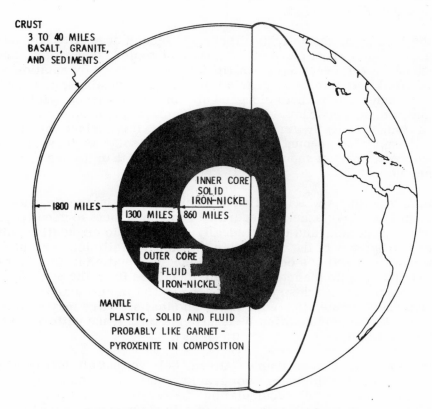

Figure 7.   Cross-section of the Earth.

a core 3400 km thick probably composed of nickel-iron alloys with densities ranging between 10 and 13. This core is enveloped by successive layers of decreasingly less dense magmas (the mantle) and the layers culminate with a thin, 30 km thick crust or outermost layer, with a density of about 2.8. This zonation occurred when the Earth heated up to about 2000° C (surface temperature) and became molten as a result of heat produced by radioactive decay, during the pre-geological stages of the Earth's development, more than 4.0 billion years ago, and before any portion of a permanent crust or presently preserved crustal rocks had formed. Most of the Earth's iron melted and flowed toward the center of the Earth as lighter substances were buoyed upward and were segregated into successive layers arranged in order of decreasing density outward from the iron and nickel core. During the heating-up process the Earth apparently lost its primaeval atmosphere, that probably consisted of molecules of the gases most abundant in the universe, the light gases hydrogen, helium, and methane, that are rare on Earth today. The increased surface temperature caused the gas molecules to move with higher velocities so that they exceeded the Earth's escape velocity and left the planet's gravitational field. The Earth's present atmosphere and sea water was derived from volatile substances present in magmas, as excess gases and steam present are given off through volcanoes by magmas as they crystallize to form the crustal rocks.

The Earth gradually cooled, and a very unstable crust formed that may originally have resembled the surface of the moon today. The original crust and its presumably cratered surface were soon modified by the processes of weathering, erosion and sedimentation. These processes could not begin until an atmosphere and surface water had accumulated, thus the water and atmosphere lacking moon has been relatively little modified in comparison with the Earth.

Chapter VI

THE ORIGIN OF LIFE

Evolution

Evolution began approximately twelve billion years ago when the elements and universe were formed with the beginning of nuclear evolution. The temporal beginning of nuclear evolution has been determined by measuring the distance to the farthest known galaxies in the universe, about six billion light years. These galaxies are receding from the center of the universe and have required at least six billion years to reach the positions they now seem to occupy. Furthermore light emitted by their stars has taken six billion years to reach us, and therefore the universe must be at least twelve billion years old.

After a period of stellar and planet formation, nuclear evolution was succeeded by chemical evolution, the formation of organic compounds of various degrees of complexity, before any living systems appeared. The organic compounds present and the composition of the atmosphere, when chemical evolution went on are not known with certainty, however there are three different methods by which diverse organic chemical compounds could have formed in either a reducing (oxygen-poor) or an oxidizing atmosphere.

Chemical Evolution

Chemical evolution occurred by polymerization of one-carbon-containing molecules, such as CO_2 (carbon dioxide) or CH_4 (methane), into larger and more complex two-carbon and four-carbon molecules. One-carbon compounds probably were present in the Earth's atmosphere as those compounds are abundant in space and have been detected on other planets and in comets, however compounds are not present in extremely hot environments, such as stars, as molecules disrupt when too hot.

Recent studies of the chemistry of a meteorite that fell in Arizona in 1969, have demonstrated that five amino acids were present, and that, at least extraterrestrially, complex organic compounds existed more than 4.5 billion years ago. Whether or not these amino acids formed by the processes of chemical evolution as discussed here, are not known. Another meteorite that fell near Murchison in Australia, was found to contain eighteen amino acids. It is fairly certain that the presence of those amino acids is not the result of terrestrial contamination, because some of the acids have unusual configurations. Amino acids formed by natural organic processes on Earth (except in procaryotic bacteria) all have "left-handed" structures, whereas those from the meteorites have both "left-handed" and a mirror-image or "right-handed" structures. This indicates that the amino acids originated from synthesis of chemicals in space. Furthermore the presence of complex organic compounds, such as methanol, formaldehyde, and cyanoacetylene, has been detected in interstellar high density gas clouds in space.

The Earth's present atmosphere began to accumulate as the crust solidified and lost volatile elements that became the atmosphere, which in its primary state probably consisted mostly of nitrogen, hydrogen, carbon monoxide, ammonia, chlorine, sulfur gases, and carbon dioxide. The gases were given off during the crystallization of igneous rocks from magma, a mixture of gaseous, fluid and solid substances, that contains an excess of gaseous and fluid (volatile) materials. Those substances in excess of the amounts required to form crystalline rocks, are lost into the atmosphere through volcanic eruptions. Presumably then, the primaeval earth had an abundant supply of one-carbon molecules in the atmosphere, and if those molecules were exposed to ultraviolet light from the sun, more complex one-carbon-containing molecules, including hydrogen cyanide, formic acid and formaldehyde could form. If formic acid and aldehyde molecules were mixed with nitrogen containing compounds, ammonia, nitric acid, or nitrates, along with continued exposure to ultraviolet light, this could result in formation of heterocyclic compounds such as amino acids, the building blocks of protoplasm.

High energy radiation in the form of cosmic rays (positively charged atomic nuclei emanating from the sun and other stars) could cause similar sequences of polymerization. This has been done experimentally in a cyclotron, by irradiating solutions of carbon dioxide and water so two-carbon substances were formed, and further irradiation resulted in four-carbon compounds being made.

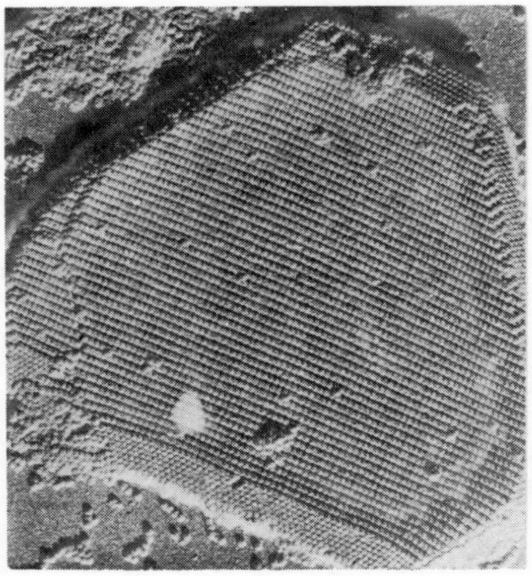

Figure 8. A virus, the southern bean mosaic virus protein, showing the arrangement of spherical molecular particles. Magnification about 25,000x. Courtesy of Dr. R. W. G. Wyckoff.

Another cause of polymerization could have been electric discharges (lightning) in the upper atmosphere where methane, hydrogen, ammonia, and water are present, and a variety of compounds, including amino acids, could be formed from these materials. H. C. Wrey and S. L. Miller experimentally created amino acids by means of electric discharges within an apparatus containing water, methane, ammonia, and hydrogen. In 1972 Dr. S. L. Miller repeated his 1953 experiment, and found that he had produced the same eighteen amino acids, and in the same relative abundances as those found in the Murchison meteorite.

Any one of the three methods could have resulted in the formation and accumulation of organic molecules, perhaps all three methods were active in early Precambrian time and resulted in the formation and accumulation of organic matter, that would have formed a film or slick on the surface of the ocean. This "organic soup" would have been an oily black or dark-brown fluid containing amino acids, carbohydrates, purines, pyrimidines, and nucleic acids.

At present there is no noticeable natural accumulation of nonorganically created organic matter. Any organic molecules newly formed today would instantly be assimilated by and converted into bacteria or other organisms, and organic matter probably could neither accumulate in easily detectable quantities, nor could it readily be distinguished from similar molecules created by living organisms.

In the early Precambrian there were no life forms to assimilate or cause decay of organic molecules as they formed, so the molecules accumulated. The organic molecules were not living because they could not duplicate all the functions of life; life forms must simultaneously display certain attributes, among which are growth, reproduction, response to stimuli, and evolution. Anyone of these attributes can be reproduced in a single nonliving system, for example, crystals grow, and peat may evolve in a sequence through lignite, bituminous and anthracite coals to graphite, and some sensitive compounds such as mercuric fulminate may react violently to the proper stimulus.

The Development of Living Molecules

It seems likely that some organic chemical compounds slowly evolved to become living systems and possibly life arose from more than one sequence of chemical evolution. The processes of polymerization may have taken place either in the oily films on the ocean surface or in slicks surrounding grains of sediments or foam bubbles on the beaches. Possibly the compounds began metabolic activity in animal-like fashion. That is they "fed" on other organic compounds present in the slicks. As the supply of organic compounds (and oil slicks) were consumed, a plant-like metabolic evolved and the organisms began to produce their own organic materials, using solar energy to convert inorganic substances. The first living system would have been arbitrarily defined as a life form, as it would have been little more than a large molecule. The virus (Figure 8) is nearly a life form as it has most, but not all the attributes of life for it can reproduce only when inside a living cell or nucleus of a cell.

Viruses are ultramicroscopic infectuous agents which cause various didsases of animals and plants. In man they cause measles, mumps, colds, flu, rabies, polio, as well as other diseases, and range in size from 10 to 150 millimicrons. The larger viruses have been photographed by means of electron microscopes and seem to be single crystals.

The only portions of an organism capable of growth are proteins containing nucleic acid, but those substances can not grow unless they are in a cell or the nucleus of a cell. Life outside the cell membrane is not possible for any of the cell's isolated components. The simplest naturally occurring substances that are capable of being self reproducible are nucleoprotein macromolecules known as viruses and genes. They are similar in chemical composition, plant viruses being composed of RNA (ribonucleic acid), animal viruses are composed of protein-coated RNA or DNA (deoxy-ribonucleic acid), and genes are composed of DNA.

Neither the virus nor gene can reproduce outside a cell and they must form a parasitic and and symbiotic relationship respectively in order to reproduce. If the virus or gene and the host cell are compatible reproduction of the virus or genes can occur. An early Precambrian virus-like form, not yet evolved into a living organism, could have fed upon or assimilated other organic matter in a saprophytic or parasitic manner to accumulate atoms for continued growth.

This could have reached a state of equilibrium, so that no longer was the host consumed or destroyed, instead a symbiotic relationship (non-destructive and mutually beneficial) was reached, and some early virus-like organism could then have been transformed into a gene giving rise to the possibility of identical replication or reproduction, and to the possibility of mutations, i.e. random changes in gene structure that would lead to biological evolution.

Laboratory Experiments

Present day laboratory experiments have resulted in reproduction of RNA by seeding a test tube, containing the chemicals present in an RNA containing virus, with a strand of RNA. The strand of RNA used to "seed" the test tube converted the chemicals into similar strands. This is not creation of life, but reproduction within a nonliving system.

Other experimenters have split and isolated portions of the nucleic acid molecules, and it is only a matter of time until some experimenter formulates or creates a DNA molecule from a nonliving source. Beyond this lies the production of living systems in scientists' laboratories. Although laboratory work on this process is still in the formative stages, some promising results have been obtained. Some experimenters have succeeded in producing short molecular structures, of the so-called "precursor molecules to life". Formation of these chain-like compounds has made many researchers optimistic about the possibility of producing living molecules in the laboratory.

BIOLOGIC EVOLUTION

Evolutionary Sequences

The successful formation of life from chemical evolution, would cause biological evolution to occur and the resultant development of a broad spectrum of life forms, that would adapt so as to be able to live in all environments capable of supporting life.

Genes and Chromosomes

Evolutionary changes and, paradoxically, inherited similarities are both determined by chemical units of heredity called genes. Genes consist of spiral, ladder-like-structured (Figure 13) molecules of DNA, in which the arrangement of the "steps" and the distribution of atoms within the structure is assumed to determine the morphology of the life form possessing those genes. Disruptions or mutations of the usual arrangement of atoms within the DNA molecule would cause evolution to occur. Sameness, sibling-parental resemblances, is the result of inheritance of unmutated parental genes. Genes are not directly visible, and are contained within elongated, striped structures called chromosomes (Figure 9) that may be seen by means of an optical microscope, within cell nuclei shortly before, during, and shortly after mitosis (Figures 10, 12) or cell division. Normally, chromosomes are not readily detectable as discrete string-like bodies within the nucleus, even though they probably are disseminated there.

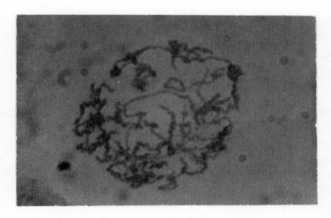

Figure 9. Human chromosomes in the late prophase stage of mitosis. Photograph courtesy of Dr. Donald Nash, Colorado State University.

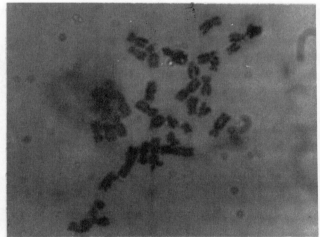

Figure 10. Mitotic chromosomes from human cells. There are twenty-three pairs of chromosomes in each human cell. Photograph courtesy of Dr. Donald Nash, Colorado State University.

Cell division or mitosis consists of first, division of the nucleus and second, division of the cytosome or remainder of the cell. The first stage of mitosis is the prophase (Figure 9), during which chromosomes become visible within the cell nucleus as long, coiled threads, and then the chromosomes pair longitudinally and form chromatids. Following this the centrioles (small star-shaped bodies) separate and the chromosomes (chromatids) contract to about one-twentieth of their original lengths, and the chromosomes can not be distinguished within the chromatids. The second stage is metaphase during which a spindle-like structure forms and the chromatids become attached to the spindle fibers, along the spindle's equatorial plane.

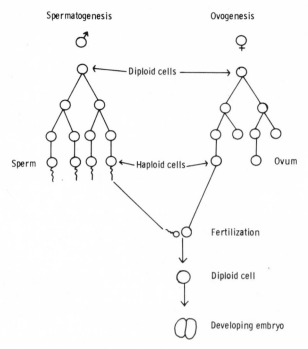

Figure 11. Meiosis diagram.

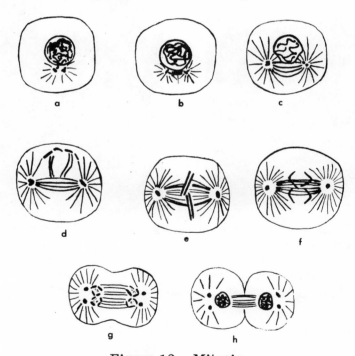

Figure 12. Mitosis.

a. Resting phase
b. Prophase, chromosomes appear
c. Late prophase, centrioles separate and chromatids form
d. Metaphase, spindle forms
e. Late metaphase, chromatids arranged along spindle
f. Anaphase, chromatids separate
g. Late anaphase, chromosomes reach opposite poles
h. Telophase, and cell division.

In the third stage, anaphase, the chromatids separate, become chromosomes again and begin to move toward the opposite poles of the spindle as the spindle fibers shorten. The final stage of mitosis is telophase in which the chromosomes merge into a chromatin network (and can not be observed) within the two newly formed daughter nuclei, and the spindle disappears as the centrioles divide and enter each of the new cells, as the cytosome divides (at right angles to the long axis of the spindle) to complete formation of the two daughter cells.

Mitosis is the means by which an organism grows as the "new cells" add to organ size.

Chromosomes are found in all cells of an organism's being, so that each cell bears a full set of chromosomes and a complete record of the genetic code that determined the individual's morphology. The genes within a chromosome are paired, one gene of each pair derived from the maternal parent and the other gene from the paternal parent.

When germ (reproductive) cells are formed, a mitotic-like reduction of chromosome number known as meiosis occurs. Briefly and simply, meiosis (Figure 11) consists of two cell divisions in each of which the chromosomes of the parent cell line up, split in half lengthwise and then separate as the two daughter cells are formed. The germ cells resulting from the second division have a reduced chromosome content are called "haploid", and contain only half the genes of each chromosome so when an haploid sperm cell fertilizes an haploid egg cell, the normal (diploid) chromosome number is restored with the resulting new individual containing chromosomes composed of equal numbers of randomly-selected maternal and paternal genes.

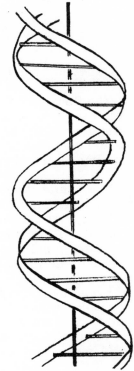

Figure 13. Diagrammatic representation of the structure of a gene, illustrating its spiral and ladder-like nature.

The chromosomal pairs contain duplicate, or overlapping gene pairs, so that an eye color determining gene from each parent is present, as well as gene pairs for height, hair color, hair curliness, and so forth. If an individual's genetic code is programmed to provide an individual with conflicting traits, only one trait can be morphologically expressed. Such an overriding trait is called dominant, and the hidden or unexpressed trait is termed recessive. For example, if your chromosomes contain genes for both blue and brown eyes, the gene for brown eyes is dominant, and you will be brown-eyed. However, you will produce germ cells half of which carry only a blue-eyed trait, and the other half will carry only a brown-eyed trait, so that you are capable of passing either genetic trait to offspring.

A linking of unlike genes for the same trait within a chromosome is called heterozygous. An individual with identical or homozygous genes for blue eyes, would not only be blue-eyed, but could only produce germ cells with chromosomes containing genes for the blue-eyed trait.

Gregor Mendel

Studies of inheritance began with the work of an Austrian monk, Gregor Mendel, in 1857. Mendel worked in comparative obscurity, and although he had no concept of genes, he studied traits involving dominance and recessiveness of inherited characteristics of peas. His paper was published in 1866, and went unnoticed until other scientists, Correns, De Vries, and Tschermak, all working independently of each other, first rediscovered Mendel's inheritance patterns and then his published paper, all shortly before 1900. The science of genetics grew from these early studies of plant inheritance by botanists.

Significance for Evolution

The forty-six chromosomes of the human cell (Figure 9) contain about 24,000 genes and provide enough genetic variability for a great diversity of morphology among man. Some gene combinations would be more favorable for survival (and reproduction!) in a given environment, and would be selected in that environment and the less favorable gene combinations would die out, or not be selected.

In a humid, warm, malaria-infested region, those individuals possessing sickle-cells that resist malarial infections, less body fat along with longer limbs to aid body heat loss, and production of sweat with low salt content, would be selected favorably over less well adjusted individuals. However, in a cool, dry climate, such individuals would be selected against because of the lethality of the sickle-cell trait when homozygous, and inability of long-limbed bodies that lack insulating fat layers to retain enough body heat to resist frost-bite and freezing.

Even though the number of extant human genes is great enough to permit a wide diversity of morphologic form, it would be difficult to formulate an entirely new animal from them or for that matter, from the extant genes of any other animal. Evolution takes place through mutations, the production of new genes from previously existing ones, by altering the structure of the DNA molecules so that permanent, and inheritable genetic changes that are expressed morphologically take place.

There are other, non-mutational changes that occur to chromosomes that are known as chromosomal aberrations. These changes occur within the nucleus of the cell and consist of chromosomes being broken and realigning with a differing order of genes or deletion of some genes from the chromosomes. These changes could result in faulty gene replication, and even deletion of major portions of offspring produced by animals with chromosomal aberrations, if the changes occurred in germ cells. These changes are not mutations, because there is no alteration of the DNA molecular structure.

Mutations

We do not know the basic causes of most mutations that occur to animals in nature, however mutated genes have been created in laboratory animals through experiments wherein the animals were exposed to radiation such as X-rays, subatomic particles, and ultraviolet light. Mutations also have been caused by exposure to some carcinogenic chemicals such as mustard gas and coal tars.

Prior to the advent of man's industrial civilization, carcinogenic (cancer-inducing- chemicals and sources of intense radiation did not normally exist over widespread areas in nature.

The paleontologic record indicates that life on Earth has undergone numerous and extensive developmental sequences because of evolution. So an effective, widespread, natural cause of mutations must exist. There is background radiation from radioactive materials in the Earth's crust, and cosmic radiation (subatomic particles emitted by stellar sources) that are uniformly distributed over the Earth and those two sources are ever-present, potential causes of mutations. Perhaps cosmic radiation emitted by our Sun has caused most of the genetic mutations observed on Earth. This radiation would be particularly effective during periods of time when the Earth's magnetic field was weak or temporarily absent, as then the full influx of cosmic particles could reach the Earth's surface and the life forms that live there.

Most mutations seem to be only minor alterations of a genes' structure, and do not involve major genetic or obvious morphologic structural changes. Probably most mutations are not only minor and unfavorable changes, but are also recessive in inheritance and so may exist without being detected for many generations.

Some mutations are dominant and cause obvious changes of morphology. The famous Ancon Ram, born in New England in 1791, was affected by a strongly expressed and dominant mutation. The ram was born with abnormally short legs, a mutation he passed on to his offspring. Thus farmers were able to use the Ancon Ram to selectively breed a race of short-legged sheep that could not easily climb or jump over the low stone fences that are used in New England to confine animal herds. In nature a mutation resulting in short leggedness would have been deleterious, and the odds for survival of the Ancon Ram would have been poor. The short legs would have prevented rapid flight and escape from predators, and would even have interferred with that prime prerequisite for evolution, transfer of genes to produce new generations. Great numbers of sheep with the mutation for short legs survive today only because it is beneficial to the herdsmen and aids them in keeping their sheep confined.

Similar mutations that would have been deleterious to animals in nature were the development of polled (hornless) cattle and white chickens and white turkeys that lacked natural camouflage. The mutations also proved to be of benefit to the herdsman-farmer, and the mutation-bearing animals increased numerically under his care.

Seemingly, mutations occur randomly, and are likely to be useless, or even harmful to the recipient. Evolution proceeds blindly along randomly oriented paths, and if it were not for natural selection, races of bizarre monstrosities would develop.

Lamarck

The Chevalier de Lamarck (1744-1829) proposed a theory of evolution wherein changes that occurred to an animal during its lifetime would be passed on to its offspring. Those changes are called somatic changes today, and include development of strength and muscles through weightlifting, or bone and organ deformation resulting from lack of vitamins and mineral nutrients. This differs from our modern concept of the causes of evolution, for we believe now that the change occurs first in the genes (germ plasm), then in the body.

Lamarck's proposed mechanism of evolution was disproved by Weismann's experimental attempt to grow tailless rats. Successive generations of rats were deprived of their tails surgically, however each new generation was born with tails. If Lamarck's ideas had been correct, eventually a race of tailless rats should have evolved. A further proof is the still present necessity for circumcision of young men in groups such as Australoids that have practiced ritual mutilation of the penis for thousands of years.

Lamarckism passed on slowly, and thrived in a modified form under the sponsorship of Lysenko in Russia until a few years ago. Apparently Lysenko's position of scientific authority depended on a political affiliation with Stalin, and his Neolamarckism did not long survive the Stalin Era.

Natural Selection

Darwin's contribution to evolution was his extensive documentation of the fact of its occurrence, and his concept of natural selection that he set forth in "The Origin of Species" in 1859. Darwin thought that natural selection proceeded by nature selecting individuals best suited for survival and reproduction, in a manner similar to man choosing livestock with desired qualities and breeding them selectively to improve strains of domestic animals.

An example of natural selection, known popularly as industrial melanism, is occurring today in Great Britain. Beginning with the industrial revolution, burning of coal deposited large amounts of soot around industrial regions of Great Britain, darkening buildings and tree trunks. This enabled some light-colored moths to develop a dark-color mutation that has become established, as those moths are better camouflaged on the no longer light-colored tree trunks. The dark, or melanistic, variety of moth is most abundant about industrial areas, whereas the light-colored variety is more abundant in areas lacking deposits of soot. Experiments have shown that bird predation rates on those moths with camouflage colors properly matched to tree trunk color is low, and predation of moths with unmatched colors is significantly higher.

Natural selection is not mainly a function of predator control, the "nature red in tooth and claw" of Victorian days. Other less obvious factors may have a far greater effect.

The Mechanisms of Natural Selection

If a pair of houseflies were to reproduce in April, and if they and all their descendants were to continue reproducing and all of them were to live until August, the result would be about 200,000,000,000,000,000,000 flies! This could not happen in nature. First of all, because flies only live about a month, but even if all the fly eggs hatched and all the young survived, it would not be long before all the Earth's organic matter would be combined into flies. The population size-limiting factors that prevent this from happening, are those factors that function in natural selection.

An important population size control factor is food supply, as sufficient and readily available food of the proper kind must be present. If the population grows too numerous, it depletes the available food supply and then starvation depletes the population. Under these circumstances natural selection would favor individuals able to adapt to and utilize unusual or new foods, or those individuals with a better metabolism so that they could survive on a reduced diet.

Disease resistance is another important factor in population size control, and animals with genetic factors that aid in disease resistance will be selected. Whole populations have been killed off by diseases such as rinderpest and bubonic plague. One of the major factors in the early American colonists' successful occupation of the eastern seacoast of the New World was the Amerindians lack of resistance to smallpox and other diseases that were unknown in the Americas prior to their introduction from Europe.

In 1880 the Navajo and Hopi Tribes, who live in the four-corners area of the United States, each consisted of about 4,000 people, at the present time the Hopis still number about 4,000 persons. The Navajo Tribe has increased to more than 180,000 individuals since 1880. Presumably the difference in population increases were caused by the Hopis living in crowded pueblos where primitive sanitation facilities allow rapid spread of fly-borne diseases, such as diarrhea, that cause deaths among infants. The Navajos live in widely spaced hogans, usually more than a mile apart and therefore beyond the limits of an individual fly's territorial ranging ability, so that fly-borne diseases were not readily spread among the Navajos. This allowed a higher infant survival rate among the Navajos and resulted in a numerical increase in their population. This is an excellent example of the control disease can exert on population size and growth.

Other population size-control factors include territorial limits. After an organism has densely populated all the space available and suitable for it, further population increases cause overcrowding that may result in development of physically weakened or mentally aberrant individuals that are unable to compete favorably with other species.

The effects of climate limit the geographic distribution of organisms to those life zones in which they are best adapted to live. Unseasonable weather, such as early fall frosts or late spring snows can cause widespread freezing and killing of plants. The normal seasonal changes of weather limit the growth and reproductive cycles of many temperate and arctic zone organisms.

Predator control also functions as old or sick and infirm individuals are killed off. Probably predators have less effect than food supply, territory, and disease resistance in controlling population size.

The Struggle for Existence

The struggle for existence is an intraspecific and interspecific competition for food, space, mates, and development of resistance to diseases. The intraspecific competition for economic dominance envisioned by Victorians, and used by them to justify the cruelties perpetrated through laissez-faire capitalism, is not at all the process of natural selection as envisioned by Darwin.

Success in the struggle for existence goes to those individuals with favorable or advantageous mutations that enable them to survive and pass their success, in the form of genes, or to the next generation. In brief, it is the ability to reproduce great numbers of vigorous, disease-resistant, climate-tolerant, metabolically-efficient, highly fecund individuals. If there are no offspring produced, then no matter how superior the genetic composition of the animal, the animal is a failure, phylogenetically speaking.

Mules, produced by cross-breeding horses with donkeys, are physically superior to either parent, but are evolutionary failures for they are sterile.

The Origin of Species

Species originate through the formation and accumulation of mutations within a population's gene pool. The relatively rarely occurring advantageous mutations would accumulate within the gene pool and would gradually alter the mean genetic composition and morphology of the animals. After a long time, enough genetic changes would have accumulated so that a new species would have formed. The formation of species is believed to be a slow, but constantly operating process.

Ernst Mayr in his book "Animal Species and Evolution", stated "A shift into a new niche or adaptive zone is, almost without exception, initiated by a change in behavior. The other adaptations to the new niche, particularly the structural ones, are acquired secondarily". Mayr feels that the isolation needed to allow genetic changes to accumulate is primarily a function of behaviorial changes and not simply or primarily geographic isolation.

If two populations of a single species become isolated from each other, and genetic exchanges between the two groups cease, the random accumulation of different mutations within each of the groups would eventually alter their morphology and genetic content so that each group would be a distinct species. Neither species would be identical to the parent species, but all three would belong to the same genus. In this way generically related species evolve.

The boundaries that separate species may consist of both genetic and nongenetic factors that can not always be used to define a species as a distinct, sharply-limited group of animals. The isolating factors may be partial (where speciation is incomplete) and range to complete separation of both genetic and nongenetic factors.

Nongenetic factors
1. geographic separation of populations
2. seasonal separation of mating times
3. separation by occupation of different habitats

Genetic factors
1. mechanical blocks to fertilization
2. incompatibility of ova and sperm

3. sterility of hybrids
4. lack of an intermediary insect (for some plants, where pollen must be spread by an insect).

The geographic separation of populations has already been briefly discussed, and study of the isolated finch and tortoise species on each of the Galapagoes Islands influenced Darwin's concept of species formation. Darwin noticed that the birds probably were descended from an ancester in common and the initial impetus to speciation was geographic isolation on the Galapagoes. Furthermore, Darwin recognized that distinct species of large tortoises had developed on some of the islands.

A more complex species is that of a population of frogs, distributed geographically continuously from New England along the coastal areas to Mexico. Obviously the frogs form a sequence of interbreeding and geographically overlapping populations. However, the breeding season in Florida does not coincide with that in New England, and furthermore frogs from Mexico are blocked (genetic incompatibility of gametes) from breeding with those from New England. Yet clearly defined species can not be made within this population, even though speciation is occurring. This form of interbreeding (partially, but geographically continuously) population is known as a Rassenkreise, and could become two (or more) distinct species by extinction of the frog population in the southern United States, and loss of the connecting link between the genetically incompatible "end" populations. Disappearance of the middle Atlantic states population would lead to formation of a New England and a southern species, as interbreeding would be blocked by the distinct mating periods. This would form allopatric species, those that occupy different territories. If because of later migrations the ranges of the species overlapped, they would become sympatric species, that is distinct species with geographic ranges that overlap, at least partially.

Most, if not all the living monkeys of the genus Macaca formerly were probably members of a single widely distributed species, with a range extending from Europe, across North Africa, the Near East, down to southeastern Asia and northward to Japan and northern China. Today most specialists recognize twelve species of macaques consisting of long-tailed (largely arboreal) and short-tailed (largely ground-living) forms, with the same general (but now largely geographically discontinuous) distribution. For example, the Barbary Ape (Macaca sylvana) lives only on Gibraltar and western North Africa, the Japanese Macaque (Macaca fucata) lives on the southern island of Japan, the best known macaque, the Rhesus Monkey (Macaca mulatta) ranges from Afghanistan to China. Most of the rest of the living macaque species are found on the southeastern Asian mainland, as well as the Indonesian Islands, Borneo, the Celebes, the Philippine Islands, and Formosa.

The occupation of different habitats (by different members of a single species) could be caused by increased predation (selective pressure) of melanistic moths living on light-colored trees and vice-versa. Similar occurrences may have led to speciation of some moths in the past, as many moth species light only upon one species of tree, and other related and nearly morphologically identical species of moths light only upon other kinds of trees.

Mechanical blocks to fertilization are exemplified most readily by plants, in which pollen grains may be of the wrong form or size to enter and fertilize the female plant, although if the pollen is introduced into the female plant surgically, reproduction will occur in some species. Incompatibility of sperm and ova either prevent fertilization from occurring or result in abortion of the fertilized egg, or failure of the zygote to become implanted.

Some closely related species (horses and donkeys) can produce offspring (mules) that are sterile. Although interspecific breeding occurs between these species, the sterile first (F_1) generation cannot produce a second (F_2) generation and maintain the population. Interbreeding of cattle with Bison, and lions with tigers produce F_1 generations with less than full viability.

Another non-genetic block to reproduction includes discriminatory mating practices such as those practiced by territorial animals (as in the arena species discussed in Chapter 12), especially the elaborate courtship rituals of some birds, such as the bower-birds of Australia and New Guinea with their "culture-like" accumulation of bright objects and construction of "avenues" leading to their hut-like bowers. Females of closely related species (or subspecies) are not attracted to bowers they deem improper or decorated with objects of the wrong color. It is interesting that male bower-birds will vandalize another male's bower, a human-like characteristic, perhaps induced by development of "cultural" objects and practices. Perhaps discriminatory mating practices are best exemplified by the legal, societal, and religious rules practiced by man. It should be of little surprise to people that such taboos do not always form effective blocks to reproduction, but do tend to isolate groups genetically.

New genera and larger taxonomic units arise because of continued accumulation of mutations within a populations gene pool, and the mean genetic structure becomes increasingly altered.

The Rates and Directions of Biological Evolution

Biological evolution does not occur at a uniform rate within all animal groups. Some animals evolve exceedingly slowly if compared with the rate of evolution of others. The conservative (evolution-wise) horseshoe crab, _Limulus_, (Figure 16), found preserved in Jurassic limestones of Solnhofen, Germany, resembles very closely the living species. Another slowly evolving genus is the inarticulate brachiopod _Lingula_ (Figure 17), that has changed very little since the Ordovician Period.

The great diversity of mammals that has evolved in the last seventy million years and the evolution of man from prehuman anthropoid ancestors within the last few million years are examples of rapid evolution. The abundance and diversity of mammal remains found within the lowermost sediments of the Paleocene Epoch, indicates how rapidly the initial evolution of mammals occurred as they evolved to fill the ecologic niches left vacant by the extinction of several reptilian groups shortly before. Extinctions and evolutionary sequences that occur rapidly cause the development of the distinctive animal groups whose abundance, wide geographic distribution, and short time range, enables us to use them as the major indices to characterize intervals of geologic time.

The directions or trends of evolution are diverse, at times seeming to be directed or meaningful, but usually seeming to be random or unoriented. No laboratory scientist with a series of unsuccessful experiments need feel discouraged, if he examines nature's experimental efforts in animal evolution, and as George G. Simpson has implied, if there is a prime director of evolution, he must be rather careless.

One evolutionary trend is that of convergence, that is, if an animal lives in a given environment, in a given manner, there is a single, external morphologic form that will be most successful for life in that environment, and biologically successful animals will evolve into that form. Examples of convergence are the shark, ichthyosaur, and porpoise (Figure 15) series, and the pterodactyl, bird, and bat (Figure 14) series. They are unrelated animals that have become similar in external body-shape, because they evolved into the body form most successful for life in the environments they occupy.

Another evolutionary trend is divergence, in which closely related animals evolve in divergent directions so they become rather dissimilar in body form. The living squid and octopods are active, predaceous cephalopods, with good eyesight, and numerous grasping tentacles, and are closely related to relatively inactive or sessile clams, (such as the shipworm, _Teredo_) whose life is spent in a bore hole in wood as a lethargic, water filtering animal, and in which locomotion is not possible in the adult stage. One must look closely to establish the presence of a genetic relationship and the morphologic features in common occasioned by

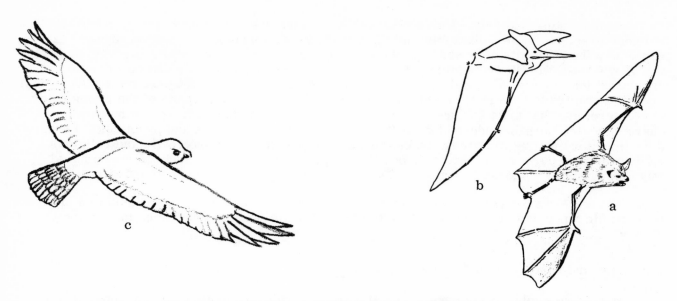

Figure 14. Convergent evolution of the bat (a), pterosuaru (b), and bird (c).

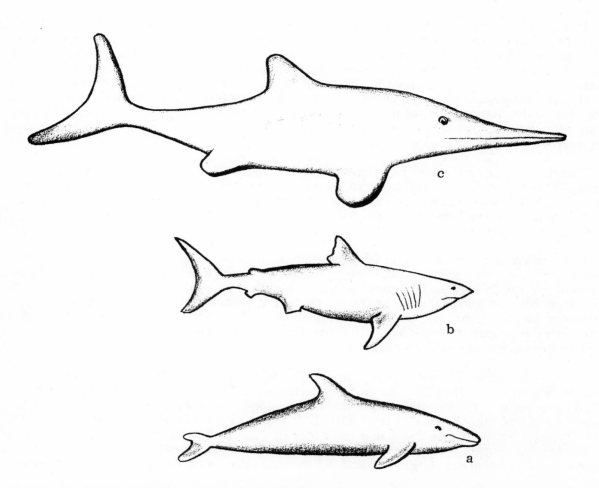

Figure 15. Convergent evolution of the porpoise (a), shark (b), and ichthyosaur (c).

the two groups having had the same generalized molluscan ancestor. It is easier for an uninformed person to misidentify a porpoise as a fish, than to see the much closer relationship of the two molluscs.

Some evolutionary trends seem to result in what appear to us to be useless developments, such as the gigantic and seemingly too heavy antlers of the extinct Irish elk (Figure 44). Extremely large antlers would probably have been more of a burden than an adaptive advantage, although we can not prove they were disadvantageous. Other evolutionary trends include the rapid development of a multitude of bizarre-appearing or uniquely ornamented species within some animal groups just before they become extinct. Late Cretaceous ammonites evolved into varied morphologic forms of doubtful selective advantage, shortly before their extinction. Variations included uncoiled, partially uncoiled, and helically coiled genera, some of which were highly ornamented with ridges and long spines.

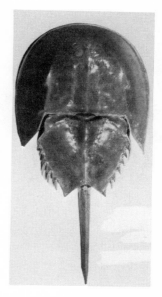

Figure 16. <u>Limulus polyphemus</u>, the living horseshoe crab or "king-crab" of the east coast of the United States. The genus has remained relatively unchanged since the Jurassic. Southern Illinois University, Edwardsville.

Rapid evolution resulting in wide morphologic divergence and then extinction is in marked contrast to the temporally long survival and morphologic stability of forms such as the opossum (Figure 62, since the Cretaceous), the coelacanth fishes (Figure 18, since the Devonian), and <u>Neopilina</u>, a living, close relative of some Cambrian segmented molluscs. This kind of survival may be in part because of the relatively unspecialized nature of the animals' diet, or morphology, or because the animals' physiology is amenable to changes of environment. For example, coelacanths were able to leave fresh water and become marine fishes. The shallow sea-water dwelling ancestors of <u>Neopilina</u> were able to adapt to life in deep sea trenches. Opposum survival may be the result of an ability to thrive on an omnivorous diet and to live in any one of many different ecologic niches.

Some Aspects of Human Genetics

Studies of human genetics are difficult in that the science of genetics is relatively young (since 1900) and human generations are too long and usually the number of offspring per parent pair is too few for effective statistical studies.

Nevertheless many genetically controlled factors of inheritance have been studied in humans. Ability to curl one's tongue, or taste the chemical PTC (phenylthiocarbamide) have been studied. Sensitivity to the taste of PTC is a genetically dominant trait, so that all children of non-tasters are non-tasters, whereas crossing a taster with a non-taster may yield offspring that may be either all tasters, or tasters and non-tasters, and crossing two tasters may yield offspring being either tasters and non-tasters, or all tasters.

We may diagrammatize the problem as follows, the symbol t represents the non-tasters gene, and the symbol T represents the dominant gene of the tasters.

Later genetic studies showed that some gene pairs lack a dominant-recessive relationship and the pairs (alleles) consisted of unlike genes that were expressed phenotypically in two or more forms or effects upon the organism simultaneously.

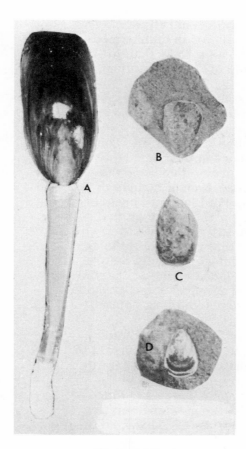

Figure 17.
A. <u>Lingula</u> sp. a living inarticulate brachiopod from the ocean off California. The species has changed but little since the Silurian. Photograph by Joe Marak.
B, C, D. <u>Lingula</u>? <u>cuneata</u> closely related Ordovician relative of the living <u>Lingula</u>, that may belong in the same genus. All specimens courtesy of Miami University, Ohio.

Figure 18.   Latimeria chalumnae, the living coelacanth (crossopterygian) fish from the Indian Ocean near the Comoro Islands. Yale Peabody Museum.

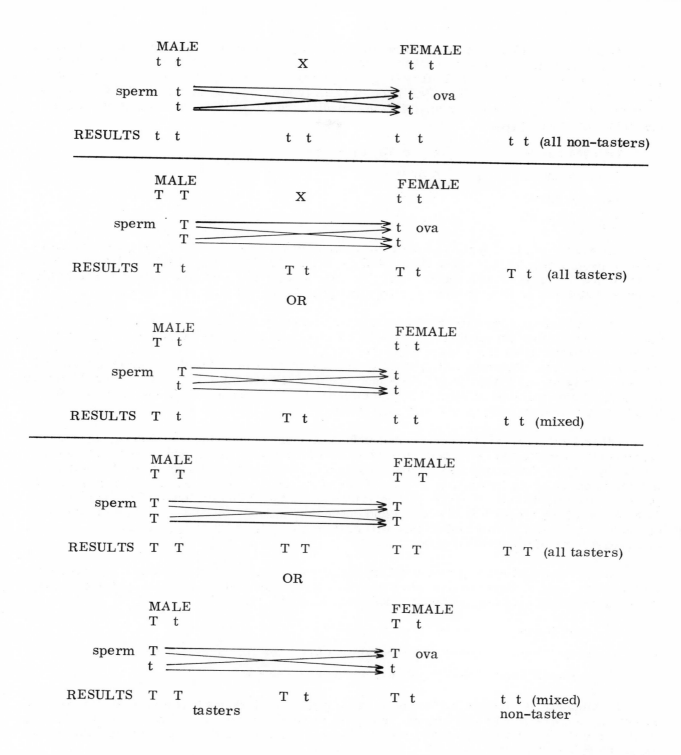

The A, B, O, blood-typing system consists of genes existing in more than two allelic forms. Types A and B are dominant to O, but A and B have no dominance over each other. Therefore, blood of phenotype A, may be genotypically AA or AO, and blood of phenotype B may be genetypically BB or BO. But blood of phenotype O must be genotypically OO. Because of these allelic differences only the following results are possible from matings of bearers of the listed blood groups:

Types A and B	A, or AB, or B, or O
Types A and A	A or O
Types A and O	A or O
Types AB and O	A or B

Knowledge of blood types is important in medicine as the A and B substances are anti-genic to people who don't possess them, and could lead to disastrous results if transfusions of mismatched whole blood are carried out. Furthermore, legal medicine has made use of blood typing to establish or deny paternity, illegitimacy and accidental child exchanges.

For example if a man (type AB) marries a woman (type O) and a child of type O is born, one could reasonably expect that he has entered into an unnecessary or misrepresented marital alliance. Furthermore if a woman (type O) with a child (type B) accuses a man (type AB) as the malefactor in a paternity suit, paternity can not be established (unless one is unfortunate enough to have an all woman jury). The man could have been the father, but so could have any one of dozens or millions of other AB type males. Legally, such tests using only the ABO blood groups, conclusively prove only non-paternity.

Other factors of inheritance studied in human blood include the MN blood group system, expressed as proteins in red blood cells, and the Rh negative (rh rh) and Rh positive (Rh Rh or Rh rh) factors that may cause natural abortions of human embryos when an Rh negative mother is carrying an Rh positive child. If any of the child's red blood cells (carrying the Rh positive foreign protein) cross the placental barrier (a theoretically impossible, but unfortunately all too frequent occurrence) and enter the mother's bloodstream an anti-Rhesus antibody is released by the mother that will destroy the child's blood cells and cause abortion or at least birth of a jaundiced child.

The presence of lethal genes (such as sickle-cell anemia, and Rh factors that occur in people) were first discovered in studies of mice that did not yield the simple ratios expected from reproductive crosses, as determined from Mendel's studies.

1. gray X gray $\longrightarrow$ all gray mice (A)
2. gray X yellow $\longrightarrow$ $\frac{1}{2}$ gray and $\frac{1}{2}$ yellow mice (B)
3. yellow X yellow $\longrightarrow$ 1/3 gray and 2/3 yellow mice (C)

B demonstrates that yellow is dominant to gray, but C shows heterozygotes that are not expected, as there should be a higher yield (3/4) of yellow mice. It was then assumed that the "yellow gene" when homozygous was lethal, that is it caused the death of individuals possessing it, even before birth.

Yy x Yy $\longrightarrow$ $\frac{1}{4}$ yy + 2/4 Yy + YY (die as embryos)

yellow x yellow $\longrightarrow$ grey + yellow + yellow
(heterozygous)   (homozygous)

Some inherited characteristics, such as color blindness and hemophilia are sex-linked and recessive. Females produce only X eggs (they are a homogametic sex) and males produce both Y and X sperm (a heterogametic sex). Males therefore determine (although not unerringly) the sex of their offspring.

An X egg + an X sperm $\longrightarrow$ an XX female zygote

An X egg + an Y sperm $\longrightarrow$ an XY male zygote

This should produce equal numbers of male and female offspring, however more male humans are born than female humans, could the cause be X-linked lethal factors?

Rarely the genetic code becomes unbalanced and may produce XO females (always sterile and incompletely developed) or XXY individuals (hermaphroditic "males" with secondary female sexual characteristics), or XYY individuals with 47 chromosomes, who are apparently overly aggressive and criminally inclined.

Blood factors have been extensively studied by anthropologists and geneticists in order to determine the genetic relationships of various human groups. Apparently this has met with varying degrees of success, as it is a relatively new development, and is complex and not yet well understood. Seemingly genetic drift has caused development of unusual ratios of blood factors in genetically isolated human groups in less than 200 years. Further study should add to the usefulness of such data. The greatest complexity of inheritable blood factors occurs among native inhabitants of humid tropical regions of the Old World where diseases are abundant, and the simplest patterns of blood factor abundance occur among aboriginal populations of isolated (or at least formerly isolated regions) such as Australia, Oceania, and the Americas.

Natural Selection and Human Evolution

Natural selection is the guiding force of biological evolution and requires differential mortality and fertility rates for its occurrence. These differential survival and fertility rates are an index of the "fitness" (in Darwin's meaning of the word) of an individual. Although survival depends upon not only "fitness", but also accidents and health factors that may be partially environmental in origin.

Modern medical science has caused lower birth rates and a correspondingly lower death rate, especially among infants, in most industrialized countries. In 1860, the infant mortality rate, before age 5, was about 25%, one hundred years later, in 1960 the 25% mortality rate was not reached until age 63 in the United States. The partial eradication of infectuous diseases as agents of natural selection could affect the genotype of living men, at least in industrial nations. Furthermore, especially in the United States, there is a differential fertility rate (caused by part of the population using contraceptives) that could further upset natural selection, as family sizes of the presumably best educated and most affluent members of our society are not being genetically determined. This could lead to rapid changes in the relative abundance of inheritable traits present in our gene pool.

Primitive men probably lived in small bands of less than 100 to as many as 500 individuals (much like modern baboon troops in size and organization), and genetic drift, that is rapid selection or establishment of genetic traits could have occurred in such groups.

Probably five factors have largely controlled natural selection of hominid species.

1. Haldane has considered disease resistance to be the major selective factor in human survival, especially since the development of large human societal groups and agriculture. There apparently are genetic factors that enhance or weaken an individuals resistance to various diseases. The sickle-cell anemia trait protects its possessors from malaria, although it selects against life at high altitudes, the presence of blood groups B and AB may help resist infant diarrhea, it is significant here that Amerindians including the Hopis, are nearly all blood group O. Smallpox resistance may be linked to the presence of the M factor, as populations continually exposed to smallpox may have a 90% incidence of M, whereas N may reach an incidence of 70 to 90% in isolated populations where smallpox does not occur. It has also been suggested that people with blood groups O, AO, and A are more susceptible to plague.

Blood type O seems to be associated with more intestinal ulcers, less bronchopneumonia, and a tendency to resist (achieve faster cures, at least) syphillis. Blood factor N may cause susceptibility to rheumatic fever, whereas Rh+ individuals may be resistant, and some forms of cancer are more prevalent in individuals with blood group A. Furthermore there is a differential fertility rate among women that is seemingly linked to ABO and MN factor frequencies.

2. Ardrey has postulated that remnant primate territorialism has played a significant part in human behavior and evolution. The group cooperation needed for territorial defense and hunting, combined with development of tool use and manufacture, and the educative processes needed to train the youth of a highly organized society have undoubtedly been among the main selective factors of pre-agricultural hominid evolution. Hominid brain size increased from less than 600 cubic centimeters in Australopithecus to about 1500 cubic centimeters in Homo sapiens over a period of possibly 500,000 years. This was undoubtedly selection for intelligence, cooperative ability (in-group), inventiveness, and territorial defense. The latter factor, territorial defense, may still be a major factor in human evolution in the form of nationalism and warfare. Man's cranial capacity has not increased during the last 40,000 years (and possibly the last 100,000 years), and humans may not be undergoing mental evolution today.

3. Another significant factor in hominid evolution during the Pleistocene would have been changes of environment. The marked, prolonged and fluctuating Pleistocene climate changes would have repeatedly changed the environments various groups of men inhabited, from warm to cool or cold, or from moist to dry, and back again. Apparently a lot of evolution takes place after occupation of a new (or climatically changed) environment, as mutations occur that increase the individual (and groups) fitness to survive under the changed conditions.

4. Perhaps the most effective present-day evolution of man is being caused by a lack of genetically selective deaths, so that genetic defects are being perpetuated in the gene pool. People with genetically caused defects, such as hemophilia, diabetes, hereditary feeblemindedness, and muscular dystrophy are kept alive by medicines or expensive surgery so that their defects are passed along to an ever-increasing number of offspring. A long term continuation of this would be deleterious to the population, not only genetically but socially as well, for such individuals may require expensive care.

It seems likely that man at the present time may, in industrialized societies, be undergoing a negative form of natural selection, caused by his own affluence and technical skills. But man as a species may have evolved (from mutations) slowly, if at all, over the last several thousand years. Nevertheless, man's extant genes provide enough variety for continued evolution and "genetic improvement" of the species, provided we are capable of implementing some form of population size and quality control.

5. Finally, groups undergoing selection and differential evolution must be isolated either behaviorally or geographically and therefore genetically, before the selective processes can cause effective differentiation of the gene pool, or accumulate mutations that are peculiar to that one population.

Chapter VIII

THE LOWER INVERTEBRATE PHYLA

The Earliest Known Fossils

The oldest alleged fossils recognized so far consist of some minute filaments and cup-shaped, algae-like bodies from the Onverwacht Series of South Africa. Engel, Nagy, et al, have determined that these plant-like fossils are about 3.5 billion years old and occur 30,000 feet below the sediments containing the rod-shaped organisms discovered by Dr. Elso Barghoorn. The rod-shaped organisms resemble bacteria and may have been similar, if not identical to the rod-shaped living bacteria called bacilli. Dr. Barghoorn discovered the specimens during examination of some three billion year old Precambrian rocks from South Africa by means of an electron microscope.

More advanced, but younger, plant-like fossils were discovered by Dr. Barghoorn in two billion year old rocks from Ontario and Minnesota. These fossils are filamentous algae resembling some living blue-green algae, spherical bacterial structures, probably coccoid bacteria, umbrella-shaped forms that resemble some living procaryote organisms that live in ammoniacal soils, as well as some unidentifiable organic structures. Many of the fossil plant-like forms closely resemble living blue-green algae that are nitrogen-fixing and photosynthetic, and perhaps they lived near the time of the initial development of photosynthesis. If this were so, it would have been the beginning of photosynthetic production of oxygen (quite likely the atmosphere then lacked oxygen, and may have been ammonia and carbon dioxide rich) and the initial development of our present day oxygen-rich atmosphere.

Other known late Precambrian plant-like remains include additional bacteria-like fossils and calcareous algal structures from the Belt Series of Montana, and coal-like beds in Scandinavia, Canada and Minnesota. Seemingly alga-like plants were geographically widespread during late Precambrian time.

The oldest known animal fossils are some approximately 720 million year old brachiopods found in Arctic Canada by Dr. Andrew H. McNair. The remains consist of paper-thin, bivalved shells about a half-inch long, that closely resemble primitive linguloid brachiopods previously known only from early Cambrian and younger rocks. Apparently animals only evolved after plants had produced enough oxygen to support metazoan life.

A greater variety of late Precambrian fossils have been discovered near Ediacara in Australia. The fossils consist of impressions of soft-bodied jellyfishes, worms, and coral-like forms in a fine-grained siltstone. No shell-bearing species are known from the Ediacara fauna, and although physiologically highly-organized forms of animal life were present during the latter portion of Precambrian time, their geographic distribution pattern was irregular. Dr. A. G. Fischer has suggested that oxygen was still scarce during late Precambrian time, and multicellular animals could only live near large colonies of oxygen-producing algae.

Most of the known Precambrian animals seem to have been either filter-feeding forms, or organisms that grazed on plants. Apparently hard parts or shells had little adaptive advantage, as long as predators were scarce or had not yet evolved. Many kinds of animals seem to have nearly simultaneously developed hard parts early in the Cambrian. It is a certainty that shell-less forms of those animals had lived in the late Precambrian, and possibly development of protective hard parts was an evolutionary response to the evolution of predators of metazoan animals.

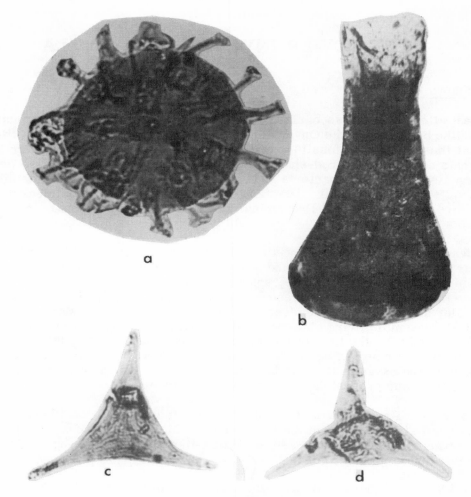

Figure 19. Protistans.
    A. <u>Hystrichosphaeridium</u>, (x500) a probable prostistan of unknown relationships.
    B. <u>Sphaerochitina</u>, (x300) a chitinozoan, one of the Protozoa with a non-calcareous test.
    C, D. <u>Veryhachium</u>, (x800) protistans? of unknown affinities that are probably related to the hystrichospheres. Photographs by courtesy of Karl W. Schwab.

The Kingdom Protista

The Kingdom Protista consists mainly of unicellular or acellular organisms that may be either plant-like or animal-like in structure or behavior. (Figure 18). Some protistans have many nuclei and may not be unicellular, but simply are not divided into cells and and therefore acellular or noncellular. This hypothesis is given added credence as not only do most protistans carry on necessary life functions such as ingestion and digestion, (or photosynthesis), egestion, assimilation, dissimilation, secretion, excretion, respiration, growth, and reproduction, but they may also react to external stimuli such as contact with objects, heat, light, electricity, and chemicals in their environment.

Within the confines of their limiting membranes protistans carry on all the life functions that in higher animals require use of millions of cells arranged in specialized organs.

Some of the higher protistans form colonies composed of many individuals, within which, each individual protistan has its own limiting membrane and usually only one nucleus. The colonies consist of cluste s of as many as several thousand individuals, and the cells may be differentiated into reproductive and vegetative (typical) individuals. The colonial proti tans' level of morphologic development grades into that of the metazoan (multicellular) animals and plants. Protistan colonies are formed of cells that can exist independently, that is all the cells would continue to live if they were separated from the colony as they could carry out all life functions except reproduction. In the least highly evolved living metazoans, sponges, the body cells are much like the "cells" of some protistans (Protozoa). However, if entire sponges are squashed and their body cells segregated, the individual cells can only live from two to twelve days independently of each other and the sponge structure. If the cells are able to reassemble within some of the sponge's mucous-like colloid, they can reform into small sponges and continue to live. In this latter respect sponges differ from all other living metazoans, in that disseminated cells of higher metazoans are not quasi-independent and die without being able to reassemble into a new organism after a short time.

The Kingdom Protista consists of two subkingdoms containing ten phyla, and are briefly characterized as follows:

Kingdom Protista

Subkingdom Monera - no definite nucleus

Phylum Schizophyta - bacteria
Phylum Myxophyta - blue-green algae

Subkingdom Protoctista - definite nucleus present

Phylum Chlorophyta - green algae
Phylum Chrysophyta - diatoms, coccoliths (minute plant-like forms)
Phylum Pyrrhophyta - dinoflagellates
Phylum Rhodophyta - red algae
Phylum Phaeophyta - brown algae
Phylum Myxomycetes - yeast, slime molds
Phylum Eumycophyta - fungi, molds
Phylum Protozoa - forams, radiolarians, largely motile and animal-like forms.

The Kingdom Protista includes the simplest life-form known (excluding the virus, which does not possess all the attributes of life) and includes both plant-like and animal-like forms. The kingdom is not subdivided into plant-like and animal-like groupings because the criteria generally used to distinguish multicellular plants from multicellular animals cannot be used to characterize entire phylogenetic groups within the protistans. Plants usually possess cellulose, chlorophyll, and are capable of carrying out the process of photosynthesis, and lack mobility. Animals are normally highly motile (at least as larvae), ingest and digest food, and lack chlorophyll and cellulose.

The criterion of possessing cellulose is not a good criterion to distinguish plant-like from animal-like protistans for some animal-like Protozoa have cellulose walls, but lack chlorophyll and capture and digest food. Furthermore the possession of chlorophyll fails to be a useable criterion to characterize plant-like forms for some of the animal-like, flagellated protozoans (Euglena) possess chlorophyll. Euglena can carry on photosynthesis if exposed to light, whenever insufficient light is present Euglena can ingest and digest food as do animals. In addition to this, some flagellates that are very closely related to Euglena (such as Khawkinea) have no chlorophyll. The presence (or absence) of chlorophyll forms the main morphologic distinction between the two genera. There are several other closely related generic pairs of plant-like and animal-like protozoans, such as Cryptomonas and Chilomonas, that obviously should not be separated and classified in different kingdoms. The ability to locomote or degree of locomotive ability, can not be used as a basis for separation into different kingdoms as many plant-like algae have motile stages and many animal-like protozoans are immobile.

The Phylum Protozoa

Although many protistan remains occur abundantly in the fossil record, few have been studied as thoroughly as have the protozoans.

The Protozoa are a phylum of complex, acellular protistans, that are usually microscopic and have a basic structure similar to that of a single cell, but with characteristics not found within single metazoan (animal or plant) cells. Furthermore specialized tissues for carrying on life process are not present, and although the ontogenetic development may be complex there is no gastrula stage of larval development.

Classification of the Phylum Protozoa

Class Mastigophora - move by means of flagella
    A. Zoomastigina - no chlorophyll, animal-like forms
    B. Phytomastigina - have chlorophyll, plant-like forms

Class Sarcodina - adults move by means of pseudopodia
    A. Rhizopoda - creeping forms, lobose or reticulose pseudopodia, some testate and some shell-less. The Foraminifera belong within this group.
    B. Actinopoda - floating forms with silicious tests
        (1) Heliozoa, fresh water, no central capsule
        (2) Radiolaria, marine, has central capsule

Class Ciliophora - move by means of cilia

Class Sporozoa - lack locomotive organs, parasitic forms, that live internally in other organisms.

Foraminifera

Foraminifera make tests of chitin, calcium carbonate (calcite), or cemented sand grains (Figure 20). Calcite is used by the majority of foraminifers, and calcareous tests secreted by those protozoans are of two main types, non-perforated with a porcellaneous luster and perforated with a vitreous and non-porcellaneous luster. The porcellaneous tests are shiny and imperforate, and perforated calcareous tests have a duller luster and the perforations may be readily observed, if enough magnification is used. Tests composed of sand grains cemented together are referred to as agglutinated or arenaceous tests, and the sand grains are held together by a secreted calcareous cementing material. Some foraminifers will only use sand grains of certain sizes or shapes to build a test, and some even restrict themselves to useage of a certain mineral, such as mica flakes. Other Foraminifera are completely unselective in choosing sand grains for test construction.

Foraminifera are separated into groups known as the "smaller" and "larger" foraminifers. Specialists normally study only one of the two groups, although this subdivision is an unnatural one and has little relationship to taxonomy. The smaller foraminifers are generally one or two millimeters in diameter, and include chitinous, arenaceous, and calcareous forms. They are normally classified on the basis of test morphology, features that can be determined from an examination of the exterior of the test. The majority of the families of the order Foraminifera belong in this group.

The larger foraminifers' tests range from about one millimeter to approximately four inches in length or diameter. This group seems to consist entirely of calcareous foraminifers, and its members are classified on the basis of their internal test morphology.

Among the better known larger foraminifers are fusulinids, spindle-shaped forms found in Pennsylvanianaand Permian rocks. The group shows progressive evolutionary changes with time and is useful for stratigraphic zonation of those rocks.

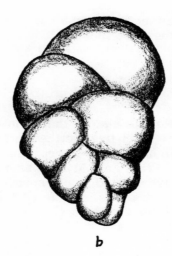
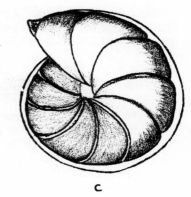

Figure 20. Foraminifers.
a. <u>Globigerina</u>, a planktonic form, consisting of a circlet of spherical chambers
b. A biserial form, that consists of a double row of chambers
c. <u>Robulus</u>, a perforate calcareous genus
d. <u>Nodosaria</u>, a uniserial form, with a single series of chambers
e. A closely coiled form, much like <u>Robulus</u>
f. A uniserial form with a chamber form that differs from those of <u>Nodosaria</u>.

    The Foraminifera, or forams ("bugs" to petroleum geologists) as they are generally called, have been studied more by paleontologists than any other protozoan group, as they have proved useful as index fossils in attempting to locate petroleum reservoirs. Their small sizes enable geologists to recover them from rock fragments ground up by drill bits, and using the principles of correlation and zonation, the ages of rocks deep below the Earth's surface may be determined. Thus petroleum geologists have been able to locate hidden structures that contain entrapped petroleum. Furthermore this method may be used to identify known reservoir rocks from which oil will not readily flow, otherwise the drill could penetrate those beds and geologists would not discover the petroleum.

Life History of Foraminifera

Many Foraminifera have a complex life history that results in dimorphism of the test types. This dimorphic variation within a species was first noticed in fossil nummulitids by Munier-Chalmas. Although Lister and Schaudin had observed reproduction of living Foraminifera in the decade of 1830-1840, it wasn't until 1935 that Earl Myers' studies confirming the observations of Lister and Schaudin were published. Myers' studies of reproduction in living Foraminifera showed that there is an alternation of generations associated with the dimorphic variations of the shell. The microspheric shell is characterized by large overall size, a small initial chamber or proloculus and its protoplasm reproduces asexually by cell division. This reproduction results in a generation with megalosphaeric shells, characterized by a smaller overall size and a larger proloculus. The megalosphaeric generation reproduces sexually, with small flagellated bodies being released as the megalosphaeric shell is abandoned. The flagellated bodies meet and exchange nuclear material through a process known as conjugation, and this results in development of a generation of microsphaeric shells.

Most if not all Foraminifera have an alternation of generations, however not all of them are obviously dimorphic.

The Actinopoda

The actinopods include the radiolarians, marine protozoans with lacework-like siliceous tests, and the heliozoans, a group of similar fresh-water protozoans. Neither group has been as intently studied as the fossil foraminifers have been, although radiolarians have been studied more than the heliozoans.

Radiolarians are characterized by delicate, intricately sculptured, internal skeletons composed of silica or strontium sulfate. They live only in the ocean, and apparently are distributed throughout all zones of the major ocean basins. The oldest known radiolarians have been found in Ordovician rocks.

The Earliest Metazoans

Colonial protozoans are largely composed of individuals with life processes that are independent, and each individual is contained within its own limiting membrane. However, in some forms generally considered to be colonial protozoans (e.g. Myxobolus of the Cnidosporidia) there is a true differentiation of cells into polar capsules and spore membranes. This would indicate a degree of interdependence or incipient interdependence as there must be cooperation among different kinds of cells for reproduction and possibly other functions to occur. In this respect colonial protozoans seemingly grade into the simplest metazoans.

The transition from colonial protozoan to simple metazoans took place during the Precambrian, possibly as long ago as two billion years. Unfortunately it is unlikely that fossils representing such transitional phases will be found.

Phylum Porifera (Sponges)

Sponges are multicellular aquatic animals that live in both the sea and fresh water. The most primitive known living sponges, Class Sclerospongia, have skeletons composed of aragonite, silica, and spongin, and fossil forms may have given rise to some of the higher sponges, the stromatoporoids, as well as some "tabulate coral-like" organisms. Sponges are characterized by possessing an internal skeleton usually composed of either spongin and opaline

Plate 2. Sponges and Coelenterates.

A.) Astraeospongia, a Silurian sponge, somewhat dish-shaped in form, with star-like spicules. B.) Hydnoceras, a Devonian sponge with a distinctive reticulated pattern resulting from the arrangement of the spicules. Courtesy of the Sternberg Memorial Museum. C, D.) Conularids, pyramidal structures of phosphatic composition that may have been protective coverings for some jellyfishes that lived in the Paleozoic. E.) Halysites, a chain-like sequence of colonial tabulate corals from the Silurian. F.) A colonial rugose coral, Columnaria alveolata with an arrangement of septa that does not clearly show tetameral symmetry that characterizes some rugose corals. G.) Favosites, a Paleozoic tabulate coral, that lacked septa (although pores with a septal-like arrangement are present), and had flat, plate-like tabulae. H.) A Cambrian jellyfish from Scandinavia, preserved as mud fillings of the central pouches. Sternberg Memorial Museum. All specimens (except B and H) are from the Geological Museum, Miami University, Ohio.

silica, or spongin, or silica, or calcium carbonate spicules, and the sponges flesh is perforated by passageways through which water currents are passed by the sponge. The water current are created by rhythmic beating of cilia within the passages, and sponge cells extract food particles and oxygen from the incoming water as it passes through the wall-like exterior of the sponge and into a central chamber or chambers. The water is expelled, usually through a single, large opening located at the top of the sponge.

The sponge's skeletal structure usually disintegrates after death and the spicules become scattered among accumulating sediments. Rarely a sponge's skeletal framework is fossilized before it disintegrates and the form of the once-living sponge is accurately preserved (Plate 2; a, b).

Sponges are locally abundant in the sedimentary rock record, however their preservation as fossils is generally sporadic and sponges are rather uncommon as fossils.

The phylum Porifera is an evolutionary dead-end as sponges did not evolve into any other animal group, and are a primitive metazoan offshoot isolated from the main stream of evolution.

Phylum Archaeocyatha (Pleospongia)

Archaeocyathids are a phylum of poorly understood, exclusively Cambrian marine organisms. The biologic relationship of archaeocyathids to the other invertebrate phyla is uncertain, although they seemingly have both sponge-like and coral-like characteristics. They differ from corals, because corals lack porous inner walls, and the coral polyp lives upon, and not within the cup-like skeleton. Furthermore, archaeocyathids differ from sponges, for sponges lack parieties (plate-like walls between, and perpendicular, to the inner and outer walls) and do not have a set of inner and outer walls. Also archaeocyathids are known only from lower and middle Cambrian rocks, the oldest known calcareous sponges occur in Devonian rocks and the oldest known corals with calcareous skeletons are found in middle Ordovician rocks.

In general, archaeocyathids consist of a cone-in-cone-like structure. The inner cone being supported by plate-like structures called parieties that are arranged perpendicular to the central axes of the cones. The space between the inner and outer cones (space where parieties are located) was probably the area occupied by most of the animal's flesh during the archaeocyathid's lifetime. The central cavity of the inner cone served as an exhalent region for water currents expelled by the archaeocyathid, after the animal had extracted food particles and oxygen from the water. In this respect, archaeocyathids were sponge-like.

Probably archaeocyathids (as are sponges) were an evolutionary dead-end and did not give rise to any other metazoan group. The phylum was a short-lived experiment in metazoan evolution that underwent a rapid and diverse evolutionary expansion before becoming extinct.

Phylum Coelenterata

The Phylum Coelenterata is composed of invertebrate animals, possessing only two well-developed cell layers (inner and outer), radial symmetry (at least in the larval stages), that lack well-developed organs. Coelenterates are further characterized by the presence (in most species) of nematocysts (stinging cells) and a lack of body cavities between the two cell layers. Adult coelenterates occur as medusae (jelly-fish) or polyps, or may consist of colonies composed of combined and modified polyps and medusae. Polyps are usually sessile forms and are attached to calcareous skeletons they have secreted, although some polyps are free-living and have no skeleton, e.g. Hydra and the sea anemones.

Presumably the primary and ancestral body form of the adult coelenterate was medusoid, although fossils of probable polypoid coelenterates have been found in Precambrian rocks.

Evidence for medusae being older is that Precambrian medusae are more diverse, more abundant and have been found in older rocks than the known Precambrian polypoid forms.

Both polyps and medusae are sac-like and hollow, and have a single opening, the mouth, surrounded by tentacles. Medusae float with the mouth and tentacles downward, whereas polyps are oriented with the mouth and tentacles upward and are attached to the sea floor, or to a skeleton by the aboral end. The two forms have essentially the same basic structural pattern, and differ mainly in orientation.

Coelenterate groups consisting of medusae reproduce sexually and those groups composed only of polyps may reproduce either sexually or both sexually and asexually. Coelenterate groups with alternating polypoid and medusoid stages reproduce asexually as polyps and give rise to a generation of medusae that reproduce sexually and the offspring become another generation of polyps. This reproductive cycle is known as an alternation of generations.

Phylum Coelenterata

Class Scyphozoa - Precambrian through Recent true jellyfishes

Class Hydrozoa - Precambrian through Recent polyps and jellyfishes, some of which secrete hard parts

Class Anthozoa - Precambrian ? through Recent corals
    Order Rugosa   - Ordovician through Permian corals, usually with a four-fold septal symmetry

    Order Tabulata   - Ordovician through Permian corals, usually with no septa (or weakly developed ones)

    Order Scleractinia - Triassic through Recent corals, with a six-fold septal symmetry.

Several coral orders of lesser paleontologic importance are not listed.

Class Scyphozoa

The class Scyphozoa consists of marine jellyfishes that are radially symmetrical, mostly lack hard parts and have a central body cavity (noncoelomate) that is subdivided into four stomach-like pouches. Fossil jellyfish are rare, but some specimens have been found in Precambrian rocks as well as in many younger rocks. Fossil jellyfish usually consist of impressions of medusae preserving the animal's outline as left in soft muds of the ancient sea floors, and as mud fillings of the four pouches of the central body cavity. (Plate 2, Figure H). Conularids are considered by many paleontologists to be scyphozoans and occur fossilized as phosphatic shells with a pyramid-like form (Plate 2, Figures C, D). These scyphozoans were unique among jellyfishes, in possessing a hard (although flexible?) external skeleton.

Class Hydrozoa

Hydrozoans may occur as either polyps or medusae, although some hydrozoan species include both forms and have an alternation of generations. Some hydrozoans are nonmarine and both polypoid and medusoid forms are known to occur in fresh water. However the fresh water species lack hard parts, do not fossilize readily and consequently their fossil record is poorly known. Many marine hydrozoans have hard parts that are easily preserved as fossils. Hydrozoan skeletons are an abundant constituent of many "coral" reefs and other sea floor sediments. Mound-like calcareous fossil structures called stromatoporoids are considered by many paleontologists to have been hydrozoans or some other sort of coelenterate. Stromatoporoid fossil remains consist of calcareous masses in the form of mounds that are characterized by a lamellar sheet-like internal structure (parallel to the mound's outer surface) that is supported by pillar-like vertical ridges. The masses range up to one or two meters across, and have been found in marine carbonate rocks of Cambrian through Cretaceous ages. Some living sponges resemble stromatoporoids closely and recently some zoologists have classified the stromatoporoids as an order of sponges in the class Sclerospongia.

Class Anthozoa

Anthozoans (corals) occur only as polyps that are relatively small and most of the coralline polyps are sessile, secrete and attach to skeletons that fossilize readily. The polyps retain vestiges of a primary radial symmetry (usually four, six or eight-fold) and have a superposed bilateral symmetry, that may be a remnant indication of a former vagrant life. The coelenteron, or body cavity, differs from that of the hydrozoans, in being subdivided by mesenteries (wall-like partitions) that extend out into the central region of the cavity and serve to increase the absorptive area of the digestive surfaces. Corals are exclusively marine and the earliest known corals may be impressions of some hard part-lacking, colonial, polypoid structures that are coral-like in form and were found in Precambrian rocks of Australia. The first known corals with fossilized skeletal structures are species of the orders Rugosa and Tabulata from middle Ordovician rocks of North America.

The rugose (formerly called tetracorals) corals (Plate 2, Figures E, F) are an extinct order of Paleozoic corals and usually possessed a crenulate or rugose outer calcareous wall or epitheca. Septa (partitions within the cup-like calyx that supported the base of the coral polyp) began ontogenetic development within the individual calyx as six protosepta. Additional septa were only added in four quadrants and thus the calyx acquired a fourfold symmetry with respect to arrangement of the septa. The four-fold symmetry however, is not apparent or readily seen in all rugose corals.

The tabulate corals (Plate 2, Figure G) are another extinct order of Paleozoic corals and the earliest known tabulate remains come from slightly older rocks than do those of the oldest known rugose corals. The tabulates are characterized by weakly developed septa, if any at all, and by the presence of tabulae, flat transverse partitions located within the tubular calcareous skeleton, that extend parallel to the base of the polyp, and the uppermost tabula supported the base of the polyp.

Early in the Triassic (or possibly late in the Permian) some rugose corals evolved into the scleractinian corals. The order Scleractinia (formerly called the Hexacorallia) ranges from the mid-Triassic through Recent and is characterized by the presence of six (or a multiple of six) septa. Species of this order occur as individually or colonially living forms.

The other known groups of corals include Recent orders with no known fossil record and some subclasses with poorly preserved or little known fossil records.

The known living and fossil coelenterates did not directly evolve into the more complex invertebrate phyla. Seemingly the more highly evolved phyla were derived from a generalized ancestor with a coelenterate level of biologic organization, and that same ancestral form may have also given rise to the rest of the coelenterates.

THE HIGHER INVERTEBRATE PHYLA

The Protostomates

The protostomates are those invertebrate phyla characterized by a similar larval development and possession of a ventral nerve cord. The protostomates include the worm phyla Platyhelminthes, Nemertinea, Rotifera, and Annelida, as well as the phyla Mollusca and Arthropoda. The Ctenophora (comb-jellies) are also protostomate-like in larval development, although some specialists consider them to be Coelenterates.

A fertilized protostomate egg cleaves to form an embryo that is a hollow sphere (blastula) one cell-layer thick. The cells at one pole of the sphere differ from those of the opposite pole (the vegetative and animal poles), and the cells of the vegetative pole invert within the sphere to form the gastrula, the next stage of larval development. This process of gastrulation or "pouching" into the sphere forms an inner (endoderm) cell layer. Following gastrulation some cells migrate into the gelatinous mesenchyme between the two cell walls (sponges and coelenterates do not develop cell layers beyond this stage). In more complexly organized animals the mesenchyme fills with cells that separate from the endoderm and those cells develop into organs. The two cell-layered (diploblastic) larva thus develops into a three cell-layered (triploblastic) larva. The more highly advanced protostomate phyla (Aschelminthes, Mollusca, Annelida, and Arthropoda) form a coelom (body cavity) within the third cell layer by a splitting of the mesoderm (a process called schizocoelomate), and some organs develop within the coelom. Further larval development may include formation of a new opening into the gastrula, located opposite the original opening (blastopore). This new opening begins to form as a cavity and then pushes through the wall so that the larva becomes tube-like in structure. Protostomates use the new opening as an anus and the old opening (blastopore) becomes the mouth.

Another line of invertebrate development (and vertebrate as well) from coelenterate-like ancestors has a similar larval developmental sequence except that the coelom forms from two pouches that grow out from the endoderm, then the pouches separate from the endoderm and continue growth to form the coeloms (eucoelomate). Furthermore these animals use the new opening as the mouth and the original blastopore becomes the anus, a condition known as deuterostomate. The deuterostomates include the Nematoda (worms) and the phyla Echinodermata and Chordata (Figure 21).

The Bryozoa and Brachiopoda

The phyla Brachiopoda and Bryozoa are characterized by possession in both of a food-catching organ (lophophore) and by having protostomate larval development, although in some of their groups deuterostomate-like cell cleavage or coelom formation may occur. Apparently the ancestors of the lophophorate phyla originated close in time and evolutionary development to the divergence of the two major lines of invertebrate descent.

Phylum Bryozoa

Bryozoans and brachiopods are descended from an ancestor in common that was presumably characterized by being both sessile and benthonic, and in obtaining food by means of filtering water currents passed over a ciliated lophophore. Brachiopods developed a bivalved shell, and evolved into larger, sexually reproducing, non-colonial forms. Bryozoan evolution trended toward sessile life and asexual reproduction, with the resultant development of tube-like dwelling structures called zooecia.

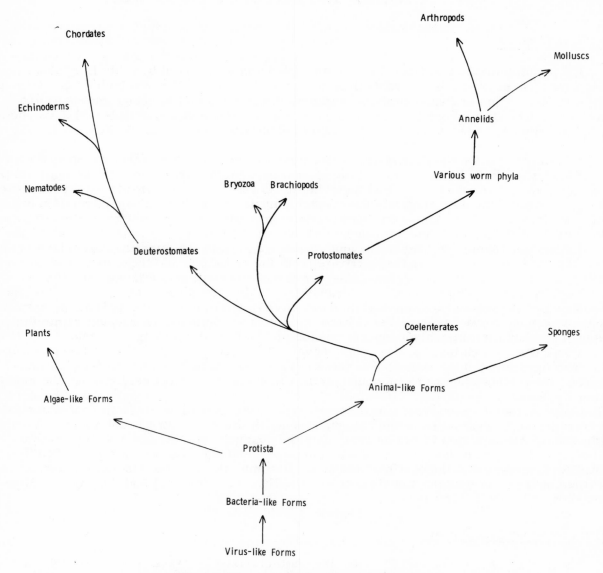

Figure 21. Invertebrate evolution.

The Phylum Bryozoa is usually classified by paleontologists as follows:

Phylum Bryozoa

Subphylum Ectoprocta (has a coelom and the anus is not enclosed by the lophophore)

Class Gymnolaemata   – marine bryozoans with no lip overlapping the mouth

Order Ctenostomata   – mouth circular and characterized by the presence of comb-like processes or spines (Ordovician-Recent)

Order Cyclostomata	- tubular, calcareous zooecia with characteristic round apertures (Upper Cambrian ?, Ordovician-Recent)
Order Trepostomata	- tubular zooecia with transverse partitions within tube; smooth topped elevations called monticules occur on the surface of the colony (Ordovician-Permian, Plate 3, Figures A, B, D, F, G).
Order Cryptostomata	- colonies may be lace-like in structure. The zooecium is short and has a constricted aperture (Ordovician-Permian, Plate 3, Figures C, E).
Order Cheilostomata	- the zooecial aperture is closed by a movable lid or operculum (Middle Jurassic ?, Cretaceous-Recent).

Class Phylactolaemata - fresh-water bryozoans with a lip overlapping the mouth (Cretaceous-Recent).

Subphylum Entoprocta (anus outside lophophore circle): This subphylum lacks a coelom and skeletal parts, is known only from the Recent, and is considered to be a distinct phylum by some specialists.

Bryozoa reproduce sexually and their fertilized eggs produce free-swimming larvae that eventually attach to the sea floor and develop into colonies by repeated asexual reproduction (budding) from the initial and subsequent individuals.

The Bryozoan polyp contains a nervous system, a well defined mouth, esophagus, stomach, intestine and anus. However there are no blood-vascular, respiratory, or excretory systems present in the phylum. Presumably gases diffuse through the exposed body surface sufficiently so that a specialized respiratory system is unnecessary. Food and waste materials are transported by the coelomic fluid to, as well as from cells, and waste materials are extracted and accumulated within cells in the stomach and tentacles and are stored there.

Brachiopods are classified into one of two classes, the Inarticulata and the Articulata, and some of the orders of the two classes are listed.

Phylum Brachiopoda

Class Inarticulata - lack complex hinge-line structures.

Linguloids	- Precambrian through Recent, chitinophosphatic shells (Figure 17).
Orbiculoids	- cap-like chitinophosphatic shells, Ordovician through Recent

Class Articulata - tooth and socket hinge-like structures

Orthids	- Paleozoic forms, usually small and ribbed (Plate 4, Figures A, B, C, D, E, J).
Strophomenids	- Ordovician through Recent forms with wide hinge lines (Plate 4, Figures F, G, I)
Productids	- globose Paleozoic forms, one convex and one concave valve.

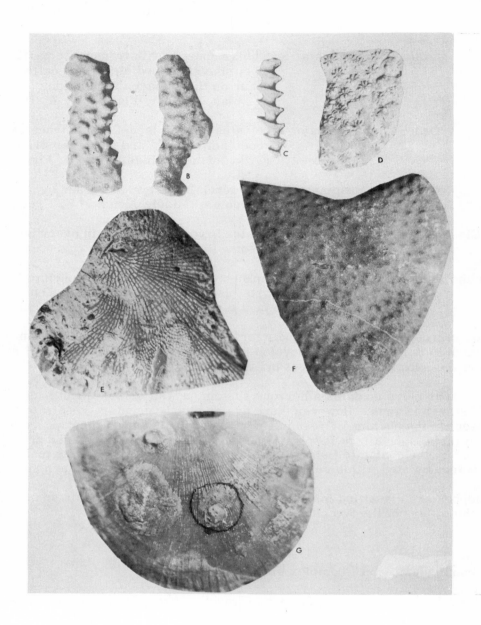

Plate 3. Bryozoans.

A, B. <u>Hallopora ramosa</u> from the Ordovician of Ohio.

C. <u>Archimedes communis</u> the spiral, auger-like, stem structure of a lacy bryozoan from the Mississippian.

D. <u>Constellaria polystomella</u> from Ordovician rocks of Wisconsin.

E. <u>Fenestella parvulipora</u>, a lacy bryozoan from the Waldron Formation.

F. <u>Monticulopora molesta</u> from the Ordovician of Ohio.

G. <u>Trematis millepunctata,</u> within the inked circle of the brachiopod shell.

All the specimens are from the Geological Museum, Miami University, Ohio.

Plate 4. Orthid and Strophomenid Brachiopods.

A. <u>Dinorthis</u> sp., pedicle valve.

B. <u>Dinorthis</u> sp., brachial valve.

C. <u>Dinorthis</u> sp., brachial valve.

D. <u>Dinorthis</u> sp., pedicle valve.

E. <u>Platystrophia</u> sp., brachial valve.

F, I. <u>Platystrophia annienna</u>, brachial valve.

G. <u>Leptaena</u> sp., brachial valve.

H. Hinge-line view of an unidentified brachiopod.

J. <u>Platystrophia ponderosa</u>, view of suture or closure line along brachial and pedicle valves.

All photographs courtesy of Dr. George Distler, Miami University, Ohio.

| Spiriferids | – Ordovician through Jurassic forms with internal spiral supports for the lophophore. |
| Terebratulids | – globose, both valves, Silurian through Recent. |

Inarticulate brachiopods are characterized by a complex musculature system for opening and closing the valves, and generally lack hinge-line structures that aid in valve articulation. The valves are either chitinophosphatic or calcareous and may have punctae (perforations extending from the inner surface of the shell nearly to the exterior). The shells are cemented directly to the substrate in some species, and shells of other species lie unattached on the sea floor, whereas shells of yet others are attached to the substrate (or within a burrow) by a fleshy stalk called a pedicle (Figure 17).

Articulate brachiopods are characterized by calcareous valves that are either punctate or impunctate, and have a well developed sequence of hinge teeth and dental sockets along the articulation line (hinge) of the valves. The muscle system that opens and closes the valves is less complex than that of the inarticulates as the interlocking tooth and socket system enables the valves to be held together more easily. The stalk-like attaching organ (pedicle) extends through an opening in the pedicle (larger) valve, and usually an internal support (crura or more rarely, spires or loops) are present and at least partially support the lophophore. The valve form and ornamentation of articulate brachiopods is generally more variable and ornate than that of the inarticulates.

Brachiopods are characterized morphologically by the presence of nephridia, a coelom, digestive system, nervous system, and a blood-vascular system within the soft-part anatomy.

The Protostomate Worm Phyla

The Phylum Platyhelminthes consists of dorsoventrally flattened, unsegmented worms with bilateral symmetry, that lack an anus or coelom. Platyhelminth worms are hermaphroditic, include marine and nonmarine forms, as well as free living and parasitic species. The worms have three cell layers, and muscular, nervous, digestive, and excretory systems. Reproduction is either sexual (hermaphroditic) or asexual (fission). No fossil Platyhelminthes are known, and Recent flatworms include such forms as planarians, tapeworms, and liver flukes. Flatworms are more advanced, with respect to organ development, than the Coelenterates and seemingly are near the base of an invertebrate evolutionary trend that culminated with development of the Arthropoda.

Rhynchocoela

The Phylum Rhynochocoela includes the nemertine worms that are characterized by possessing an alimentary canal with both a mouth and anus, and a blood-vascular system consisting of a median dorsal and two lateral blood vessels. The nervous and excretory systems are similar to those of the flatworms. The anterior end of the nemertines has a long, retractile proboscis that normally is lodged in a sheath that may be a coelom, and the proboscis is a tactile organ that can be used for defense. Reproduction is either sexual or asexual (spontaneous fragmentation). There are no known fossil nemertines.

Aschelminthes

The Phylum Aschelminthes includes marine, fresh-water, and parasitic forms. The best known aschelminthe worms are the rotifers or "wheel animalcules", so called because of a circlet of cilia, arranged around the anterior end of the animal, that beat with a wave-like, or seemingly rotational movement. Rotifers have a body cavity that is not a true coelom, and digestive, excretory, and reproductive systems that generally are more advanced than those of the lower worm phyla. There are no known fossil remains of aschelminthes. The

trochelminth larve of annelids and molluscs is similar
to rotifers in general appearance, and indicates that
those phyla are descended from a rotifer-like
ancestor.

Annelida

The Phylum Annelida consists of segmented
worms that possess a true coelom, a double ventral
nerve cord, well developed organs for excretion,
respiration, digestion, and a ventral blood vessel
that carried blood away from the heart. Blood is
returned to the heart through a dorsal blood vessel.
The exterior of an annelid is covered (usually) by a
nonchitinous cuticle. Some annelids live in moist
soils (earthworms), or fresh-water (leeches), and
some live in the ocean (clamworms). Reproduction
is sexual and some annelids are hermaphroditic.
Annelid worms have left fossil remains in the form
of calcareous tubes (Figure 22) constructed by tube
dwelling forms, burrows excavated in the sea floor,
trails or trackways, casts of worm's bodies, and
jaw-like masticatory structures that are known as
scolecodonts.

Figure 22. Serpula, calcareous
tubes secreted by
annelid worms that
lived within. Uni-
versity of Kansas
Geological Museum.

Annelids have evolved morphologic features
not present in the other phyla, such as segmentation, leg-like parapodia, presence of a true coelom,
an outer protective covering or cuticle, and have a
single preoral segment. The annelids form an
evolutionary link between the other worm phyla and
the arthropods on one line of descent and lead to the
molluscs along another line of descent.

Onycophora

The Phylum Onycophora, with at least two known fossil forms, the Cambrian Ayshaeia
from Canada and another genus that may have come from Precambrian rocks of Sweden, and
one living genus, Peripatus, is intermediate between the Annelids and Arthropods. Some
specialists consider the onychophorans to be subphylum of the Arthropoda. Peripatus has both
annelid and arthropod morphologic features and is an ideal non-missing "missing link".

The Phylum Mollusca

The Phylum Mollusca is comprised of six classes each of which is characterized by bilateral symmetry, a muscular foot (that may be modified, e.g. into tentacles), a dorsal heart,
usually an external calcareous shell, a mantle (fleshy lobe-like lining of the shell, although it
may be modified), and a complete digestive tract.

Phylum Mollusca

Class Monoplacophora - primitive fossil and living segmented molluscs.

Class Polyplacophora - only the shell is segmented, and the animals are generally known as chitons.

Class Scaphopoda - burrowing forms with tusk-like shells.

Class Rostroconchia - bivalved shells with fused hinges.

Class Gastropoda - usually with coiled shells and a "coiled" body.

Class Pelecypoda - bivalved shells and no cephalization.

Class Cephalopoda - active predators with well-developed eyes and a head that is armed with tentacles.

Monoplacophora

The monoplacophorans are a group of living and early Paleozoic molluscs with Phrygian cap-like, asymmetrically peaked shells. The living monoplacophoran, Neopilina, has a segmented body and each segment contains paired muscles, gills, and nephridia. Furthermore the nervous system and blood vessels show a segmental arrangement and the presence of this segmentation indicates that molluscs were derived from an annelid or annelid-like ancestor. Although the oldest known monoplacophoran remains are from Cambrian rocks, the group undoubtedly evolved in the Precambrian.

Polyplacophora

The polyplacophorans, or chitons, are characterized by a segmented shell composed of eight individual plates. The plates of an individual chiton are held together by a muscular girdle, and the plates are rarely found fossilized. Only the shell is segmented, so chitons differ from monoplacophorans in having an unsegmented body. Chitons differ from snails as chitons' have not undergone torsion (a process that results in the "looped" intestine present in most snails), and by the snail's having non-segmented shells that are usually coiled. The chitons' geologic range is from the Ordovician into Recent.

Scaphopoda

The Scaphopoda are burrowing molluscs with tusk-like shells that are open at each end so water currents may be drawn in the upper end and food particles filtered out by the gills before the current is expelled through the lower end. The oldest known fossil scaphopods are from Silurian rocks.

Rostroconchia

An extinct class (Paleozoic) of bivalved molluscs with nearly inflexible hinges. They evolved parallel to pelecypods, and like scaphopods and clams were filter-feeding animals.

Gastropoda

The class Gastropoda includes both shelled (Plate 1, Figure F) and shell-less snails (slugs and sea hares). Most snails undergo a process called torsion during larval development. As torsion occurs the head and muscular foot remain stationary and the visceral mass rotates through an angle of as much as 180°, so that the anus and the mantle cavity (an open body cavity that surrounds the anus and gills) are moved upward to a position above the head. As a result of the twisting some of the organs on one side (usually the left) of the body fail to develop and the visceral mass and mantle become spirally coiled. The shell is secreted by the mantle and acquires a spiral structure from the coiling of the mantle. In some gastropods the primary twisting of the viscera and nervous system is reversed and those organs become secondarily straightened.

Gastropods characteristically have a well-developed muscular foot which is used as a locomotor organ for creeping. The head is well-developed, and has eyes, sensory tentacles, and a mouth with a rasp-like or file-like dental apparatus that may be used by herbivores to shred vegetation or by carnivores to bore through mollusc shells and shred the contents. Marine and some fresh-water gastropods have gills, and the other fresh-water and terrestrial gastropods breathe by means of "lungs". The earliest known gastropods are from Cambrian rocks.

Pelecypoda

Pelecypods, or clams, are characterized by bivalved shells (Plate 5, Figures A, D) that are reminiscent of brachiopod shells. However, valves of individual clams, except for those of oysters and a few others, are mirror images of each other, as the two valves of most individual clams are identical in size and the line of symmetry is between the valves and along the hinge-line. The two valves of an individual brachiopod are not mirror images of each other and the line of symmetry is perpendicular to the hinge-line so that both valves of an individual must be divided in half, in order to symmetrically "halve" a brachiopod.

Clams lack development of sensory organs and a head, and obtain food by straining food particles from water currents passed through net-like gills. The valves are lined internally by two lobes of flesh called mantles that secrete the shells. Many clams become permanently attached to the substrate either by cementing one valve in place or by attaching a series of hair-like strands (byssus) that extend from the valves to the substrate. Other clams excavate permanent burrows in sand, mud, wood, or even consolidated rocks, and yet other clams are free-living and either wander about by burrowing (Venus, Mya) beneath a thin cover of sea floor sediments, or "hop" (cockle shells or Cardium) by thrusting the muscular foot out between the valves. Some clams (such as scallops or pectens) "jet" across the substrate by rapidly closing the valves and expelling a stream of water that propels the animal along.

Cephalopoda

Cephalopods are active predators and are characterized by having well-developed heads with eyes that range from being "pin-hole" camera-like in structure, to eyes similar to those of the vertebrates in form (in coleoids). The muscular foot is modified into tentacles (from eight to about ninety-four) and serves to seize prey and additionally as a locomotor organ in some species. The mantle is modified into a collar-like cloak around the anterior end of the body portion of the animal and functions to gather water that is expelled through a tubular structure (hyponome) by contracting, thus providing the "jet-propelled" method of swimming that is characteristic of living cephalopods. The mouth is located centrally within the circle of tentacles and contains a parrot's beak-like structure used for biting and tearing prey. Living cephalopods (Nautilus is an exception) have an ink sac that expels a brown or black fluid through the mantle cavity when the cephalopod is frightened or annoyed. The fluid apparently forms an effective screen through which predators cannot see and may also function to deaden the predators sense of smell. The class Cephalopoda is subdivided into several orders and subclasses as follows:

Subclass Endoceratoidea - Ordovician and Silurian nautiloids with mostly straight cone-like shells, with deposits within the siphuncle.

Subclass Actinoceratoidea - Ordovician through Carboniferous nautiloids, generally with straight cone-like shells and secondary deposits within the chambers.

Subclass Nautiloidea — Cambrian through Recent nautiloids with straight to tightly coiled shells, with a centrally or nearly centrally located siphuncle and straight or gently flexed septal edges. The living Nautilus belongs to this subclass.

Plate 5. Pelecypods and Cephalopods.

A.) Durania, a cluster of cone-shaped clam shells from the Niobrara Chalk of Kansas. B.) A straight-shelled nautiloid cephalopod from the Paleozoic. C.) The septal surface of a nautiloid showing the position of the siphuncle. D.) Inoceramus, a large clam from the Cretaceous of Kansas. E, F.) Actinocamax, a squid pen, belemnoid, from the Niobrara Form-Formation of Kansas. Specimen (B) is in the Miami University Museum, the other specimens are in the Sternberg Memorial Museum.

Plate 6. Ammonoids.

A.) Euaspidoceras, an ammonite from the Jurassic of Europe. Miami University, Ohio. B.) Tragodesmoceras, a Cretaceous ammonite from Kansas. This specimen is preserved in a limestone block that forms a portion of the exterior eastern wall of the Fort Hays Kansas State College Science Building. C.) A goniatite ammonoid, probably a clymeniid with an extremely simple suture pattern. Courtesy of the Sternberg Memorial Museum. D.) Baculites, a largely uncoiled Cretaceous ammonite from the Pierre Shale of South Dakota. Courtesy of the Sternberg Memorial Museum. E.) Tornoceras uniangulare, a goniatite ammonoid from the Arkona Shale of Devonian age. Miami University, Oxford, Ohio.

Plate 7. Arthropods.

A, B.) Insects preserved as carbonized films from the Tertiary Florissant Shales of Colorado. C.) Phacops, an enrolled trilobite, presumably a protective or defensive posture. D.) Elrathia, a Cambrian trilobite from Utah. E.) A large may-fly-like insect from the Florissant Shales of Colorado. F.) A nearly complete eurypterid from the Silurian Bertie Waterlime of New York. G.) An abdominal view of an excellently preserved crab from the Eocene of Egypt. H.) Dorsal view of another well-preserved crab. All photographs on this plate are by courtesy of the Sternberg Memorial Museum.

Plate 8. Echinoderms.

A.) An ophiuroid (brittle starfish) from the Jurassic Solnhofen Limestone of Germany. B.) A crinoid, showing arms branching off from the calyx or body. C.) A free-living or stemless crinoid from the Jurassic Solnhofen Limestone of Germany. D.) Isorophus cincinnatiensis, an Ordovician edrioasteroid from Ohio. E.) An echinoid, from the Cretaceous, characterized by a rounded test. F.) Carneyella pilea, an edrioasteroid from the Late Ordovician of Ohio. G.) Blastoid, Troosticrinus reinwardti, from the Silurian. These primitive forms are more elongate than later genera. H.) Pentremites elongatus, a Mississippian blastoid characterized by a "bud-like" shape. The specimens are from the Sternberg Memorial Museum (A, B, C) and Miami University, Ohio (D, F, G, H).

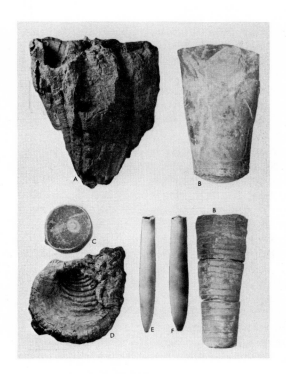

Plate 5.

Plate 6.

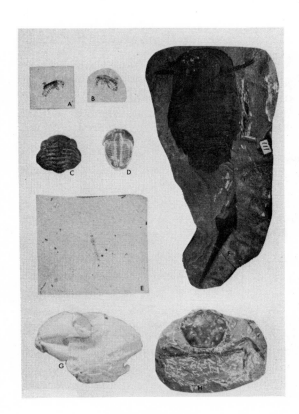

Plate 7.

Plate 8.

Subclass Bactritoidea	– Ordovician through Permian cephalopods with straight, cone-like shells, a ventrally located siphuncle, and straight septal edges.
Subclass Ammonoidea	– Devonian through Cretaceous cephalopods that resemble nautiloids, but differ in having ventral siphuncles and septa with flexed or crenulate edges (Plate 6, all figures).
Subclass Coleoidea	– Devonian ? and Carboniferous through Recent cephalopods that are characterized by internal shells or hard parts (or none at all), eight or ten grasping tentacles, and well-developed eyes. Nearly all living cephalopods belong to this subclass, including squids and octopods. The coleoids are very highly evolved predators, paralleling fish in function, and the largest known invertebrate, Architeuthis, is a squid that may grow to a length of 52 feet. (Plate 5, Figures E, F).

Cephalopod shells range in form from straight to highly coiled, and are characterized by being subdivided into chambers by partitions known as septa. The septal edges (contact of septum with outer wall of shell) are characteristically straight or gently flexed in the nautiloids, and are normally highly flexed in ammonoids. The chambers are connected by a generally hollow tube-like structure, the siphuncle, that in life contained an extension of the mantle with blood vessels. This structure extends rearward from the fleshy portion of the cephalopod, and may enable the visceral mass to deposit calcium carbonate layers within the shell or siphuncle, subsequent to the original formation of the shell.

The Phylum Arthropoda

The Phylum Arthropoda contains more species than all the other phyla combined. Probably 750,000 species of Arthropods have been described, and most of those are living insects. Living arthropods range in size from less than one mm (some spiders and mites) to nearly twelve feet across (Alaskan King Crab). They have also diversified into flying, land-dwelling, marine, and fresh-water forms, and rival the vertebrates in their adaptability.

Arthropods are characterized by segmentation, a jointed and shell-like external skeleton (exoskeleton) and a pair of appendages (legs, antennae, or mouth parts) for each segment. The nervous system is well-developed, especially in flying forms, and concordantly the respiratory and excretory systems are more efficient than in the less active invertebrate phyla.

Phylum Arthropoda

Supersubphylum Protarthropoda	– Precambrian ? and Cambrian through Recent forms (onychophorans, tardigrades, etc.) that differ markedly from the rest of the Arthropods, and some authorities place these forms in a separate phylum.
Supersubphylum Euarthropoda	– Cambrian through Recent forms, that constitute nearly all the species in the phylum.
Subphylum Trilobitomorpha	– Cambrian through Permian species, including trilobites and trilobite-like arthropods. This subphylum is characterized by presence of antennae (one pair) and the paired appendages are mostly legs with little modification. (Plate 7, Figures C, D).

Subphylum Chelicerata	– Cambrian through Recent species that are characterized by claws (pincers), no antennae and a division of the body in two portions. Spiders, horse-shoe "crabs", and eurypterids belong to this subphylum (Plate 7, Figure F).
Subphylum Pycnogonida	– Devonian through Recent arthropods characterized by claws and a lack of well-developed abdomens.
Subphylum Mandibulata	– Cambrian through Recent arthropods that are characterized by possessing either one or two pairs of antennae, and have several pairs of appendages modified to function as mouth parts (specialized feeding apparatus). Insects, crustaceans (crabs, shrimp, etc.) and myriapods (centipedes, etc.) belong in this subphylum. (Plate 7, Figures A, B, G, H).

Arthropods undoubtedly evolved in the Precambrian, however there are few (trackways, and possibly an onychophoran) known fossil remains from that era. The first well-preserved and readily geologically dated arthropod remains are those of trilobites (Olenellus) from basal Cambrian rocks. Trilobites were fully developed arthropods, however they were primitive, for their paired appendages (legs of each segment) are largely unspecialized and have not evolved into any specialized mouth parts, although the first pair are modified into antennae. Furthermore, there is but little fusing of segments into plates except for the head (cephalon).

The trilobitomorphs probably gave rise to the chelicerates late in the Precambrian or early Cambrian. The chelicerates have no antennae, and developed both head and thorax (fused segments) regions. The abdomen is segmented and is readily visible as the posterior portion of the animal. Large pincers or claws are present, and some larval chelicerates (especially horse-shoe "crabs") are very trilobite-like in appearance. Horse-shoe "crabs" or xiphosurans (Figure 16), first appeared in the Cambrian and evolved into a form essentially the same as the living species by the Jurassic. The eurypterids, or sea-scorpions, were probably mostly fresh-water dwelling forms (Plate 7, Figure F) that had pincers and a scorpion-like body form, although only one eurypterid had a "stinger" at the tip of its tail. Nevertheless they were aquatic and were not ancestral to true scorpions.

Arachnids include spiders, scorpions, ticks, and mites. Scorpions, in essentially a modern-appearing body form, appear in the Silurian and are presumed to be the first known land-dwelling animals, although some specialists suspect that Silurian scorpions (Palaeophonus) may have lacked spiracles (openings to an air-breathing organ) and could have been aquatic. Spiders are known from Carboniferous (one specimen that may be a spider is known from the Devonian) through Recent rocks.

The Subphylum Pycnogonida (sea spiders) is of little importance paleontologically, although their fossil record begins in the Devonian. They resemble chelicerates in having pincers, but differ in many other respects and have been placed in a separate subphylum.

Some specialists believe the Subphylum Mandibulata arose from Cambrian trilobitomorphs, and other specialists believe the group to be an independent line of evolution (derived from pre-arthropods) that parallels trilobitomorph and chelicerate development. The earliest known mandibulates are some crustacean remains from early Cambrian rocks. The crustacea radiated into several evolutionary lines and developed bivalved, nearly clam-like forms (ostracodes and some branchiopods), swimming forms with elongate abdomens (shrimp), sessile and attached forms with conical shells (barnacles), and larger, actively walking (or swimming), bottom-dwelling forms with large pincers (the lobsters and crabs, Plate 7, Figures G, H).

In the Devonian two more lines of mandibulate evolution appeared, the insects and the myriapods. The first known insect (Rhyniella), from Scotland, is a primitive wingless form with living relatives. Winged insects are first known from Pennsylvanian rocks, and include dragon fly-like forms, cockroaches, cricket-like forms and may flies. Beetles are first found from Permian rocks as are fly-like and moth-like forms. Social insects (bees and wasps) first appear in Jurassic sediments, ants appear in the Cretaceous, and all become more abundant in the Cenozoic. The earliest myriapods are found in the late Silurian (as millipedes, or thousand-legs) and became more abundant (at least as fossils) in the Pennsylvanian, where the first centipedes are found fossilized.

The Arthropoda are the highest evolutionary development of the protostomate line of descent, and insects are probably the most highly evolved arthropods. Insects include flying, burrowing, ground-surface dwelling, and aquatic forms, a range of adaptability that has only been exceeded by the vertebrates, who probably are the insects' chief biologic competitors.

The Deuterostomates

Deuterostomates are characterized by possessing dorsal nerve cords, larvae in which the blastopore becomes the anus, and coelom formation (where present) occurs by means of pouches budding out from the mesoderm and separating. This line of descent is distinct from that of the protostomate line and the separation occurred near the coelenterate level of development. The Nematoda (a class of unsegmented roundworms, usually placed in the Phylum Aschelminthes), are seemingly primitive members of the deuterostomate line. Living Nematodes are either parasitic or free-living, and the free-living species live either in soil, freshwater or salt water. Apparently true coelom formation does not occur in the nematodes, and the living forms mostly are specialized and thus probably differ from the hypothetical nematode worm-like deuterostomate ancestor of the echinoderms.

Presumably an ancestral deuterostome with a worm-like body form became a benthonic (sea floor-dwelling), filter-feeding animal that gave rise to two lines of descent. One line remained free-living (although perhaps sluggishly so) and evolved into vertebrates, and the other line of descent evolved into the sessile, filter-feeding echinoderms, free-living echinoderms are derived secondarily from attached forms.

Phylum Echinodermata

The Phylum Echinodermata is an exclusively marine phylum characterized by the presence of a coelom, (evolved independently of the protostomate coelom), a skeletal structure of finely porous calcium carbonate, a five-fold radial symmetry (although free-living forms may have a superposed bilateral symmetry), and a water-vascular system. The water-vascular system consists of a five-fold sequence of internal canals that circulate water within the echinoderm. Possibly the system developed as a food gathering (filtering) mechanism, with a secondary respiratory function. Use of the water-vascular system in locomotion apparently developed only after some echinoderms became free-living.

Phylum Echinodermata

Subphylum Homalozoa — Cambrian through Devonian echinoderms lacking radial symmetry, and the body form is essentially asymmetric. Members of this subphylum are called carpoids, and usually are un-attached.

Subphylum Crinozoa — Cambrian through Recent echinoderms that are characterized by cup-like bodies, radial symmetry, and (in most) stalk-like stems that attached to the sea floor. Some crinoids were free-swimming (Plate 8, Figure C, Plage 9, Figure D)

Plate 9. Crinoids and Starfish

A.) <u>Uintacrinus socialis</u> colony from the Cretaceous of Kansas. These crinoids lived as planktonic colonies near the ocean surface and probably fed on microscopic life forms. The slab measures 44 inches by 88 inches and preserves a large number of calyces with long flowing arms. It was discovered in the Smoky Hill chalk, Niobrara Cretaceous of western Kansas. Collected and prepared for exhibition by George F. Sternberg. Print courtesy of the Sternberg Memorial Museum, Fort Hays Kansas State College, Hays, Kansas. Mr. Myrl V. Walker, Director of Museum. B.) Crinoids from Crawfordsville, Indiana with stalks, calyces and arms well preserved. Specimens from the Sternberg Memorial Museum. C.) Asteroid-like starfish from early Paleozoic rocks of Ohio. Specimens from the Miami University, Ohio.

Class Blastoidea	– Silurian through Permian forms that lack appendages, instead they have brachioles on the cup that is composed of symmetrically arranged plates (Plate 8, Figures G, H).
Class Crinoidea	– Ordovician through Recent forms with arm-like appendages attached to a cup (that has symmetrically arranged plates), (Plate 8, Figure B; Plate 9, Figure B).
Class Cystoidea	– Ordovician through Devonian crinozoans with irregular plates that are characterized by the presence of pore rhombs or diplopores, specialized external openings related to the internal water-vascular system.
Class Edrioblastoidea	– Ordovician forms with no appendages at all.
Class Eocrinoidea	– Cambrian and Ordovician forms that lack arms, but have stick-like brachioles and cystoid-like cups.
Class Parablastoidea	– Ordovician forms that are blastoid-like in many respects.
Class Paracrinoidea	– Ordovician crinozoans that are cystoid-like, but have a peculiar arm structure.
<u>Subphylum Asterozoa</u>	– Ordovician through Recent Echinoderms, with star-shaped bodies, that are radially symmetrical and free-living.
Class Stelleroidea	– An Ordovician starfish group, the somasteroids, probably gave rise to the two living starfish subclasses, the Asteroidea (Plate 9, Figure C) (characterized by wide based arms not sharply defined from the body) and the Ophiuroidea (Plate 8, Figure A) (characterized by a sharply defined body, or central disk, and long, snake-like arms).
<u>Subphylum Echinozoa</u>	– Cambrian through Recent echinoderms, that are nearly all free-living, nearly globular (or a flattened variant thereof) in form, and lack arms or appendages.
Class Helicoplacoidea	– Early Cambrian, free-living forms with spirally coiled bodies.
Class Edrioasteroidea	– Cambrian through Pennsylvania echinozoans, that lacked stems, were disc-like to globular in body form and many were attached to the substrate during life. (Plate 8, Figures D, F).
Class Holothuroidea	– Devonian through Recent echinozoans with a sac-like body form, that rested on one side on the sea floor. The mouth, surrounded by tentacles, is located at one end of the body so that holothurians, unlike other free-living echinoderms that are radially symmetrical do not travel on their oral surfaces.

Class Echinoidea   – Ordovician through Recent echinoderms that are radially (some with superposed bilateral symmetry) symmetrical and have a biscuit-shaped test or corona that is covered with short spines in life (Plate 8, Figure E).

Class Ophiocistoidea   – Ordovician through Devonian echinozoans that resemble young echinoids more than any other group, and are problematical as to their true relationship.

The ancestral echinoderm was very likely a sessile, attached, sea-floor dwelling form that filtered water currents to obtain food. This ancestral echinoderm evolved into a variety of stalked forms that acquired radial symmetry and "arms" used to capture food. Although the oldest known echinoderms with hard parts (skeletons) are from the early Cambrian, the group must have originated in the Precambrian, underwent morphologic diversification, and developed a calcium carbonate skeleton during that era, as echinoderms are a widely diverse and highly evolved group in the Cambrian.

The next trend of echinoderm evolution was the development of free-living, but still sea floor-dwelling forms. Some groups (the carpoids) retained a vestigial stalk, whereas other groups (the helicoplacoidea, holothurians, starfish, and echinoids) lost all vestiges of a stalk and became well adapted to wandering about the sea floor. Although all the free-living forms are radially symmetrical, or at least retain strongly developed vestiges of radial symmetry acquired as an inheritance from sessile ancestors, some have developed (echinoids) a superposed bilateral symmetry, as an adaptation to the uni-directional travel of widely wandering animals.

Echinoderms are a marine-dwelling offshoot of chordate evolution, and did not give rise to any other animal groups. Seemingly the echinoderms are an evolutionary "dead-end", although they have diversified into a large number of distinct groups.

Chapter X

THE CHORDATES

Origin of the Chordates

Although some specialists have speculated that early Paleozoic fishes with bony armor-like plates evolved from a somewhat morphologically similar echinoderm (carpoids) group, it is more likely that chordates and echinoderms both arose from the same ancestral stock.

Phylum Chordata

Subphylum Stomochorda — Cambrian through Recent free-living, worm-like and attached forms lacking true dorsal nerve cords and vertebrae. The graptolites (Ordovician through Mississippian) belong here.

Subphylum Urochorda — Only Recent forms are known, (the tunicates) with sac-like bodies that are attached to the sea floor and filter food particles from self-created water currents.

Subphylum Cephalochorda — known only from Recent forms, (Amphioxus or Branchiostoma) that are filter-feeding forms with fish-like bodies.

Subphylum Vertebrata — Ordovician through Recent forms characterized by vertebrae, a dorsal nerve cord and a dorsally located main artery. The subphylum includes all vertebrates from fish through mammals.

Poorly known Paleozoic fossils that may be chordate remains include conodonts, amber spheres, archaeognathids, graptolites, and pterobranchs. David Jensen and Halsey Miller said in part (in an article discussing this problem).

"It is quite probable that conodonts, Archaeognathus and Youngquistina are not vertebrates, however it is very probable that they are fragmentary remains of Chordates, possibly from an unrecognized and undefined subphylum. Recent Cephalochorda and Urochorda seem to be highly modified, sessile or nearly sessile forms descended from more active, and unknown ancestors. The Recent forms lack hard parts; perhaps their ancestors possessed some bonelike or phosphatic structures, that were discarded during the trend away from a more active life.

Early chordates (late Cambrian through Ordovician) include: graptolites, pterobranchs, conodonts, 'amber' spheres (Stauffer, 1935), Archaeognathus, Youngquistina, ostracoderm denticles and plates, and unclassified dentine-like and bone-like fragments reported by Denison (1967).

With the exception of graptolites and pterobranchs, the remaining Chordate fragments can be characterized in that they consist of calcium phosphate, and occur in marine sediments. Calcium phosphate is typically a Chordate structural substance. It occurs in living invertebrates only as setae (external) of some marine worms and as statocysts of some marine jellyfishes. Complex, internal tissues of calcium phosphate seem to be a chordate trademark."

Paleozoic graptolites and pterobranchs were branching, colonial forms, lacking bonelike hard parts, and with a generally conceded relationship to each other and the living protochordate phyla. The Ordovician ostracoderm denticles and plates were the protective and supporting structures (all probably of mesodermal origin) of primitive agnathan fishes, related to the living hagfishes and lampreys.

Conodonts, archaeognathids, (Figure 23) and amber spheres are similar morphologically and physiologically in that they are small, consist of calcium phosphate, have lamellar microstructures, are translucent to transparent, and generally are amber in color. Conodonts and archaeognathids may have bone-like material attached to their bases, and are tooth-like in structure.

The morphologic and chemical (physiologic) similarities indicate a genetic relationship. Possibly the structures came from either (a) three distinct but related chordates, or were (b) three different structures of the same chordate.

Although the structures are similar in morphology and composition, they may be unrelated as they do not have the same geologic time ranges, although they do occur together locally. Conodonts are known to range from late Cambrian to Middle Triassic rocks. The amber spheres range from Ordovician into late Paleozoic, and possibly late Cretaceous rocks. Archaeognathids have so far been found only in Ordovician rocks, several speciments from the early Ordovician Dutchtown Formation of Missouri, and three specimens from the middle Ordovician Harding

Figure 23. Youngquistina, a problematic conodont-like fossil, that may be the remains of an Ordovician protochordate. Courtesy of the Sternberg Memorial Museum.

Sandstone of Colorado. Ostracoderms range from the early Ordovician of the Baltic Sea region and mid-Ordovician of the United States into the Devonian System. Thus the geologic range of conodonts indicates that they could not have been ostracoderm parts, nor would it have been likely that the early Ordovician archaeognathids from the United States functioned as ostracoderm parts. Furthermore, ostracoderm plates are exceedingly abundant within the Harding Sandstone, and archaeognathids are rare and do not occur in any reasonable ratio with any of the various ostracoderm remains. In addition Denison has indicated that conodonts, (and probably the archaeognathid combs) as well as the bone-like substance discovered by him in the Harding Sandstone differ markedly histologically from vertebrate bone.

Furthermore it seems likely that both conodonts and archaeognathids were probably internal and of mesodermal origin, in that conodonts broken during the conodont bearing animals' lifetimes show sutures along which regrowth took place, and the sharp tips of the conodonts and archaeognathids do not show wear or signs of abrasion. In addition to this, living chordates lack external calcium phosphate structures of non-mesodermal origin. Such flesh covered structures could have functioned as (a) scale-like elements, (b) internal supporting structures, (c) an internal filtering apparatus, or (d) otoliths.

Externally conodonts are morphologically like the placoid scales of sharks. However, conodonts internal structure and basal bone-like attachments are very non-placoid. Although both conodonts and archaeognathids resemble gill rakers of some living fishes, gill rakers are generally soft and flexible. The archaeognathids comb-like array of denticles closely resembles in form the rasping "teeth" of hagfishes. However, hagfish "teeth" lack bony basal attachments, are not translucent, and are concave-convex, not rounded in cross-section as are the denticles of the archaeognathid combs. Both conodonts and archaeognathids occur attached to a bone-like substance. This bone-like substance should have provided the major internal, supporting structures of the animal(s) in question. Therefore, conodonts and archaeognathids were most probably accessory, attached structures of a decorative, or protective, or scale-like nature or were an internal filtering apparatus. The amber spheres could have been scale-like elements, or otoliths, in that they lack bone-like attachments, and seemingly occurred as hollow spheres with a lamellar wall, unattached to bone or to each other in flesh.

The relationship of conodonts to archaeognathids is still not determinable, and solution to the problem must await thin-sectioning and histologic study of an archaeognathid with its bone-like base and non-destructive chemical analyses of both conodonts and the known archaeognathid specimens.

Classification of the Vertebrata

Subphylum Vertebrata

Superclass Agnatha	– Primitive fishes, ostracoderms from the Ordovician through the Devonian, with lampreys ranging from the Pennsylvanian into the Recent. Agnathaus are jawless, fish-like vertebrates, with (usually) no paired fins, one nostril, and only one or two semi-circular canals in the inner ear. Most fossil forms (ostracoderms) have bony armor-like plates over the head and thorax.
Superclass Gnatho- stomata Class Elasmo- branchiomorphi Subclass Placoderm	– Devonian through Carboniferous and Permian ? fish with jaws, some lacking true teeth, and with true paired fins. Some had lungs, and some had the head and thorax armored with bony plates, and in some the head articulated on a "ball-joint" socket with the thorax.
Subclass Chondri- chthyes	– Devonian through Recent fishes (sharks, rays, skates, chimaeras, etc.) that lack bone, have cartilagenous skeletons, and denticle-like (placoid) scales. There is no swim-bladder or functional lung.
Class Teleostomi Subclass Osteichthyes	– Devonian through Recent fishes (includes the majority of living fishes) characterized by the presence of rayed fins or fleshy-lobed fins, usually scales (no bony armor-like plates) are present and primitively lungs were present. Most living species have a swim-bladder, derived from the primitive lung.
Class Amphibia	– Late Devonian through Recent vertebrates characterized by smooth, moist, scale-less skins (in most species), cold-bloodedness, and shell-less eggs that develop into gill-breathing aquatic larvae (in most species).
Class Reptilia	– Pennsylvanian through Recent vertebrates with scaled skin (of ectodermal origin, therefore unlike mesodermal fish scales), cold-blooded (at least in living species), that mostly lay shell-ed (amniote) eggs on land, with no larval stage during ontogeny. The mandible consists of more than one bone, and only one inner ear bone (stapes) is present.
Class Aves	– Jurassic through Recent, mostly winged, (and mostly able to fly) vertebrates, characterized by the presence of feathers (some scales also present), warm-bloodedness, amniote eggs, and extensive young care.
Class Mammalia	– Triassic through Recent land and water-dwelling vertebrates with hair, warm-blood, mammary glands, three inner ear bones, and a mandible composed of only dentary bones.

Superclass Agnatha

The oldest known fossil remains that are generally considered to be those of vertebrates are small scale-like and bone-like fragments from lower Ordovician rocks of the Baltic Sea region. Similar, but younger fragments have been found in the Middle Ordovician Harding Sandstone of Colorado. Although no complete skeletons of vertebrates have been found from Ordovician rocks, paleontologists consider the fragments to be partial remains of ostracoderms, small, filter-feeding, dorsoventrally flattened, bottom-dwelling fishes. Typically, ostracoderms' head and thorax regions were covered with an interlocked sequence of armor-like bony plates (Plate 10, Figure E). Filter-feeding was carried on by inhaling water through the mouth and straining out food particles while exhaling water through gills, where respiration also took place. This respiratory-feeding system is similar to that of the protochordates, and in addition is not unlike the echinoderms' water-vascular system; perhaps both systems were inherited from a more primitive, water-filtering ancestor in common.

Ostracoderms lack jaws and true teeth, and generally speaking lack paired fins, although some species have a pair of pectoral fins. It is rather unlikely that any known ostracoderm gave rise to any living fish groups, other than the lampreys and hagfishes (cyclostomes). The lampreys (as did ostracoderms) lack jaws, true teeth, paired fins, and have a single nostril, and only one or two semicircular canals. Lampreys differ from ostracoderms in lacking (lampreys) bony armor plates, and in possessing a cartilaginous skeleton and a parasitic mode of life (they attach to bony fishes, rasp through their flesh and suck out body juices). The oldest known fossil lamprey is from Pennsylvanian rocks, and the group could be the highly specialized descendants of an ostracoderm group, or representatives of a separate line of descent, derived from the same ancestor as the ostracoderms. (Figure 25).

Dr. Alfred Romer proposed the concept that the earliest vertebrates evolved in fresh-water and then entered the sea after a long period of non-marine evolution into various fish groups. Romer's evidence is mainly based on physiologic studies of kidneys of living fish groups. R. H. Denison studied the paleoecology of the Ordovician ostracoderm remains and concluded that they lived in a near-shore marine environment, and that the earliest fish were of marine origin.

All living echinoderms and living protochordates dwell only in the sea and all known fossil remains suspected to be those of protochordates and echinoderms are found preserved only in marine sediments. It seems likely therefore that the ancestral "echinochordate", echinoderms, protochordates and the earliest vertebrates were marine. Later, some early fish-like vertebrates migrated into fresh-water (possibly as early as Precambrian or Cambrian time) where an evolutionary radiation resulted in the formation of the modern fish groups (sharks, ray-fins and choanichthyes) that became physiologically adapted to life in fresh-water, then individuals of those fish groups remigrated into the sea, and their descendents still retain vestiges of a prior adaptation to life in fresh-water.

Superclass Gnathostomata
Class Elasmobranchiomorphi
Subclass Placodermi

Placoderms are primitive fishes with true jaws that evolved from gill bars that rotated forward, the upper pair becoming affixed to the base of the cranium to form the upper jaw, and the lower pair uniting to form the mandible or lower jaw. True teeth were not present in all placoderms, some had sharply pointed bony flanges exposed along the oral surfaces of the jaws, and these flanges functioned as "teeth". True teeth evolved from scales located along the lip-region or edge of the mouth, as determined by comparative study of shark teeth and sharks' placoid scales, for those scales or denticles are tooth-like in form and structure.

Placoderms were a morphologically varied group, and included some forms with bony plates vovering a heavily armored head and thorax region. Generally the armor was similar to that of the ostracoderms, except placoderms had a ball and socket joint between the head and thorax (Plate 10, Figure D; Plate 11, Figure C). Those groups with bony armor included both

Plate 10. Paleozoic Fishes.

A. Artist's concept of early amphibian-like fish crawling out on land. Probably the fish is Eusthenopteron. Saint Louis Museum of Science and Natural History.

B. Eusthenopteron, a restoration of a Devonian crossopterygian fish. The living fish was about 2 feet long. Saint Louis Museum of Science and Natural History.

C. Osteolepis, preserved remains of a crossopterygian fish. The head is on the left, and most of the body scales are present. Sternberg Memorial Museum.

D. Restoration of a fossil placoderm, probably Coccosteus, from the Devonian. Saint Louis Museum of Science and Natural History.

E. Fossilized remains of an heterostracan ostracoderm. The head shield is on the right and a portion of the scale covered tail is to the left. Sternberg Memorial Museum.

Plate 11. Fishes.

   A.) Fossilized skeletons of two perch-like fishes from the Green River Shales of
Wyoming. B.) <u>Carcharodon</u>, large (about six inches long) tooth of a Miocene shark from South
Carolina. The shark in life may have been nearly 80 feet long and was related to the modern
"Man-eating" or great white shark. C.) <u>Bothriolepis</u>, head and thoracic armor of an arthro-
dire from Devonian rocks of Canada. D.) Calcified vertebra of a shark from the Cretaceous
Niobrara Chalk beds of Kansas. Normally shark vertebrae are cartilaginous and are not pre-
served. All photographs courtesy of the Sternberg Memorial Museum.

small and large genera, one of which, Dinichthys, was the largest (up to 26 feet long) predator known to have lived in Devonian seas. Some other placoderms were skate or ray-like and lacked bony armor plates. A group of shark-like fishes (Acanthodians or spiny sharks) was former formerly considered to be placoderms by paleontologists, and although others classify them as aberrant, but true sharks, however they seem to be teleostome fishes.

It is likely that placoderms gave rise to some, if not all, of the higher fish groups. Although fossil placoderms are known from both marine and fresh-water sediments, it is quite likely that they evolved in fresh-water.

Subclass Chondrichthyes

The Chondrichthyes are an evolutionary "dead end" that did not give rise to another vertebrate class. They evolved from some other fish group (placoderms?) in fresh-water, and the first known fossil remains of chondrichthians are those of well-developed, though primitive sharks (Cladoselache) from Devonian marine sediments in Ohio. Acanthodians may be a closely related group, even though most of them were fresh-water dwelling forms.

During the Mississippian Period sharks probably were very abundant in the sea, and numerous teeth of many varieties of mollusc-eating and more actively predaceous sharks have been found in sediments of that age. Although sharks are generally thought of as voracious predators, several shark groups (both extinct and living) independently evolved into forms with flat-crowned, pavement-like dentitions that were used to crush and eat shelled molluscs. Many of the Mississippian sharks (bradyodonts and cochliodontids) were of this type, and some of them may have evolved into the living chimaeras or file fish. The living skates and rays (descended from Mesozoic sharks) are modern pavement-toothed mollusc eating sharks. Remains of well-preserved sharks with the normally cartilaginous vertebrae calcified have been discovered in the Cretaceous Niobrara Formation of Kansas (Plate 11, Figure D), although only teeth of sharks are usually found fossilized (Plate 11, Figure B).

Class Teleostomi
Subclass Osteichthyes

The class Osteichthyes (bony fishes) includes two major subdivisions, the Sarcopterygii (lobe-finned fishes and lungfish) and the Actinopterygii (ray-finned fishes). Both subdivisions originated in fresh-water, and most of the Sarcopterygians few living members are fresh-water dwellers, however the great majority of living actinopterygian species are marine.

The earliest actinopterygians (paleoniscids, a now extinct group) were covered by parallelogram-shaped, thick, bony scales (ganoid scales), and had functional lungs. Some living fishes are closely related to the paleoniscids and are relicts of that early stage of bony fish development (chondrostean stage). Representatives include the African fishes Polypterus and Calamoichthyes, both of which have functional lungs. A slightly more advanced stage of development is exemplified by the sturgeon and the spoonbill, neither of which have functional lungs (the lungs have evolved into swim-bladders). The paleoniscids were the ray-finned fish group that was most abundant during the Paleozoic.

The second stage of ray-finned fish development (the Holostei) became the numerically dominant group of ray-finned fishes during the Mesozoic and a typical primitive holostean is the Triassic fresh-water fish, Semionotus. Many holosteans retained ganoid scales, but none had functional lungs. Living holostean fishes are the fresh-water dogfish or bowfin (Amia) and the garpike (Lepidosteus). Although the living holosteans are fresh-water forms, most Mesozoic holosteans were sea-dwelling fishes.

The most highly evolved ray-finned fishes, the teleosts, first appeared with the evolution of Leptolepis in the late Triassic, and by late Cretaceous time teleosts had evolved into a variety of genera. Most living fishes are teleosts, they are quite varied in form, and range from primitive kinds such as the Recent herring and fossil forms such as Xiphactinus (Cretaceous, Plate 12, Figures A, B) to more advanced forms such as the perches (Plate 11,

Figure 24. Fragment of a large clam shell (Inoceramus) from the Cretaceous chalk beds of Kansas with remains of a small actinopterygian fish (Kansius) preserved on the interior of the shell's surface. Apparently these small fishes lived within the clams, possibly in a commensial relationship. Courtesy of the Sternberg Memorial Museum.

Figure A). Some apparently evolved commensal relationships with invertebrates (Figure 24), and live in close association with coelenterate "jellyfishes" and polyps, or molluscs.

The Sarcopterygii first appeared in the Devonian and evolved along two lines of descent, the crossopterygians and the dipnoans (lungfishes). The dipnoans, of which three genera are still living, have functional lungs and evolved a specialized dentition for eating fresh-water molluscs. The lungfish did not evolve into land-dwelling vertebrates or any other fish group. They are archaic remnants of an evolutionary "dead-end".

The oldest known crossopterygian fishes are also from Devonian rocks, and they too lived in fresh-water. Of the two groups of crossopterygians, only one, the coelacanths, have a living species, Latimeria chalumnae (Figure 18), that lives today in the Indian Ocean near the Comoro Islands. The other crossopterygian group, the rhipidisteans (Plate 10, Figures A, B, C) gave rise to amphibians late in the Devonian Period, and the rhipidistean fishes as such, became extinct in the Permian.

Class Amphibia

The earliest known amphibians, from late Devonian sediments of Greenland, have many features in common with crossopterygian fish. One of the better known genera, Ichthyostega, has a skull bone pattern similar to those of rhipidistean fishes, but with reduced or no opercular bones. Furthermore Ichthyostega had fish-like scales, a laterally flattened, fish-like tail, and teeth with complex labyrinthine infoldings of enamel identical to the rhipidisteans' tooth structure. The tetrapod limb bone structure was essentially present within the crossopterygians' fleshy, lobe-like fins. Crossopterygians had pelvic and pectoral girdles as well as homologs of the major limb bones. A leg structurally capable of use in terrestrial motion was present in the rhipidistean fish before the amphibians evolved.

According to Dr. Alfred Romer, the rhipidisteans' ability to travel on land (and consequent evolution into amphibians) was an adaptation to remain in water. Apparently they lived in regions of seasonal (monsoonal) rains, and during the dry season, as creeks and ponds dried up, those fish best able to wriggle or walk along dry creek beds to a permanent water hole were more likely to survive. They already had lungs (present in probably most if not all primitive true fishes) and were "pre-adapted" for life on land.

In the Mississippian Period amphibians became more abundant, both in numbers and variety and among the more predominant descendants of the ichthyostegids (an order of the

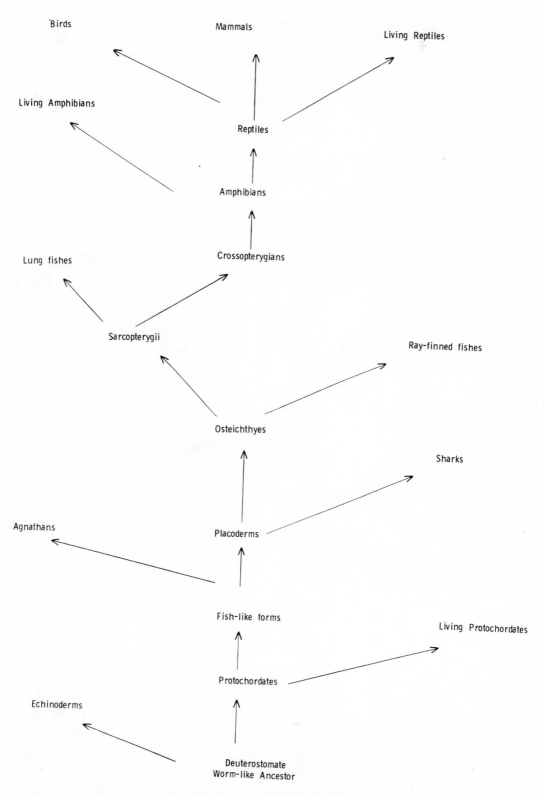

Figure 25. Evolution of fish.

Plate 12. Fish-within-a-fish.

A.) The giant Kansas Cretaceous fish <u>Xiphactinus molossus</u> with a smaller fish, <u>Gillicus arcuatus</u> within the abdominal cavity. Specimen now exhibited in the Sternberg Memorial Museum. Collected and prepared for exhibition by George F. Sternberg. Photo by E. C. Almquist. Print courtesy of the Sternberg Memorial Museum, Fort Hays Kansas State College Museum, Hays, Kansas. Mr. Myrl V. Walker, Director of Museum. B.) Preparation of large fish skeleton (shown displayed in Figure A) for collecting. The specimen has been carefully uncovered and the fragile bones hardened with a filler. The specimen is ready to be blocked out and framed. Plaster will then be poured to completely cover and support the specimen during transportation to the preparation laboratory in the museum. Print courtesy of the Sternberg Memorial Museum, Fort Hays Kansas State College, Hays, Kansas. Mr. Myrl V. Walker, Director of Museum.

subclass Labyrinthodontia) were the many forms of labyrinthodonts (so named because of the labyrinthine infolds of enamel in their tooth structure). By Permian time the labyrinthodonts were the dominant land animals (even though many reptiles lived at that time), and this dominance was personified by Eryops (Figure 27), a short-legged, stocky-bodied animal with an ominously large and toothy mouth. By the end of the Triassic the labyrinthodonts died out, and their only descendants may be frogs and toads, a relatively meek, though noisy group.

The subclass Lepospondyli (Figure 26) consists of some legless forms and some salamander-like Paleozoic genera that may have given rise to the present day salamanders and apodans (legless tropical amphibians with no known fossil record).

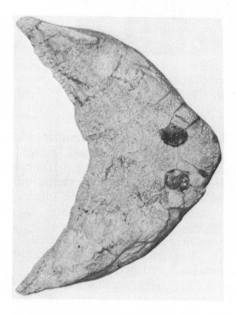

Figure 26. Diplocaulus, the arrow-head shaped skull of a water-dwelling amphibian whose remains have been found in lower Permian rocks. Sternberg Memorial Museum.

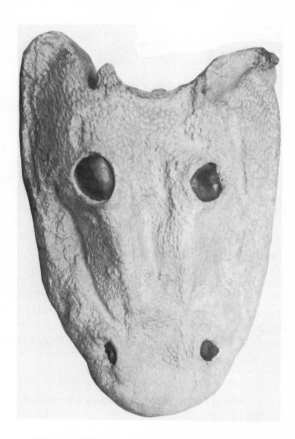

Figure 27. Eryops, the skull of a large carnivorous labyrinthodont amphibian that was one of the dominant land animals of Permian time. Sternberg Memorial Museum.

Class Reptilia

Reptiles very likely developed from Labyrinthodont amphibians during late Mississippian time, and the oldest known reptile remains (Romeriscus) were found in early Pennsylvanian sediments of Nova Scotia by Dr. Donald Baird. It is difficult to distinguish the skeletons of advanced seymouriamorph amphibians (e.g. Seymouria and Diadectes) from the skeletons of primitive reptiles such as Limnoscelis (Figure 28). The skeletal criteria used to distinguish Recent reptiles and amphibians (reptiles have two sacral vertebrae, five toes, and one occipital condyle, and amphibians have one sacral vertebra, four toes, and a double occipital condyle), are not distinctive or definitive enough for use in identifying fossils. The seymouriamorph amphibians were formerly considered by paleontologists to have been reptiles, and the reptile-amphibian "boundary-line" is difficult to define.

Figure 28.   Limnoscelis, a primitive reptile (cotylosaur), about 5 feet long, from Permian rocks of North America.   Yale Peabody Museum.

In general, primitive reptiles lack an amphibian-like otic notch, and their eardrums have migrated downward and rearward to near the jaw articulation.   Seemingly, the earliest known reptiles were largely water-dwelling forms and thus were not morphologically greatly different from amphibians, although some early Mississippian seymouriamorph amphibians (perhaps on the line of reptile descent) were active, walking forms that may have largely dwelled on land. The greatest distinction is probably in the mode of reproduction.   Amphibians as a general rule, lay their eggs in water, and the eggs develop into free-swimming larvae that meta- morphose to become adults.   Reptiles usually lay a specialized type of egg (amniote, Plate 1, Figure B) on land that develops directly into an adult without a larval stage and metamorphosis. Amniote eggs could have originally been laid either on land or in water, and still would have had selective value, as there would have been no free-swimming larval form exposed to preda- tors.   Furthermore eggs laid on land, especially if buried, would have resulted in an even higher survival rate for the young as there were fewer predators (if any) actively hunting for food on land.   Quite likely most early reptiles and amphibians were fish-eating animals, and the land did not become a major source of food materials for predators before late Carbon- iferous time.

We are not certain that the amniote egg was developed by the animals now considered to be the earliest known reptiles, or by later evolved reptiles, or if the egg was developed by what we now consider to be a fossil amphibian.   But the amniote egg was developed far enough back in time that it is present in all living reptile groups (at least ancestrally) and in two other classes (partially so in mammals) that are descended from reptiles.

The amniote egg is characterized by being protected by a limey or leathery outer shell, with an inner membranous lining, the chorion.   These layers help protect the egg from dessication and injury.   The embryo is surrounded by another membrane, the amnion, that contains a fluid within which the embryo develops.   This is analogous to the amphibian eggs' pond water.   The embryo feeds from an attached yolk sac as growth and development take place, and this same type of egg is laid by birds and the monotreme mammals.

Class Reptilia

Subclass Anapsida
     Order Cotylosauria   - the "stem reptiles"
     Order Chelonia   - turtles

Subclass Lepidosauria
    Order Eosuchia   - extinct lizard-like forms
    Order Squamata   - lizards and snakes
    Order Rhynchocephalia - fossil and living lizard-like forms

Subclass Archosauria
    Order Thecodontia   - stem of the archosaurs
    Order Crocodilia   - crocodiles and alligators
    Order Pterosauria   - flying reptiles
    Order Saurischia   - dinosaurs
    Order Ornithischia   - dinosaurs

Subclass Euryapsida
    Order Araeoscelidia   - extinct lizard-like forms
    Order Sauropterygia   - plesiosaurs
    Order Placodontia   - marine reptiles

Subclass Ichthyopterygia
    Order Ichthyosauria   - ichthyosaurs

Subclass Synapsida
    Order Pelycosauria   - sail-finned reptiles
    Order Therapsida   - mammal-like reptiles

The oldest known reptile remains are classed within the order cotylosauria, and the cotylosaurs probably gave rise to the rest of the reptilian groups (Figure 29). Turtles are specialized descendants of cotylosaurs that have a shell (carapace, the upper portion, and plastron, the lower portion) developed from expanded and fused ribs that grow out so as to cover and include the limb girdles within the shell. Nevertheless, turtles retain a relatively primitive skull type that is reminiscent of the cotylosaurs. The stem of turtle evolution is unknown, and some paleontologists used to think that a small Permian reptile, Eunotosaurus, that had expanded, touching ribs and some other turtle-like features was the ancestral form, this is considered to be unlikely by most paleontologists at the present. Undoubted turtles (e.g., Proganochelys) are found in the Triassic and those primitive genera evolved into more advanced turtle groups. (Plate 13, Figure C).

The eosuchians were lizard-like reptiles that evolved in the Permian from cotylosaurs, and became extinct in the Eocene. Prior to that time (Jurassic) they gave rise to lizards and subsequently, by some becoming burrowing forms and undergoing loss of limbs, snakes arose in the Cretaceous. The most primitive snakes are the boids (Figure 35), the poisonous elapids are more advanced, and the pit vipers are the most highly evolved snakes. Probably the first poisonous snakes evolved in the Miocene. Lizards and snakes are the most abundant and widely distributed (geographically) of modern reptiles. During the Cretaceous a group of lizards (the mosasaurs, Plate 14, Figures A, B) became specialized for life in the sea and developed into forms that were as long as 30 feet (Figure 34) and had paddle-like limbs and flattened tails for use in swimming.

Sphenodon, the Tuatara, is a living, lizard-like member of the rhynchocephalia. Essentially the rhynchocephalians are an

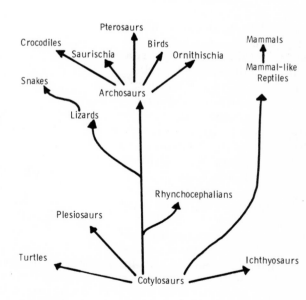

Figure 29. Reptile evolution.

early Mesozoic reptile group, that has managed to survive as other reptile groups became extinct.

Thecodonts, a Triassic reptile group, gave rise to the archosaurs or ruling reptiles. Probably the ancestral thecodont was closely related to the eosuchians, however, typical (but not all!, Figure 30) thecodonts were bipedal, slightly-built reptiles with long tails used for balance. One line of archosaur evolution became birds, and is considered to be a separate vertebrate class, the Aves. Crocodiles and alligators evolved in the Triassic from an unknown thecodont ancestor, as the known Triassic crocodilians may be evolutionary cul-de-sacs. The largest known crocodile was Deinosuchus, probably 40 to 50 feet long as adults, from the late Cretaceous. Crocodiles are the largest living reptiles, for both the Indian Gavial and the southeastern Asian salt water crocodile may be as long as 25 feet when fully grown.

The pterosaurs or flying reptiles were another successful attempt by archosaurs to develop an aerial group, although birds were more successful and have survived much longer. The oldest known pterosaurs are found in early Jurassic rocks (Figure 36) and were relatively small forms (wingspread of a foot or so) with elongate tails and toothy snouts. Many bird-like features such as hollow bones, large sternal bones,

Plate 13. Marine reptiles.

A.) Artist's restoration of the short-necked plesiosaur, Trinacromerum, from the Kansas chalk beds. Painting by Charles Bonner, courtesy of the Sternberg Memorial Museum. B.) Nearly complete skeleton of a Jurassic ichthyosaur from Lyme Regis in England. Saint Louis Museum of Science and Natural History. C.) Protostega, a large Cretaceous marine turtle from the chalk beds of Kansas. Courtesy of the Sternberg Memorial Museum.

prominent bosses for attachment of flying muscles to the humerus, and the pelvis fused to the lumbar vertebrae were present. Late Cretaceous pterosaurs (Pteranodon, Plate 16, Figure A) became gigantic with wingspreads of about 25 feet. These large forms lacked teeth and tails. In view of the pteranodonts' (and other pterosaurs) large processes for attachment of flight

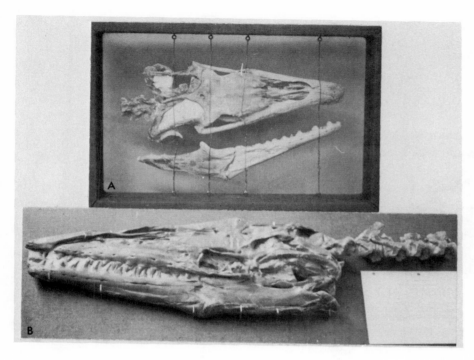

Plate 14. Mosasaurs.

A.) <u>Platecarpus</u>, an open mount of the skull of a medium-
sized (about 18 feet total length) mosasaur from the Cretaceous
chalk beds of Kansas. B.) <u>Tylosaurus</u>, an excellently preserved
skull of a large (about 30 feet maximum length) mosasaur from
the Cretaceous chalk beds of Kansas. Both photographs courtesy
of the Sternberg Memorial Museum.

muscles, it would seem reasonable that those reptiles had large, strong muscles used for flight and were not "weak gliders". Furthermore if they were active, strong fliers, they may well have been warm-blooded.

The Saurischia are one of the two archosaur orders (Figure 31) usually called dinosaurs, although the two orders are no more closely related to each other than they are to birds or crocodiles. The oldest known saurischian remains are from Triassic rocks and are of relatively small, bipedal, carnivorous species. Dr. John Ostrom has proposed the interesting thesis that dinosaurs were warm-blooded reptiles, and

were capable of sustained activity. Evolution of the group led to development of large, bipedal carnivores (Plate 17, Figures D, E, F) that culminated in <u>Tyrannosaurus</u> (Plate 18, Figure A) a 50 foot long late Cretaceous genus, and in development of the large sauropod dinosaurs. The sauropods (Figures 32, 31) secondarily reverted to a four-footed stance (necessitated by their tremendous bulk, some were more than 80 feet long with body weights of as much as 50 tons), and presumably were mainly vegetarians or omnivores. Among the better known sauropod genera are <u>Bronto-saurus</u> (67 feet long and weigh-

Figure 30. Skull of a phytosaur, a group of specialized thecodont reptiles that resembled crocodiles in appearance. Yale Peabody Museum.

ing 30 tons) and <u>Diplodocus</u> (87 feet long and weighing 15 tons) of Jurassic age. A brachiosaur from Africa has been estimated to exceed 75 feet long and a weight of 80 tons.

The other dinosaur group is the order Ornithischia, that consisted mostly of smaller-sized animals, but with a greater variety of body forms. The earliest known ornithischian remains are from Triassic sediments of South Africa, and the ornithischians differ from saurischians in pelvis structure, in being less adapted for bipedal walking, and in being entirely herbivorous. Ornithischian evolution resulted in development of several distinctive groups; the ornithopods that culminated in the bipedal duck-billed dinosaurs (hadrosaurs or trachodonts, one species discovered by Dr. William Morris in Baja, California was 100 feet long,

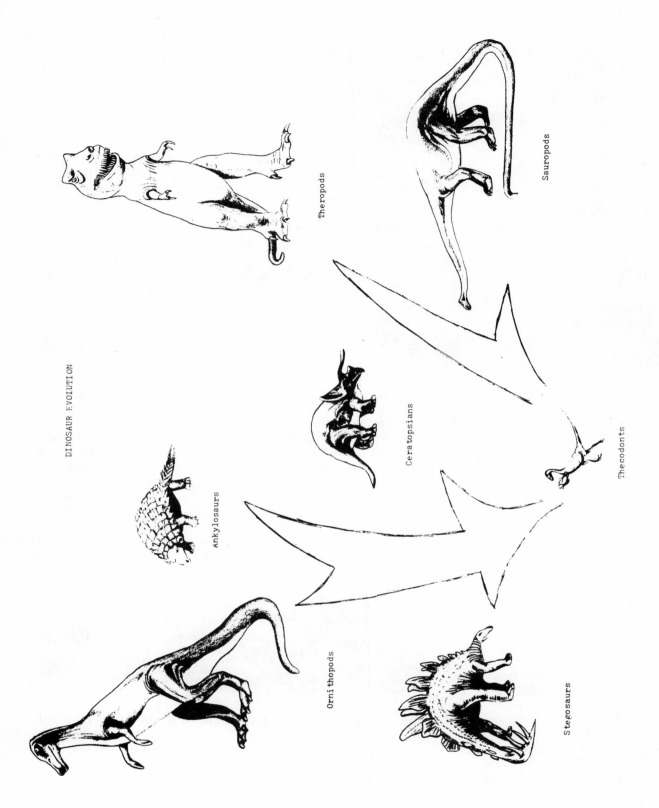

DINOSAUR EVOLUTION

Theropods

Sauropods

Ceratopsians

Thecodonts

Ankylosaurs

Ornithopods

Stegosaurs

Figure 31. Dinosaur evolution.

Plate 15. Plesiosaurs.

A.) Probably the most complete small (length ten feet), short-necked plesiosaur skeleton (Trinacromerum?) known. This specimen discovered by M. C. Bonner of Leoti, Kansas, in the Niobrara Cretaceous of western Kansas. Prepared for exhibition by George F. Sternberg. Print courtesy of the Sternberg Memorial Museum, Fort Hays Kansas State College, Hays, Kansas. Mr. Myrl V. Walker, Director of Museum. B.) The largest fossil reptile skull and lower jaw thus far collected in Kansas. Brachauchenis is the largest of the short-necked plesiosaurs with a skull reaching more than sixty inches in length. Discovered in the Cretaceous Greenhorn Formation of western Kansas and collected and prepared for exhibition by George F. Sternberg. Print courtesy of the Sternberg Memorial Museum, Fort Hays Kansas State College, Hays, Kansas. Mr. Myrl V. Walker, Director of Museum.

Plate 16. <u>Pteranodon</u> and chalk beds.

A.) The most unusual of all the large flying reptile (<u>Pteranodon</u>) skulls ever found in western Kansas. No explanation has yet been given for this greatly enlarged or inflated crest which gives the skull a total length of over 2019 mm (about 80 inches). Collected in the Niobrara Cretaceous of western Kansas and prepared for exhibition by George F. Sternberg. Print courtesy of the Sternberg Memorial Museum, Fort Hays Kansas State College, Hays, Kansas. Mr. Myrl V. Walker, Director of Museum. B.) Typical exposures of Smoky Hill chalk of the Niobrara Formation, Upper Cretaceous, of western Kansas. These exposures are northwest of Wakeeney, Kansas, on the Garrett Ranch. Several excellent fossil specimens have been found and collected from this area. Print courtesy of the Sternberg Memorial Museum, Fort Hays Kansas State College, Hays, Kansas. Mr. Myrl V. Walker, Director of Museum.

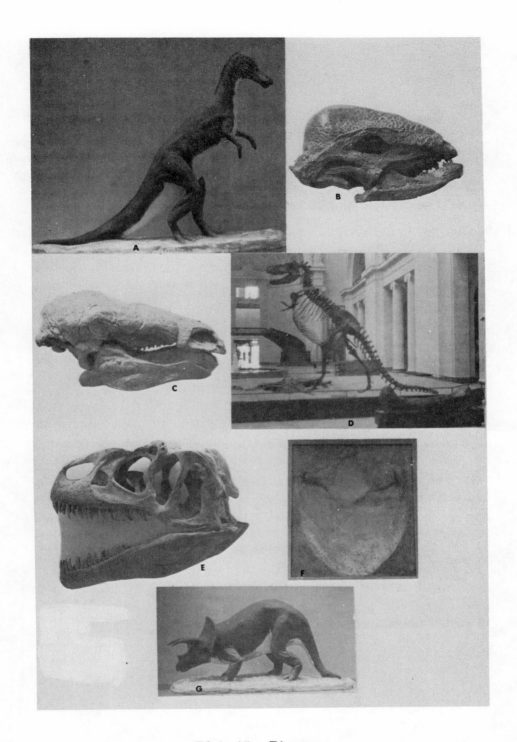

Plate 17. Dinosaurs.

A.) Model of Trachodon (or Hadrosaurus), an herbivorous duck-billed dinosaur from the late Cretaceous. B.) The skull of a late Cretaceous ornithopod (Stegoceras) usually referred to as a "bone-headed" dinosaur, because of its thick skull and relatively small brain case. C.) The skull of Trachodon, a duck-billed dinosaur. D.) The skeleton of Gorgosaurus, a large carnivore that lived in the Cretaceous. Chicago Museum of Natural History. E.) The skull of Antrodemus (Allosaurus) a late Jurassic and early Cretaceous carnivore. Saint Louis Museum of Science and Natural History. F.) The footprint of a large three-toed carnivorous dinosaur from Cretaceous sediments of Utah. G.) Restoration of Triceratops, a horned, late Cretaceous herbivorous dinosaur. All photographs (except D and E) are from the Sternberg Memorial Museum.

Plate 18. Dinosaur restorations.

A.) <u>Tyrannosaurus rex</u>, a life-sized model at the Saint Louis Museum of Science and Natural History. B.) <u>Triceratops</u>, a life-sized model at the Saint Louis Museum of Science and Natural History.

Plate 17, Figures A, C) of the Late Cretaceous, the 20 foot long quadrupedal stegosaurs (Figure 33) of Late Jurassic and Early Cretaceous time, that were characterized by alternating rows of erect triangular plates down the back, and spiked tails. The Late Cretaceous (up to 20

Figure 32.   A prosauropod or primitive sauropod dinosaur. Yale Peabody Museum.

Figure 33.   Stegosaurus, a restoration of the large herbivorous dinosaur made famous by a poem citing the supposed relationship of its small brain-size and a much larger sacral ganglion. Sternberg Memorial Museum.

foot long) armored dinosaurs or ankylosaurs (Plate 17, Figure 3) that had a four-footed stance with the body held close to the ground, and the dorsal side of the body covered by a series of bony armor-like plates, some of which had bony spikes, were another ornithischian group. The horned dinosaurs or ceratopsians of the Late Cretaceous, that possessed bony frills extending from the parietal regions out over the neck, and spike-like horns (in many genera, but not all) on the nose or over the eyes, were also ornithischians. The best known ceratopsian was Triceratops, a 16 to 20 foot-long reptile weighing perhaps seven tons. (Plate 17, Figure G; Plate 18, Figure B).

The subclass Euryapsida includes the araeoscelids (Permian through Triassic), an extinct, lizard-like group; the placodonts, a Triassic group that was "walrus-like" and had crushing dentition for eating molluscs, and the Sauropterygia, or plesiosaurs, (Plate 15, Figures A, B) that lived during the Jurassic and Cretaceous and evolved from short (about 10 to 20 feet long) forms into late Cretaceous species, some of which (Elasmosaurus) had a maximum length of 50 feet. Plesiosaur limbs were modified into paddles and their bodies were short and broad. One line of plesiosaur evolution, exemplified by Trinacromerum, developed short necks and long skulls (Plate 13, Figure A), and the other line developed long necks (up to twice the length of the body in Elasmosaurus) with relatively short skulls.

The ichthyosaurs (Plate 13, Figure B) lived from the Triassic into the Cretaceous Periods and were a group of marine, fish-like reptiles. In general body form the ichthyosaurs foreshadowed swordfish, bottle-nosed dolphins, and imitated sharks.

The subclass Synapsida is known from remains found in Pennsylvanian and Permian sediments and begins with the evolution of pelycosaurs or sail-finned reptiles that ranged (as adults) from about three to about twelve feet in length. Most of them had elongated neural spines that extended upward from the vertebrae, and it is assumed that the spines supported a web-like "sail" during the animals' lifetime. The function of the "sail" is not known, but it

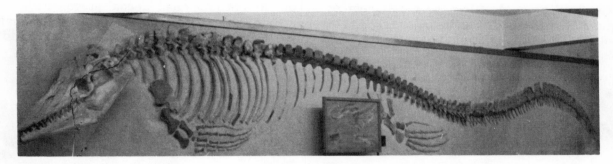

Figure 34. <u>Tylosaurus</u>, a thirty foot-long marine lizard (mosasaur) from Cretaceous chalk beds in Kansas. Courtesy of the Sternberg Memorial Museum.

Figure 35. The python (a member of the boidae) is one of the most primitive living snakes. These constrictors have vestiges of hind limbs and well-developed paired lungs. In more highly evolved snakes, only one lung is present and the vestigial limb bones are absent. Saint Louis Zoo.

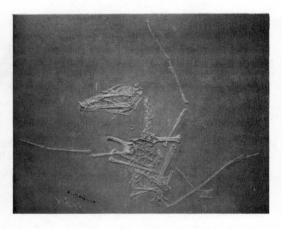

Figure 36. A toothed pterosaur (<u>Dorygnathus</u> sp.) from the late Jurassic of Germany. Yale Peabody Museum.

may have been a body temperature regulating device. One line of pelycosaur descent (dimetrodonts) gave rise to the more advanced therapsids or mammal-like reptiles.

The therapsids lived from Permian into Triassic times, and included both carnivorous and herbivorous forms. Several lines of evolutionary development occurred among the therapsids (Plate 19, Figure E), the most important of which (to us mammals) led to the development of mammals. Many mammalian features developed within the reptilian therapsids; secondary palates, double ball-joint of the occipital condyle, specialized teeth (incisors, canines, premolars, and molars), scapulae with spines and fused coracoids, hair (at least in the form of whiskers or vibrissae), and very likely warm-bloodedness (because of the presence of an insulating covering of hair). It is difficult to distinguish mammals from mammal-like reptiles, as the two groups grade into each other, for many mammal-like reptiles possessed essentially mammalian features, and many apparently true mammals retained essentially

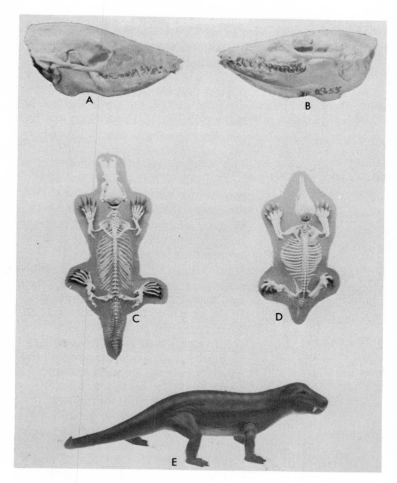

reptilian morphologic characteristics. The criteria generally used to distinguish mammals from reptiles include the presence in mammals of three inner ear bones, reptiles have only one, the stapes. The other two bones of the mammalian inner ear are derived from the articular and quadrate bones of the reptilian jaw to skull articulation. In addition mammals have a mandible that consists of a single pair of bones, the dentarys, with the skull to jaw articulation being between the squamosal and dentary bones. By using these criteria the living monotremes (Plate 19, Figures C, D) may be classed as mammals, although they are reminiscent of mammal-like reptiles as they lay eggs, have a flat scapula (no spine), separate coracoid and interclavicle bones, unfused cervical ribs, no auditory bulla and a middle ear that is only partially enclosed. Their stage of body skeletal development is more reptilian than that of some mammal-like reptiles.

Plate 19. Primitive mammals and mammal-like reptiles.

A, B.) Skull of a primitive insectivore from North American Tertiary deposits. Courtesy of the Sternberg Memorial Museum. C.) Skeleton of Ornithorhynchus anatinus, the duck-billed platypus, a living egg-laying mammal from Australia. D.) Skeleton of an echidna (Zaglossus or Tachyglossus), another living egg-laying mammal from Australia and New Guinea. E.) A restoration of Cynognathus, a mammal-like reptile. In some restorations Cynognathus is shown with a covering of hair. C, D, E. Saint Louis Museum of Science and Natural History.

Class Aves

The earliest known bird remains are those of Archaeopteryx (Figure 40) from Jurassic limestones in Germany. Essentially, Archaeopteryx was a slightly modified reptile with feathers, and impressions of those feathers were found with the four known skeletons. The fossilized remains were crow-sized, long-necked, with a double row of feathers along the tail, no beak was present and the jaws had teeth. Undoubtedly Archaeopteryx was warm-blooded and could fly. Perhaps feathers evolved (from scales) primarily as insulation for a warm-blooded, active reptile and became flying surfaces secondarily.

Birds may have survived (as pterosaurs did not) because of several factors that were probably lacking in pterosaur life and morphology. Seemingly the pterosaur wing membrane if torn could not have been used for flight, and pterosaur leg development was poor, so that they were inefficient in running on the ground or swimming in water, and very likely, pterosaurs had little or no young care in a typical reptilian fashion.

In Late Cretaceous rocks of Kansas the remains of two distinct kinds of tooth-bearing birds have been found. One group, known as Ichthyornis, is a series of birds that skeletally

Figure 37. Restoration of the wingless but toothed diving bird Hesperornis whose remains have been found in the Cretaceous chalk beds of western Kansas. Painting by Charles Bonner, courtesy of the Sternberg Memorial Museum.

are much like some living shore birds. However, they were described by Professor O. C. Marsh (Ichthyornis dispar, Figure 39) as being toothed. A restudy of Marsh's specimens in the 1950's by some scientists led them to conclude that Ichthyornis was not tooth-bearing, and the jaw associated with Marsh's type specimen was that of a young mosasaur and not that of a bird. Recently (1970) Professor Myrl Walker, Director of the Sternberg Memorial Museum, obtained another specimen of Ichthyornis cf. I. dispar, complete with fragments of toothed upper and lower jaws. Therefore at least some of the varied kinds of bird remains referred to Ichthyornis were tooth-bearing, however, not all members of the genus are well enough known from fossil remains to demonstrate that all the described species were tooth-bearing, or if some were more closely related to modern birds and lacked teeth. The other group (Hesperornis, Figures 37, 38, and Baptornis) consists of relatively large-footed, nearly wingless, toothed, swimming and diving marine birds, that are not related to any living birds. The latest Cretaceous greensands of New Jersey have yielded bones of sea and shore birds that belong to families living today, and remains of the oldest known hawk have been recovered from late Cretaceous nonmarine sediments in the Western Interior of the United States. Cenozoic bird faunas were essentially the same as those living today, although the development of large, (up to seven feet tall), ground-living, flightless, carnivorous birds early in the Tertiary (before mammalian carnivores became numerous) was an unique event in bird evolution.

Class Mammalia

The earliest known mammals are docodonts from upper Triassic rocks, and quite likely the oldest known specimen is a nearly complete skull and lower jaw of an Erythrotherium-like form from South Africa. Docodonts had skeletons much like therapsid (mammal-like) reptiles, and some retained the articular bone of the jaw, although the typical mammalian jaw to skull articulation had developed. Essentially these animals were in-between the full mammalian and mammal-like reptile status.

Class Mammalia

Subclass Prototheria
    Order Monotremata   – egg-laying forms, the living platypus (Ornithorhynchus) and the spiny anteaters (Zaglossus and Tachyglossus), unknown as fossils before the Pleistocene.

Figure 38. Hesperornis, a toothed,
wingless, diving,
marine bird from the
chalk beds of western
Kansas. Yale Peabody
Museum.

Figure 39. Ichthyornis dispar, a toothed,
but modern-appearing, bird
from the Cretaceous chalk
beds of western Kansas. The
type specimen is in the Yale
Peabody Museum.

Subclass Uncertain - method of reproduction unknown
    Order Docodonta   - the oldest known mammals, late Triassic through
                                    Jurassic, jaws may retain reptilian elements, skele-
                                    tons rather therapsid-like.

    Order Triconodonta   - Late Triassic through lower Cretaceous, small (house-
                                    cat sized at largest) carnivorous mammals with no
                                    known descendants. Possibly these mammals evolved
                                    independently of the therapsids.

Subclass Allotheria - method of reproduction unknown
    Order Multituberculata   - Late Jurassic through early Eocene herbivorous
                                    mammals whose appearance and adaptations were
                                    rodent-like. It is likely that the evolution of true
                                    rodents may have led to extinction of the multi-
                                    tuberculates.

Subclass Theria - method of reproduction unknown
    Infraclass Trituberculata - Lower Jurassic through lower Cretaceous mammals,
                                    some of which may have given rise to marsupial and
                                    placental mammals, although paleontologists do not
                                    generally agree as to which trituberculate group
                                    (symmetrodonts or pantotheres) were the ancestral
                                    forms.

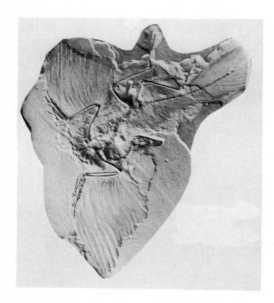

Figure 41. An egg-laying mammal, the echidna (Tachyglossus setosus), in its normal day-time activity, sleeping. This specimen in the Saint Louis Zoo seemingly feels secure enough to not roll up and protect its abdominal region.

Figure 40. Archaeopteryx, the oldest known bird from Jurassic limestones near Solnhofen, Germany. The outlines of feathers show well, extending rearward from the wings and outward along the elongate tail. Photograph of a plaster cast of the original specimen. Sternberg Memorial Museum.

Infraclass Metatheria - marsupial or "pouched" mammals

    Order Marsupialia   - Late Cretaceous through Recent mammals characterized by (in most marsupials) birth of immature young that crawl into a pouch (marsupium) and attach to teats until a semi-independent stage is reached. A pair of marsupial bones that support the pouch are present, and the bones articulate with the pubes.

Infraclass Eutheria - placental mammals

    Order Insectivora   - Early Cretaceous through Recent primitive placental mammals, some of which gave rise to the higher mammals. Living insectivores are shrews, moles, Old World hedgehogs, and "flying lemurs".

    Order Tillodontia   - Paleocene and Eocene, large (some were bear-sized) primitive placentals, with a poorly understood relationship to other mammals.

    Order Taeniodontia - Paleocene and Eocene herbivores that evolved from insectivores, as a short-lived and unsuccessful experiment in evolution.

Order Chiroptera	– Eocene through Recent bats, the only mammal that has developed true wings and flight. The wing membrane is stretched between the digits and is a less readily damaged wing than that of the pterosaurs.
Order Primates	– Cretaceous through Recent, largely arboreal and tropical-region dwelling monkey and monkey-like mammals.
Order Creodonta	– Late Cretaceous through early Pliocene primitive "carnivores" that preceeded true carnivores and were replaced by them.
Order Carnivora	– Paleocene through Recent carnivores including dogs, cats, weasels, raccoons, bears, seals, walruses, hyaenas and their carnivore ancestors.
Order Condylarthra	– Late Cretaceous through lower Pliocene primitive ungulates (transitional from insectivores to true ungulates) that gave rise to elephants, sea cows, artiodactyls and perissodactyls as well as some other groups.
Order Amblypoda	– Paleocene through lower Oligocene archaic ungulates. Some (uintatheres) were large with grotesquely ornamented skulls.
Order Proboscida	– Eocene through Recent, elephants, mastodons, and their close relatives, mostly characterized by tusks and trunks.
Order Sirenia	– Eocene through Recent sea cows (manatees and dugongs), the "mermaids" of medieval sailors.
Order Desmostylia	– Miocene and Pliocene amphibious, marine, subungulates related to sirenians and elephants, characterized by relatively short (seven to eight feet long) bodies, that were stocky and had massive legs.
Order Hyracoidea	– Lower Oligocene through Recent conies, rabbit-like subungulates with hooves, that are the most generalized subungulates known.
Order Embrithopoda	– A large horned subungulate, only one genus (Arsinotherium) is known, and its remains are from Oligocene rocks of Egypt, and show some degree or relationship to the hyraces.
Order Notoungulata	– Paleocene through Pleistocene ungulates, largely from South America. They were hoof or claw bearing herbivores not unlike the primitive ungulates from the Northern Hemisphere.
Order Astrapotheria	– Paleocene through Miocene ungulates from South America, characterized by large size, large canine teeth, and seemingly the development of an elephant-like trunk in some forms.

Order Litopterna   - Paleocene through Pleistocene hoofed ungulates from South America, that evolved into horse-like and camel-like forms.

Order Perissodactyla - Eocene through Recent ungulates with an odd number (one, three or five, although the front feet of some may have four) of toes. Horses, tapirs, titanotheres, rhinoceroses and chalicotheres are the main groups of living and extinct perissodactyls.

Order Artiodactyla   - Eocene through Recent ungulates characterized by an even number of toes, (two, four, or five in some fossil forms). Typical artiodactyls are pigs, hippopotami, bison, cattle, deer, camels, and sheep. There is a great variety of extinct fossil forms.

Order Edentata   - Paleocene through Recent mammals that are mostly from South America, and include a toothless anteater (Myrmecophaga) sloths (living tree sloths and extinct, large, ground-living sloths), and armadillos.

Order Pholidota   - Oligocene through Recent forms characterized by the living pangolin or scaly anteater of Asia and Africa.

Order Tubulidentata - Eocene through Recent genera represented today by the aardvark, a termite-eating African mammal that resembles the anteaters.

Order Cetacea   - Eocene through Recent marine mammals known as whales, porpoises, and dolphins. The earliest known cetaceans were very whale-like in appearance, but retained some skull characteristics suggestive of descent from land carnivores.

Order Rodentia   - Paleocene through Recent mammals with large incisor teeth used for gnawing. Squirrels, rats, mice, beavers, guinea pigs and chinchillas are among the better known living rodents, and numerically they are the most diversified mammal order.

Order Lagomorpha   - Paleocene through Recent mammals with long legs, long ears, large incisor teeth (hares and rabbits) and some short-legged, short-eared forms (pikas). The known fossil forms are much like living ones.

It is quite likely that mammals, as we define the class today, evolved (Figure 42) from more than one therapsid group. In the late Triassic the two mammalian orders (docodonts and triconodonts) are rather reptilian in skeletal structure and seemingly did not give rise to any other mammals. The change from mammal to reptile, is usually considered to be signified by development of the dentary to squamosal articulation for the jaw and incorporation of the prior jaw-skull articulating bones (articular and quadrate) as two (incus and malleus) of the three inner ear bones. Apparently these changes did not occur simultaneously, as some early mammals with the dentary to squamosal articulation still retain the articular bone on the jaw, and some mammal-like groups evolved that did not become fully "mammalian", and apparently did not give rise to any higher or more fully mammal groups.

The monotremes (Figure 41), known only from Pleistocene and living forms, are structurally equivalent to a late Triassic or early Jurassic mammal group, and may be survivors

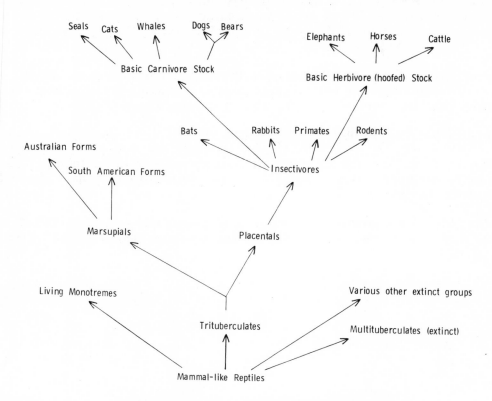

Figure 42.   Evolution of mammals.

of some early Mesozoic mammals, or possibly descendants of a therapsid reptile group that independently evolved across the reptile-mammal "boundary".

In the Jurassic three more mammal orders evolved, one of which, the multituberculates, was the longest-lived mammal group known, and became extinct without giving rise to any other mammals. The other two orders (both included within the infraclass Trituberculata) gave rise to the marsupial and placental mammals. The line of descent from therapsid reptiles to trituberculates is unknown, and forms grading from trituberculates into marsupial or placental mammals are also unknown.

The evolution of marsupial and placental mammals took place at the same time, that is, placental mammals are not descended from marsupial ancestors, but are a parallel line of evolution. Probably both those mammal infraclasses had evolved at least by early Cretaceous time.

The oldest known marsupial remains are from late Cretaceous rocks, and small opossum-like marsupials were probably abundant on all the major land masses. During late Cretaceous time South America and Australia (including Tasmania and New Guinea) became isolated from the other major land masses as continental drift began to break up the Mesozoic continents. Thus those two continents became isolated before the greater portion of placental evolution took place. Australia was probably isolated first, and had at that time a fauna that we may presume to have been composed of reptiles, including some remnant late Cretaceous archosaurs, birds, monotremes, perhaps some other Mesozoic mammals, and marsupials. True placental mammals may have not been present on Australia or they may have become extinct there after the separation of the continents. If Australia drifted away in the late Cretaceous (and the earliest known placentals are early Cretaceous), the latter assumption would seem plausible.

Marsupials in Australia evolved into three main groups and developed into forms that filled niches mainly occupied by placental mammals elsewhere in the world. The dasyuroids evolved into mole-like forms (Notoryctes), an anteater (Myrmecobius), the Tasmanian wolf (Thylacinus), the Tasmanian devil (Sarcophilus) and into weasel-like or cat-like forms (Dasyurus).

The second group, the perameloids, is an evolutionary intermediate between the first group and the diprotondonts. The perameloids (bandicoots) are a group of long-snouted omnivorous forms that are somewhat rabbit-like in appearance.

The diprotodonts evolved into the phalangers, or Australian "possums" that generally are squirrel-like in form, the koala bear (Phascolarctos), the wombat (Phascolomys), a large woodchuck-like form, and into the wallabies and kangaroos, that are rather well-known grazing forms with a well-developed ability at hopping. Very few fossil marsupials of pre-Pleistocene age are known from Australia.

A parallel, but less extensive, development of marsupials occurred in South America. Probably South America became separated from the other continental masses after the

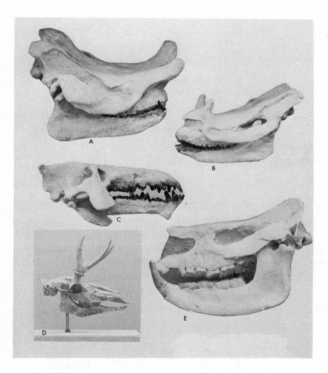

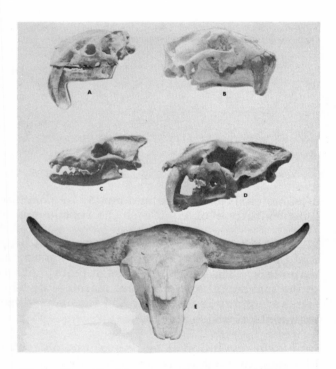

Plate 20. Some tertiary ungulates.

Plate 21. Tertiary carnivores and Bison.

A, B.) Titanotheres (Menodus sp.), early Cenozoic perissodactyls of large size that ate soft vegetation. C.) Archaeotherium scotti, a pig-like artiodactyl from Oligocene rocks. D.) Merycocerus warreni, a Miocene deer-like form from North America. E.) Teleoceras ? a short-legged, semi-aquatic rhinoceros from Pliocene deposits of Kansas. All photographs courtesy of the Sternberg Memorial Museum.

A.) Thylacosmilus, a Pliocene "saber-toothed, cat-like" marsupial from South America. B.) Hoplophoneus, an Oligocene true saber-toothed cat from North America. C.) Canis dirus, the dire wolf from the Pleistocene La Brea pits of Los Angeles. D.) Smilodon, a Pleistocene saber-toothed cat from the La Brea pits. E.) An extremely large-horned fossil Bison from Pleistocene deposits of the western United States. All specimens were photographed by courtesy of the Sternberg Memorial Museum.

separation of Australia (probably also in the late Cretaceous, but a few million years later). The South American marsupials evolved into a variety of possums, including the living "North American" species, the caenolestoids, small mouse-like or rat-like forms that lack marsupial pouches, and a group of large carnivorous forms that were not related to those of Australia. The carnivorous forms include <u>Borhyaena</u>, Miocene dog-like forms, and <u>Thylacosmilus</u> (Plate 21, Figure A), Pliocene, cat-like forms with large, stabbing canine teeth similar to those of the placental saber-toothed cats (Plate 21, Figures B, D) of the northern hemisphere.

The most primitive placental mammals are the insectivores (Plate 19, Figures A, B) and the oldest known members of that group are from lower Cretaceous rocks. Although we do not have much knowledge of early insectivore evolution, it seems likely that they gave rise to the rest of the placental mammals. Late Cretaceous insectivores seemingly evolved into three known divisions, the deltatheridian creodonts (formerly considered to have been insectivores) that gave rise to only the carnivorous creodonts that are now extinct, the leptictids that may have evolved into condylarths (and then the ungulate orders) and the rest of the placental orders, including the living carnivores. Even though most of the placental orders do not have as yet discovered pre-Cenozoic fossil remains, their evolution and the initial splitting up of the insectivore "stocks" must have begun in the Cretaceous. In this respect it is significant that Late Cretaceous creodont, condylarth, and primate remains have been discovered recently.

Some arboreal insectivores probably evolved into bats, and another arboreal insectivore group evolved into tree shrews and primates.

Rodents probably evolved directly from insectivores although some specialists think that rodents may have been derived from some early primates, that became gnawing herbivores.

Nearly all the remainder of the placental mammals evolved from one or the other of two stocks. The true carnivore stock evolved into a variety of land-dwelling groups that are specialized as to hunting style. Among the various groups are stalking hunters, the cats, group or pack-hunting forms, dogs (Plate 21, Figure C) and their close relatives, the large omnivorous bears. Weasels and ferrets are slender forms that hunt burrowing mammals, and raccoons are largely nocturnal omnivores of small size.

An early offshoot of carnivore evolution (although some scientists think condylarths may have been ancestral) led to the development of whales very early in Cenozoic time. The earliest known whales were long (<u>Basilosaurus</u> was as long as 70 feet), slender forms with carnivore-like skulls, although the nostrils had already migrated on top of the skull, as in modern whales. These primitive whales evolved into the stocky-bodied, living toothed-whales, such as the sperm whales and porpoises, and into the whalebone whales that are filter-feeding

Plate 22. Bison.

A.) Artists conception of an extinct species of long-horned bison on the prairies of western Kansas.
B.) Model of extinct <u>Bison</u> species, from the Pleistocene of North America. The painting and the model are both in the Sternberg Memorial Museum.

forms, generally of large size. The largest animal known (living or fossil) is the modern sulphur-bottom or blue whale (a whalebone whale) that as an adult, may be 100 feet long and weigh 120 tons or more.

In the mid-Cenozoic, two other lines of carnivore evolution resulted in the development of three new groups of marine mammals. Those forms are less modified for aquatic life than the whales, and are the living seals, sea lions, and walruses.

Nearly all of the remainder of the placental mammals are descendants of the condylarth stock, that arose from insectivores in the Cretaceous. Subsequent to the condylarth stage, development followed three distinct evolutionary lineages, (a) that of the subungulates (a largely African group), (b) the ungulates, and (c) those forms endemic to South America.

Figure 43.   The skull of a small deer, Leptomeryx, from the Oligocene and Miocene rocks of North America. Courtesy of the Sternberg Memorial Museum.

Subungulates are probably descended from small, hoofed, Hyrax-like (but unknown) forms that lived early in the Tertiary. These primitive forms may have lived in Africa, and gave rise to a variety of subungulates, including the giant, horned Arsinotherium (an extinct, evolutionary "dead-end"), the elephants (Figures 45, 46, 47) and mastodonts, the sea cows, (aquatic, flippered herbivores) and the desmostylids, extinct amphibious forms that lived along the Pacific Ocean shores.

Most of the living herbivorous, land-dwelling animals are hoofed and belong either to the Perissodactyla or to the Artiodactyla. The perisodactyls are probably the older of the two groups and were the numerically dominant hoofed mammals early in the Tertiary. Evolutionary trends within that group led to development of swift, one-toed grazers with high-crowned teeth (horses), and bulkier, horned, herbivorous forms, such as the largely American titanotheres, and the rhinoceros (Plate 20, Figures A, B, E), an Old World group that is not closely related.

Figure 44.   Megaloceros, skull and antlers of a giant deer known as the "Irish elk", whose remains are rather abundant in some Pleistocene deposits of Europe. Courtesy of the Sternberg Memorial Museum.

The artiodactyls are the most abundant hoofed mammal group today. They have followed several evolutionary trends and most have become long-legged animals with each foot so constructed that they stand on the tips of two toes (hooves). The Suina (pig-like forms and hippopotami) are primitive and tend to have elongate canine teeth, an omnivorous diet, and no horns or antlers (Plate 20, Figure C). Ruminants are both more numerous and more advanced than the Suina, and are characterized by "cud-chewing" and compartmented stomachs useful for storing materials cropped during

Figure 45.   Restoration of a mammoth (<u>Mammuthus</u>), the woolly coat, probably characteristic of most if not all mammoths, is not present on this model.   Courtesy of the Sternberg Memorial Museum.

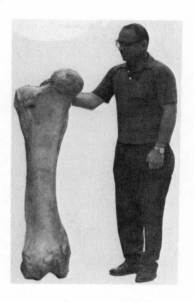

Figure 46.   A femur of one of the largest mammoths (<u>Mammuthus</u> sp.) dis- covered so far.   Courte- sy of the Sternberg Memorial Museum.

Figure 47.

   A.) Artist's restoration of a group of shovel-tusk- ed mastodons (<u>Amebelodon</u>?) during the Pliocene in western Kansas.   B.) Jaw of a shovel-tusked mastodon (<u>Amebelodon</u>?) from Pliocene sediments of Kansas. Photographs on this plate are by courtesy of the Stern- berg Memorial Museum.

grazing, that later are regurgitated and chewed more thoroughly ("cud-chewing") before being reswallowed and further digested. The more primitive ruminants include camels, llamas, and oreodonts (Figure 43), and some extinct forms, all of which lack horns or antlers. Slightly more advanced ruminants are represented by some other primitive forms, that are hornless and antlerless and have large upper canine teeth. The most advanced ruminants are the tropical area dwelling giraffes that are horned browsers (Figure 44) and deer that are antlered, usually only the males, temperate region browers, and the bovoidea (Plate 21, Figure E; Plate 22, Figures A, B) that are mostly horned, usually in both sexes, and are grazers. The most primitive bovoids are the Old World antelopes that gave rise to the living cattle, bison, sheep, and goats. The American antelope (Antilocapra) is seemingly a separate line of descent (Plate 19, Figure D) with some features that are bovid-like.

Several primitive ungulate groups developed in South America during the Cenozoic, independently of the more advanced northern hemispheric ungulates. This was made possible by the geographic isolation of South America because of late Mesozoic continental drift. The order Notoungulata was roughly equivalent to the more primitive northern hemispheric ungulates, and included forms that had five or three toes, a few had horns, some had an elongate proboscis, some were rodent-like, and others were horse-like. The order Astrapotheria were mostly large, tusk-bearing forms that were either hippo-like or elephant-like in appearance. The litopterns range from condylarth-like forms into some one toed ungulates that were extremely horse-like. Other litopterns were more camel-like in body form.

The order Edentata is another characteristically South American group that consists of sloths, anteaters, and armadillos, and may be descended from ungulate ancestors. Edentates may be toothless (origin of the name) or have simple peg-like teeth lacking enamel. Armadillos are covered by corneous scutes that provide an armor-like shell, and include large, extinct fossil forms (Glyptodon) that were as long as nine feet and successfully entered and lived in North America in the late Pliocene through the Pleistocene. Sloths are best known as small, sluggishly-moving, tree-dwelling animals that are mainly nocturnal and spend most of their time hanging upside down. Although there are no known fossil remains of tree sloths, fossil remains of the larger, ground-dwelling sloths are abundant in South America from the Oligocene through the Pleistocene, and in Pleistocene sediments of North America. The largest known forms were 20 feet long and were larger than living elephants.

The third group of edentates is the South American anteaters (Myrmecophaga) and related fossil forms, and they are the only really toothless edentates.

Although the armadillos and ground-sloths were able temporarily to complete successfully with North American mammals, the great majority of the South American ungulates became extinct after more highly evolved ungulates from the northern hemisphere entered South America in the Pleistocene. Possibly the glyptodonts and ground sloths were hunted to extinction by man.

THE PLEISTOCENE EPOCH

Pleistocene Defined

The term Pleistocene was first proposed by Charles Lyell in 1839 as a replacement name for the Newer Pliocene that Lyell had defined and named in 1833. The Newer Pliocene had been defined by Lyell on a faunal basis, ninety percent of the fossilized mollusc species found in sediments of that age could be found living in modern seas. Sediments located near Val di Noto, Sicily, were cited by Lyell as containing a typical Newer Pliocene fauna, and even after Lyell replaced the term Newer Pliocene with the term Pleistocene, the same criteria for definition by means of the fossil fauna contained in the rocks and the same type section applied to the Pleistocene. After the term Newer Pliocene was discarded, the Older Pliocene became known as the Pliocene.

Because the lower boundary of the Pleistocene Epoch may be determined by Lyell's still valid definition based on the contained fossil fauna, the geologically latest glacial stages need not have occurred throughout the entire Pleistocene, or have been confined to the Pleistocene. A potassium-argon radioactive age determination of a sample from a volcanic ash bed in Africa that overlies a slightly younger Pleistocene fauna than the one contained in sediments Lyell designated as the type section in Sicily, gave an age of 1.85 million years. Therefore the Pleistocene probably extends over at least the last two million years, and possibly the last three million years.

Relation to Man

A brief discussion of the history of the Pleistocene Epoch is necessary to understand the effect widespread ice sheets and arctic climates had on the evolution of Homo sapiens, and may yet have on modern men's distribution and survival. Either melting of the ice with a resultant rise in sea level, or a renewed spreading of ice sheets would seriously affect men's survival, cultures and geographic distribution (Figure 49).

The Glacial Stages

At least four major glaciations separated by warm interglacial stages occurred during the Pleistocene, and at least one of those major stages, the Wisconsinan, had several substages marked by lesser advances and retreats of the ice sheet.

THE KNOWN MAJOR PLEISTOCENE GLACIAL STAGES

North American Terms	ALPINE AREA	NORTHERN EUROPE
Wisconsin Glacial Stage	WÜRM GLACIAL	WEICHSEL GLACIAL
Sangamon Interglacial	"THIRD INTERGLACIAL"	EEM INTERGLACIAL
	RISS GLACIAL	SAALE GLACIAL
Illinoisan Glacial Stage	"SECOND INTERGLACIAL"	HOLSTEIN INTERGLACIAL
Yarmouthian Interglacial	MINDEL GLACIAL	ELSTER GLACIAL
	"FIRST INTERGLACIAL"	CROMER INTERGLACIAL
Kansan Glacial Stage	GÜNZ GLACIAL	MENAP GLACIAL
Aftonian Interglacial	DONAU-GUNZ INTERVAL	WAAL INTERVAL
	DONAU GRAVELS	EBURON COLD CLIMATE
Nebraskan Glacial Stage	WARM? INTERVAL	TEGELEN INTERVAL
	BIBER GRAVELS	BRÜGGEN GLACIAL?

European and American geologists use distinct sets of terms for the glacial stages of their continents, however, they agree that glacial and interglacial stages occurred synchronously on both continents, but the correlations of the stages are uncertain, except for the Wisconsin-Würm-Weichsel.

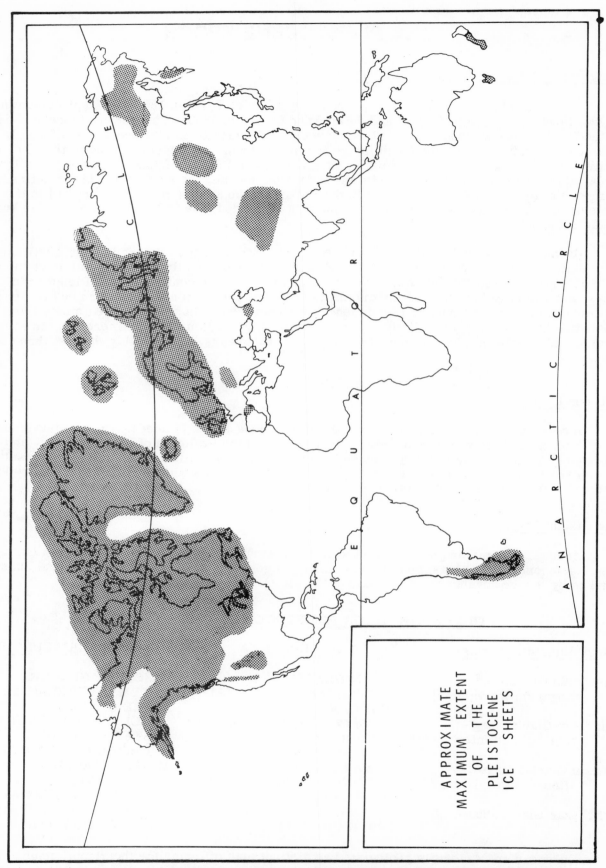

Figure 48.   Approximate maximum extent of the Pleistocene ice sheets.

The most widespread glaciation in North America (Figure 48) was that of the Nebraskan ice sheet, and it could well have eroded away or covered over most if not all traces on the continent of any older and less extensive glaciations. By correlating studies of deep sea sediments that contain records of glacial stages in the form of alternating cold and warm water faunas with the preserved continental sedimentary record, we may learn precisely how many major and minor ice sheets existed during, and prior to the Pleistocene.

Glacial Chronology

Estimates of the time span occupied by the glacial stages range from 500,000 years to more than 10,000,000 years. Although the temporal length of the glacial sequences has been hotly debated by glacial geologists, there are some radioactive age determinations that indicate a short readvance of the Wisconsinan Ice Sheet occurred about 11,200 B.P. in Wisconsin, so a still active, though retreating glacier existed at that time. Presumably this short readvance was followed by 5,000 year period of melting. The world climate remained cool until about the second century A.D., when a warming trend began that reached a peak between 1100 and 1300 A.D., and was warmer than the present. Following this a cooler climate, much like that of the present day, prevailed until 1450 A.D. From 1450 to 1550 the world climate seems to have been warmer, but gave way to a renewed cold spell from 1600 until 1850. Another warm period began in 1850 and lasted until about 1940, but has seemingly been succeeded since then by a new cooler climate and the last major North American ice sheet was completely melted by 6,000 B.P., at which time the Hypsithermal or "Thermal Maximum", a slightly warmer climate than that of the present time prevailed. The "Thermal Maximum" was followed by the Little Ice Age or Neoglaciation (4,500 B.P.) during which the glaciers now present in some of the 48 contingent mainland United States reformed.

The initial (?) major (Nebraskan) ice sheet in North America may have formed approximately 1,000,000 years ago, as a till bed in Nevada, probably a portion of the Kansas Glacial State sediments, has been determined by the potassium-argon age determination method to have formed before 700,000 years ago. This would indicate an older age, probably 1,000,000 years for the beginning of the Nebraskan Glacial Stage, although some recent evidence indicates an older glaciation occurred three million years ago in the Sierra Nevada of the western United States, and three million year old glacial sediments have been identified in drill cores taken from the North Atlantic Ocean.

Glacial sediments older than 3,000,000 years, have also been discovered in Antarctica, but whether these older glaciations were confined to Antarctica, or were local glacial sequences is not certain. There is some evidence (tills and deep sea sediment cores) that indicates the presence of glaciers on Antarctica and Alaska through much of the Cenozoic, beginning about 10,000,000 years ago.

The Earth's Surface Area

The Earth has an area of approximately 197 million square miles, of which 71% (about 140 million square miles) is ocean covered. The remainder of about 57 million square miles is land area, of which nearly 10% is still ice covered (Plate 23, Figures A, B) mostly in Greenland and Antarctica, about 15% is permafrost, and approximately 25% is arid or desert land. Only about 2% of the Earth's land surface has a Mediterranean climate, the climate zone considered most pleasant and usually preferred by European Caucasoids and their descendants.

Volume of Ice on Land

Greenland has an area of about 630,000 square miles and Antarctica has an area of about 4 million square miles. The ice sheets that nearly cover these land masses range from a few hundred feet to a maximum of 10,000 feet in thickness. If the average ice thickness were between one mile and one and one-half miles, the Greenland and Antarctic ice caps would contain

Epochs	Glacial and Interglacial Stages	Hominid Cultures and Genera
	Recent--5,000 B.P.	
Pleistocene	Wisconsinan (Würm-Weichsel)	farming and herding Magdalenian culture Solutrean culture Cro-Magnons-Aurignacian culture Neanderthalers-Mousterian culture
	Sangamon (Eem)	Homo sapiens Acheulean culture
	Illinoisan (Riss-Saale)	Homo erectus
	Yarmouthian (Holstein)	Homo sapiens ?
	Kansan (Mindel-Elster)	Homo erectus Abbevillian culture
	Aftonian (Cromer)	
	Nebraskan (Günz-Menap)	Homo erectus ? Australopithecus spp. Eoliths
	"Villafranchian" 3,000,000	
Pliocene	 9,000,000?	Australopithecus spp. Eoliths ? Ramapithecus spp.
Miocene		"Kenyapithecus" spp. Ramapithecus spp.

Figure 49. Chart of Glacial Stages correlated with the known hominid cultures and remains.

a total of nearly 6,000,000 cubic miles of ice. If this volume of ice were to melt and spread over the Earth's ocean area of 140 million square miles, sea level would rise about 200 feet.

Pleistocene Changes of Sea Level

Sea level will continue to rise as the remaining land-locked glacial ice melts. Sea level seems to have risen at least four inches during the last century, and most glaciers have seemingly shrunk during the same period. We do not know if this warming trend, that started about 1850, will return. However sea level seems to be rising, at least locally, about one foot per century, in spite of the renewed cold climate.

Previous warm interglacial periods have resulted in glacial ice melting and causing higher sea levels that formed wave cut benches and shoreline deposits at least 100 feet above the present day sea level. Some geologists have found evidences of pre-Pleistocene shore lines nearly 300 feet above the present-day sea level.

During the maximum extent of the ice sheets, the Earth's land surface was about 30% ice covered, and North America may have been partially covered by as much as twelve million cubic miles of ice. So much water was removed from the oceans and locked up in glacial ice on the land surface that sea level was lowered as much as 350 feet.

Plate 23. Antarctic Glaciers.

A.) A view of the area surrounding an iceberg as seen from an ice cave inside an iceberg near Hallett Station. Official U. S. Navy Photograph. B.) Aerial view of Meserve Glacier in Wright Valley. Official U. S. Navy photograph.

This lower sea level resulted in deposition of partially preserved beach sands and dunes far off the present-day shore line, and mastodons, mammoths, and other animals wandered across the exposed and dry former sea floor. Siberia and Alaska were connected by the then water-free Bering Straits, as a 120 foot lowering of sea level would cause Asia and North America to be connected by a land bridge.

Extent of the Ice Sheets

Despite the extensive ice sheets that covered much of Europe, North America and part of Asia, large portions of those continents remained ice-free. Siberia was largely unglaciated, although cold climates and perma-frost must have been widespread there. Other ice-free areas may have included a corridor leading southward from Canada along the eastern flank of the Rocky Mountains to the southern Great Plains. Furthermore, much of the coastline of the Arctic Ocean may have been relatively ice-free and unglaciated, thus permitting men and animals to live along that coast and to migrate from the Old World into the New World.

Eastern North America was partially covered by a large ice sheet, the edge of which extended south from the Arctic Ocean along the Atlantic Coast to New York City, thence westward through the site of present-day Saint Louis to northeastern Kansas. From Kansas the edge of the sheet extended northward through the Dakotas to the Arctic.

Other large ice sheets were present over portions of the North American Cordillera, the Alps and southern Germany, Scandinavia, and northern European Russia. In addition many other areas were covered by smaller glaciers.

Interglacial Ages

During the interglacial stages the warm climate zones expanded and their northern boundaries shifted toward the polar regions. Some of these shifts brought warmer annual temperatures to northern regions than those present today. Glaciologists have estimated that a mean annual temperature rise of 7° F would cause widespread tropics and melting of the remaining glacial ice.

Sediments deposited during the interglacial stages contain fossils, such as pollen grains, plant remains, snail shells, or bones of organisms that could only have lived in the areas where they were found if the climate had been warmer than at the present. Near Toronto in Canada interglacial (Sangamon) sediments called the Don beds contain fossils (trees, molluscs, vertebrates) indicative of a climate with a mean annual temperature 5° F warmer than that at the present for the Toronto area. The Scarborough beds overlie the Don beds, and contain fossils (trees, insects) indicative of a climate slightly cooler than that now prevalent in the Toronto area. The interglacial sediments are overlain by Wisconsin tills, indicating a return of extensive glaciation.

Pluvial Climate

The pluvial climates are thought to have coincided at least partly with the glacial stages as expansion of the ice sheets brought polar climates and the middle-latitude belts of rain-bringing cyclonic storms southward, and caused the other climate zones to migrate toward the equator. The horse-latitudes, a zone of descending dry air shifted southward so that deserts such as the Sonoran and Sahara, became rather well-watered grasslands with extensive lakes developed in basins that are not dry (playas), or have become smaller saline lakes (Great Salt Lake) that lack river outlets to the ocean.

Causes of Glaciation

The causes of the cyclic glaciations have been the subject of much speculation and little enlightenment. Apparently the cycles were irregular and not periodic, so that a regular, self-perpetuating cause seems unlikely. The ice sheets also varied in extent as well as temporal spacing. A temperature decline (the Earth's mean annual temperature) of 3° to 14° F would cause a return to glacial conditions approaching those of the Pleistocene maxima.

Possibly the glaciations were caused by factors such as continental drift, in that the northern hemisphere continents moved so as to form a nearly enclosed Arctic Sea and oceanic warm-to-cold area circulation patterns became restricted. This could have resulted in a higher evaporation rate over the Arctic leading to a radiation-reflecting cloud cover and increased snowfall and formation of glaciers. Or perhaps the sun undergoes as yet undetermined major fluctuations of its output of radiation. The most frank appraisal is that we just do not know what causes major glaciations.

Chapter XII

PRIMATE EVOLUTION

Early Primate Evolution

Primate evolution began with the appearance of the plesiadapids in the late Cretaceous. The earliest known primate, Purgatorius, was described from study of one tooth from Cretaceous rocks by Dr. Leigh Van Valen. The tooth is very insectivore-like in structure and also seems to have a close relationship to condylarths. Fifty more teeth of a closely related species were found in early Paleocene rocks; and from mid-Paleocene rocks at least ten genera of primates are known. Presumably primates underwent a rapid diversification early in the Cenozoic. Primates (following Simons, 1972, Primate Evolution) are classified as follows:

Order Primates

Suborder Prosimii

Infraorder Plesiadapiformes (Cretaceous through Eocene)

Infraorder Lemuriformes (Eocene through Recent)

Infraorder Lorisiformes (Miocene through Recent)

Infraorder Tarsiiformes (Eocene through Recent)

Suborder Anthropoidea (Oligocene through Recent)

Infraorder Platyrrhini (Oligocene through Recent)

Infraorder Catarrhini (Eocene through Recent)

Superfamily Oreopithecoidea (Miocene through Pliocene forms)

Superfamily Cercopithecoidea (Oligocene through Recent)

Superfamily Hominoidea (Eocene through Recent).

The tree shrews (Tupaia, Figure 50) are small squirrel-like, tree-living insectivores that seemingly are primate-like and

Figure 50. Tupaia sp., the living tree shrew that seemingly represents an evolutionary link between insectivores and primates. Saint Louis Zoo.

Figure 51. The potto (Perodicticus potto), a loris from Africa. This is one of the most geographically widespread of the living prosimians. Saint Louis Zoo.

some specialists consider them to be primitive primates, although others believe them to be specialized insectivores. The tupaiids are characterized by relatively large brains, an eye socket not open to the rear, opposable "thumbs" and big toes, and lemur-like middle ear structures. Primates could well have originated from this insectivore group, however, the oldest known fossil suspected to be a tupaiid is from Paleocene rocks.

The plesiadapids are Late Cretaceous and Early Tertiary primates with chisel-like incisor teeth, and possibly were rather closely related to rodents. The known fossil remains of plesiadapids indicate that they had claws, a lemur-like inner ear region and molar teeth. The members of this group may all be aberrant forms, and were not directly ancestral to the living higher primate groups.

The lemuroids (Figure 51) are more typically primate-like, and living forms are arboreal, rather cat-like or squirrel-like nocturnal animals, with bushy fur, and eyes that are directed more laterally than in higher primates. The "thumb" and great toes are well-developed and have flat nails as do those of higher primates, although the other digits (especially the second) may have claw-like nails. The lemurs possibly did not give rise to any higher primates, although this is problematical. Lemurs, plesiadapids, lorises and tarsiers are generally grouped together and called prosimians by some taxonomists.

The tarsiers are small, nocturnal animals (a single living genus Tarsius is known from the East Indies and Philippines Islands), with large, forwardly directed eyes, long tails, and a reduced nose and snout region that results in a monkey-like face. Fossil tarsiers have been found in Eocene rocks of Europe and North America, and survived into the early Miocene in North America. Possibly some North American tarsier (or lemur) reached South America by "rafting" or "island-hopping" during the Oligocene and gave rise to the South American (Platyrrhine) monkeys. Tarsiers have relatively large braincases, a higher-primate-like inner ear structure, and are believed to have given rise to the Old World primates (Catarrhines). The Old World and New World monkeys do not have a common origin or direct ancestor among the tarsiers, and are two genetically distinct but morphologically equivalent animal groups.

Platyrrhine monkeys evolved on the South American land mass after it had become isolated from the rest of the continents by continental drift, and the South American monkeys evolved parallel to, but distinct from the Old World monkeys. The two monkey groups differ in that the Platyrrhines tend to have long tails, no ischial callosities, a smaller body size, and thumbs that are not readily opposable. Furthermore three premolar teeth are present (dental formula $\frac{2 - 1 - 3 - 3}{2 - 1 - 3 - 3}$, where Old World monkeys and apes have a dental formula of $\frac{2 - 1 - 2 - 3}{2 - 1 - 2 - 3}$). The nostrils are unusually far apart and cause the nose to appear to be flat (platy = flat, rhine = nose).

The marmosets, perhaps the more primitive of the two platyrrhine families, are small, squirrel-like, bushy-haired primates that are characterized by claw-like nails, loss of the last molar ("wisdom-tooth") and lemur-like incisor and canine teeth.

The cebids are more numerous and varied and are characterized by being larger, with less fur, and a prehensile tail. Typical cebids include the capuchin (Cebus), squirrel (Saimiri, Figure 52), howler (Alouatta), and spider (Ateles) monkeys. The oldest known fossil remains of Platyrrhine monkeys are from Oligocene rocks, however their fossil history is poorly known.

The oldest known fossil ape-like or monkey-like Old World primates are the rather primitive genera Pondaungia and Amphipithecus (with three rather than two premolar teeth) from the late Eocene sediments of Burma. Both genera are known from lower jaw fragments only, and both have five-cusped ape-like teeth that include both tarsioid and monkey-like features. The two genera may be an evolutionary stage intermediate between tarsiers and Old World monkeys and apes, but are generally classified among the Hominoidea.

Figure 52.   Squirrel monkeys (Saimiri sp.), New
World monkeys characterized by long
tails and an exceptional ability at leaping.
Saint Louis Zoo.

Figure 53.   Macaca sp. demon-
strating the typical
quadrupedal walking
posture of monkeys,
in which the palms
contact the ground
and the hips are
elevated.

Old World monkeys seemingly evolved from tarsiers (Old World monkeys and apes may have a single
tarsier ancestor in common) and are characterized by
the presence of only two pre-molar teeth, ischial callosities, four-cusped molar teeth, and a tendency to
have relatively larger brains. In addition Old World
monkeys tend to have cheek pouches, either no tails or
short tails that are non-prehensile. Their nostrils are
closer together than those of the New World monkeys, and
they tend to have generally larger body sizes. They were
all originally arboreal, but some more progressive groups, macaques (Figure 53) and baboons,
have developed into largely terrestrial animals, some of them lack tails, and most have a relatively large body size, and effective societal organizations.

An Oligocene primate (Oligopithecus) from the Fayum beds of central Egypt must have
been ancestral to the Old World monkeys. This is inferred from a study of the teeth Oligopithecus, as they seem to have some monkey-like characteristics.

The earliest known Old World monkeys are found in Miocene sediments, although their
evolution probably began in the Eocene. Initially the group would have been characterized by
specializations for arboreal life, such as long tails, quadrupedal locomotion, opposable thumbs,
and a "hand-like" foot structure. They probably had a thin hair distribution, with nearly naked
faces and may have resembled the living African green, vervet, and Diana monkeys (Cerco-
pithecus sp.), and possessed cheek pouches for temporary food storage, and simply constructed
stomachs (not for a specialized diet as in the more advanced arboreal forms).

Two more advanced evolutionary lines seem to have diverged from the primitive forms.
One line led to development of long faces, larger size, and a terrestrial mode of life. The
macaques (Macaca) are probably representative of the early ground-dwelling forms, and are
still partially arboreal, although some species are nearly tailless. A few intermediate forms
lead to the larger, more fully terrestrial baboons (Papio, Mandrillus, and Theropithecus), with
dog-like muzzles, large canine teeth and larger body sizes.

Baboons compete, often successfully, with man for food and living space. They are a line
of monkey evolution paralleling that of the terrestrial apes, man.

Figure 54. A siamang, <u>Symphalangus</u> sp. or <u>Hylobates</u> <u>syndactylus</u> (specialists fail to agree whether or not the siamang is a distinct genus), a close relative of the gibbon. Both are relatively primitive living great apes from southeastern Asia that are characterized by extremely long arms, and relatively short body length. Saint Louis Zoo.

The second line of Old World monkey evolution led to development of small, specialized arboreal monkeys with complex stomachs and a restricted diet. They lack cheek pouches and have long tails and flat faces. Typical representatives are the langurs and leaf monkeys (<u>Presbytis</u>), and the proboscis and colobus monkeys (<u>Colobus</u>).

During the early Oligocene two (<u>Parapithecus</u> and <u>Apidium</u>) primitive catarrhine primates lived in what is now central Egypt. Their remains were formerly classed in the superfamily Parapithecoidea, although they are poorly understood and may be primates that have not advanced very far beyond the tarsier level of evolution. Probably they are not related to any of the living apes or monkeys, as they have an aberrant dental formula with three premolars, instead of two. Presently they are considered to be cercopithecoids.

Ape Evolution

Apes, or pongids (Figure 55), are characterized by their ability to assume an erect posture, although only the gibbon normally walks erect (Figure 56), the presence of five-cusped molar teeth, no tails (at least in living forms), no ischial callosities (except for some gibbons), relatively larger brains, relatively long arms and short legs, rather "hand-like" feet, large body size, and a "swinging" form of branch to branch (using hands) locomotion known as brachiation. There are four living groups, the gibbons and siamangs, orangutans, chimpanzees, and gorillas. The gibbons are the most primitive and arboreal, and ability at brachiation and the degree of arboreal life decreases among the larger forms, so that gorillas have become secondarily largely terrestrial forms. The great weight of adult male gorillas, from 400 to 600 pounds, prevents them from readily climbing and traveling among trees.

During the early Oligocene a portion of the shore line of the Mediterranean Sea was located in what is now central Egypt. Where rivers entered the sea, a group of coastal plain sediments, now known as the Fayum Beds, were deposited. Many fossil ape remains have been collected from the Fayum Beds, including the genera <u>Proliopithecus</u>, a hominoid of doubtful relationship, in that it has been called a gibbon, or related to the other great apes or to man, but may be a generalized ape. <u>Aegyptopithecus</u>, is more advanced and is the oldest known undoubted great ape and is possibly the ancestor of both man and the living great apes. The genus <u>Aeolopithecus</u> is also present and is possibly a primitive gibbon, as it is more gibbon-like than <u>Proliopithecus</u>. The Fayum Beds contain fossilized remains of creodont carnivores, rodents, bats, hyraxes, dugongs, mastodonts, birds, corcodiles, and fish. The kinds of animals and plants (fossilized tree trunks up to 100 feet long) present in the beds with the primates indicate that the environment was a humid tropical forest along the coastal lowland next to the Mediterranean Sea.

The ape <u>Pliopithecus</u> from Miocene and Pliocene sediments is paradoxical as it has some characteristics of the gibbons, but has a long, unape-like tail, and also has some prosimian and ceboidean-like characteristics, but it could well have been descended from <u>Aeolopithecus</u> and could also have given rise to the gibbons, or been an offshoot of gibbon evolution.

Figure 55. Young orangutan with typical infantile facial features that differ markedly from those of the adult male. Saint Louis Zoo.

Figure 56. Skeleton of adult gorilla showing normal walking and standing posture for most great apes. The hips are held relatively low, and knuckles contact the ground. Saint Louis Museum of Science and Natural History.

Our knowledge of the early Tertiary stages of primate evolution is largely based on the fragmentary remains of an incompletely known sequence. It seems likely that the first apes were generalized in that relatively long arms and brachiation, the accompanying tree-limb to tree-limb locomotion method that is characteristic of the modern great apes, did not develop before the Miocene, except in the gibbons (Figure 54).

The gibbons (Hylobates) are the smallest (up to three feet tall and about 13 pounds in siamangs) and most primitive of the living great apes. They are almost completely arboreal, but are the only living great apes to normally walk erect when on the ground. They have extremely long arms, long enough to touch the ground when standing erect, although they normally walk with their arms held upward and waving rather awkwardly to help preserve their balance. Their brain size is about 90 cubic centimeters, and the brain lacks convolutions, although it is relatively large for a mammal that size.

The orangutans (Pongo) are more advanced and larger, up to five feet tall and 165 pounds, living great apes than the gibbons, and also are arboreal forms. The cranial capacity is relatively large, up to 550 cubic centimeters, however the paleontologic history of the orangs is unknown, but they may have had an origin close, if not similar, to that of the gorillas and chimpanzees.

Very likely in late Oligocene or early Miocene time a short-armed ape, possibly Aegyptopithecus or an unknown, but closely related form gave rise to the ancestors of the chimpanzees, the gorillas, possibly the orangs, and to men (Figure 57). At least one species of Aegyptopithecus, or a descendant thereof, became specialized for arboreal life, by developing long arms and the ability to brachiate, thereby giving rise to the tree-living modern great apes. Another species retained the more primitive and relatively short arm length and became specialized for terrestrial life and eventually evolved into man, the ground-living ape.

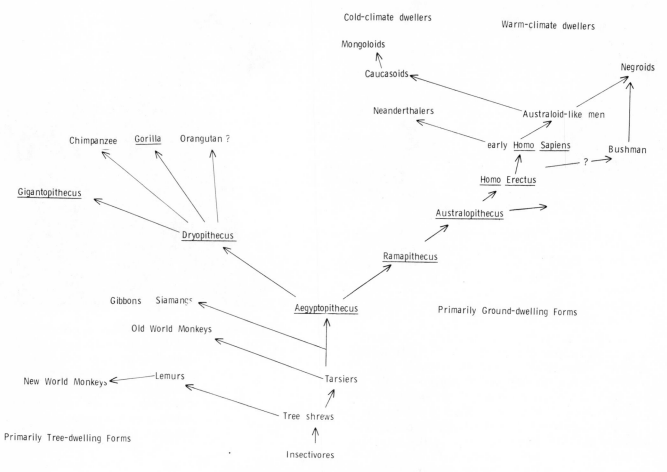

Figure 57. Evolution of man.

Dryopithecus was a variegated ape genus of Miocene and early Pliocene times and included a number of species ranging in three size groups, from that of a small ape (pgymy chimpanzee), a chimpanzee sized, and a gorilla sized group. The genus was distributed over a geographically wide area, including portions of Africa, Europe, and southern Asia. Variation among species belonging to the genus was such that some remains now considered to belong within Dryopithecus were described as distinct genera, "Proconsul" and "Sivapithecus" among other names. The name "Proconsul" was rather humorously based on the name of a chimpanzee, Consul, formerly an inhabitant of the London Zoo, and was not intended to indicate the burgeoning intelligence or leadership of the Proconsul line.

Skulls of **Dryopithecus** ("Proconsul" from east Africa) indicate that the cranium of that species was rounded with a low vault, had rather weakly developed brow-ridges, and was only slightly prognathous. Furthermore, the postcranial skeleton indicates that bipedal posture was possible and the arms were not specialized for brachiation.

Dryopithecus remains were first found in association with fossil oak leaves (the source of the generic name, Dryo = oak, pithecus = ape) and other plant fossils that indicate Dryopithecus lived in forested regions, with a tropical climate. In France and Spain dryopithecine remains have been found associated with fossil bones of elephants, tapirs, rhinoceroses, carnivores (bears, cats and smaller forms) pigs, and deer, that indicate warm, nearly tropical forests, with some interspersed grasslands. In Africa the associated animal fauna is very similar to the one from Europe. The Indian dryopithecine fossils from the Siwalik Hills are associated with a distinct fauna, that is related to the late Miocene and early Pliocene faunas of Europe, and consists of elephants (four-tusked forms), rhinoceroses, other ungulates including deer and pigs, some carnivores (hyaenas and creodonts), and giraffes. Again the fauna indicates a warm, nearly tropical climate, and an area with forests and some grasslands.

Dryopithecus was formerly considered to be ancestral to both man and the great apes, Dr. Louis Leakey, however, has recently discovered the remains of an older ape that he thought was a man-like dryopithecine ape, "Kenyapithecus" africanus. The species "Kenyapithecus africanus" is considered by some specialists to be a synonym of Dryopithecus nyanzae, and not at all man-like. Dr. Leakey's new species came from the lower Miocene of Africa, in rocks which had been deposited at the time the earliest known dryopithecine apes lives. This may indicate that the ancestors of man may have been a distinct evolutionary sequence before Dryopithecus evolved. Furthermore it seems likely that the ancestral gorilla, probably Dryopithecus major, and the ancestral chimpanzee, possibly Dryopithecusnnyanzae, were genetically distinct in the Miocene Epoch. If this is so, then ancestral hominids were almost certainly evolving as a genetically separate and distinct lineage during that epoch.

Fossil remains of apes and other primates are rare and usually consist of maxillary or mandible fragments and teeth. The scarcity of primate remains is probably caused by the preference of primates for living in tropical or subtropical forests, and forest environments are not ideal for the fossilization and preservation of bones. Teeth are harder and resist crunching by scavengers and weathering better than bone. Perhaps jaw fragments occur more abundantly as fossils because of a lack of edibility of such nearly meatless and relatively thick-boned parts.

Gigantopithecus was a genus of large apes that lived in India during the Pliocene Epoch at least five million years ago and possibly as long ago as nine million years. Some additional specimens found in China came from much younger, early or middle Pleistocene sediments. So far only four jaws (Figure 58) and more than 1,000 isolated teeth of Gigantopithecus have been found, and those only from China and India. The first scientifically studied tooth was obtained from a Chinese drugstore, where fossil bones were being sold as dragon remains to be ground-up for medicinal use.

The jaws are large, with massive, heavy bone, and the teeth are flattened on the occlusal surface and do not interlock as do the teeth of an ape. According to Dr. Elwyn Simons, individuals of Gigantopithecus may have weighed 600 pounds and been as tall as eight feet, and were heavy, ground-living, gorilla-like apes, with man-like dentition. It seems probable that an ape as large and heavy as Gigantopithecus could not have successfully lived in and traveled among trees, but such an ape could have competed successfully with other primates on the ground. Large size is apparently a distinct advantage in competing with closely related or morphologically similar forms for occupation of the same ecologic niche in a given area.

Gigantopithecus apparently lived in a grasslands region and may have been the first fully terrestrial hominoid, because of body size and the environment inhabited. Gigantopithecus very likely was not a meat-eating primate, although with its large size and accompanying strength, it could easily have become a successful predator of smaller primates and other vertebrates. The usually fruit-centered diet of primates would not have been available on the grasslands, and Gigantopithecus had adapted to a diet of grasses and grass seeds. Gigantopithecus' tooth row sequence consisted of small and peglike incisors, canine teeth worn flat from grinding, and flattened (from grinding) cheek teeth. There are no diastems in the tooth row, similar to those present in a typical ape's tooth row. The flat-crowned canine teeth and lack of diastems cause the teeth of Gigantopithecus to resemble those of man. The resemblance is apparently an adaptive one, in that both were descended from, or still were, (as was Gigantopithecus) largely graminivorous (grass and seed eating) animals. Gigantopithecus may have descended from Dryopithecus indicus, a species of large, gorilla-sized and conventional ape from late Miocene or early Pliocene sediments of India.

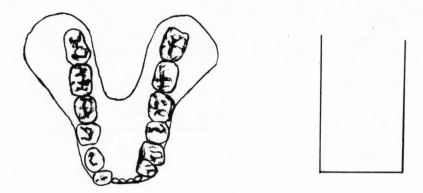

Figure 58. Gigantopithecus jaw, with the U-shaped dental arcade characteristic of pongids.

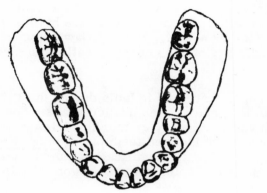

Figure 59. Ramapithecus jaw, with the V-shaped tooth-series characteristic of hominids.

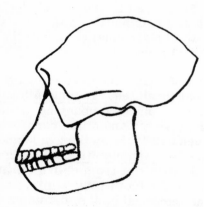

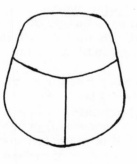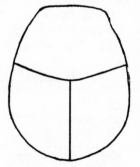

Figure 60. Australopithecus skull, a side view of A. africanus, showing the lack of highly developed sagittal crests and brow ridges that are present in A. robustus. In this respect A. africanus is more like Homo.

Figure 61. Skull form, long and broad heads, shown from above.

The fossils found associated with the Chinese Gigantopithecus include remains of an orangutan, dogs, bears, cats, hyaenas, elephants (mastodonts), badgers, civets, porcupines, pigs, goats, deer, bovids, giant pandas, rhinoceros, tapirs, horses, and chalicotheres (a horse-like, but claw-bearing animal). Dr. Elwyn Simons has discussed this fauna and its significance in interpreting the environment of Gigantopithecus. He concluded that most of the larger mammals were known chiefly from milk teeth and that the bones were predators' "bone-piles" that had been accumulated by dogs, the Indian Dhole, whose remains had also been found in the deposit. Dholes are pack hunting animals that kill deer, sheep, water buffaloes, bears, and tigers, and use caves as lairs. Dr. Simons further noted that many of the bones and teeth had been gnawed by porcupines, and an alternative explanation is that the bones are from porcupine burrows, where they had been dragged to be gnawed.

The fauna consists of woodland-dwelling forms, the orang, civet, tapir, cat, and dog, and of a grasslands-dwelling fauna, horse, rhinoceros, goat, giant panda, and the bovid, indicating that the environment was a savannah (or grasslands) region with interspersed local woodlands. The Indian Gigantopithecus species was found associated with horse and elephant bones, indicating that it too lived in a grasslands area.

Skeltons of Oreopithecus, (superfamily Oreopithecoidea) a long-armed ape capable of brachiation have been found in early Pliocene coal beds of Italy. A study of the teeth of Oreopithecus indicate that it is not on the line of descent of man or any of the other living great apes, and probably is a member of a distinct line of ape-evolution, and may possibly be related to Apidium, as Oreopithecus is similar to that form and has three instead of two premolar teeth.

The living chimpanzees are classified into two species, the larger (Pan troglodytes) reaches a height of five feet and may weigh as much as 150 pounds and the smaller species is the pygmy chimpanzee or Bonobo (Pan paniscus). The two species occupy distinct geographic areas separated by the Congo River, with Pan troglodytes living north of the river.

The living gorillas (Gorilla gorilla) consist of two subspecies, a mountain-dwelling form from central Africa, and a more abundant lowland-dwelling form from dense forests. Adult gorillas may reach a height of six feet and weigh as much as 600 pounds. Cranial capacities of the chimp (350-400 cc) and the gorilla (500-600 cc) are relatively large and these genera are probably the most intelligent of the living apes. However they seem to differ markedly in temperament, gorillas are patient and calm, whereas chimpanzees are excitable and active, so that it is rather difficult to meaningfully equate their "intelligence quotients". Both genera tend to develop rather heavy brow-ridges and sagittal crests along the vault of the cranium, especially in older males. Enlarged canine teeth set in a U-shaped dental arch are further skeletal distinctions between man and these apes. Furthermore, even though these apes are largely ground-dwelling forms, although secondarily so, they travel terrestrially with the quadrupedal posture characteristic of most primates.

"Man" Defined

Before we can discuss fossil men and man-like fossils, it is necessary to determine how to distinguish them from each other and from apes (Plate 24, Figures A, B, C, D, E, F). The similarities of the living great apes to modern man are manifold and include such features as lack of tails, presence of five-cusped teeth, consumption of a varied diet, the ability (of most) to walk upright, flexible and opposable thumbs, color-sensitive binocular vision, and the ability to use and make tools. As Vernon Reynolds remarked, apes also possess the mental processes of imagination, creativity and sympathy. David Premack and his fellow researchers have managed to teach Sarah, a chimpanzee, to read and use, but not write, 120 plastic heiroglyphs and to solve simple sentences. Other researchers, the Gardners, William Lemmon and Roger Fouts, among others, have studied and taught chimpanzees to use and recognize as many as 200 of the "word symbols" used by human deaf-mutes. Washoe, a chimpanzee, was raised in species isolation by the Drs. Gardner in Nevada, and when introduced for the first time to other chimpanzees, she signed, "They are insects." A social comment combining a concept and a value judgment. After a training session, Washoe signed, "Now time to eat, Jack, you

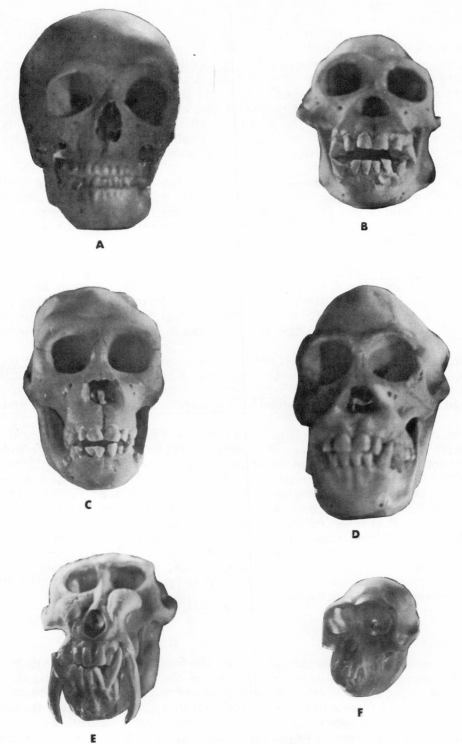

Plate 24. Primate skulls.

A.) <u>Homo sapiens</u>, modern man, with a nearly worldwide distribution. The skull lacks a saggital crest, and has a large cranial capacity. B.) <u>Pan</u>, the living chimpanzee from central Africa. Smaller cranial capacities of the great apes are readily apparent. C.) <u>Gorilla gorilla</u> from central Africa. The large sagittal crests of the apes are indicative of power-powerful jaw muscles. D.) <u>Pongo</u>, the living orangutan from southeastern Asia. E.) <u>Papio</u> sp., a living baboon from Africa and southern Asia. F.) Mangabey (<u>Cercocebus</u> sp.) a living Old World monkey. The specimens are on display in the Saint Louis Zoo.

and me, and Roger, and Booie (another chimp), go in car, get food and sweet drink." On another occasion one of the apes observed an airplane fly overhead and signed, "I want to ride in one of those." The apes can communicate with each other, and it will be interesting to learn whether or not communicating mothers teach their offspring the sign language.

Apes differ from modern men in that apes lack speech, a complex communication and idea exchange system largely based on vocal sound production and aural reception. Apes differ morphologically from men in the obvious factors of skull and facial profile, hirsuteness (hairiness), relative arm length, and foot structure among other characteristics. There is little difficulty distinguishing <u>Homo sapiens</u> from the living great apes. But if we examine the paleontologic record of men and apes, the obvious morphologic differences found in the living forms seem to disappear as the fossil forms converge toward an ancestor in common.

Paleontologists have adopted the shape of the mandibular dental arch and tooth row as the criterion to distinguish apes from hominids. An apes mandibular tooth row has parallel sides, and is "U" shaped, whereas in hominids (man and his less than human ancestors) the mandibular dental arch and tooth row is open, or more nearly "V" shaped. The earliest recognized hominid, characterized by possessing an open, man-like dental arch, is <u>Ramapithecus</u> (Figure 59) known from Miocene and Pliocene sediments of India, Africa, Europe, and China. Obviously paleontologists must depend upon skeletal and not cultural characteristics for their taxonomic determinations of fossil hominids; artifacts found in the general area were not necessarily manufactured by the primate whose bones were found lying closest, and more likely no artifacts may occur nearby at all. Paleontologists cannot determine the degree of social organization, the presence or absence of speech or other behavioral patterns formerly used by the bones' now extinct proprietors.

Anthropologists used to define man as the "tool maker" and considered a tool to be any natural object modified by the user for a specific function. If this definition is used, man would have to include chimpanzees as they have been observed in the wild by Jane van Lawick-Goodall using twigs and leaves as "tools" to obtain termites and water that would otherwise have been inaccessible to them. According to Dr. L. S. B. Leakey, we shall either have to redefine man, or admit a chimpanzee representative to the United Nations.

Man's tool-making is more abstract than that of any of the other tool-making animals; man will fashion a tool, the only function of which is use in the manufacture of another tool. As an example, a man can chip a cutting edge on a piece of flint and use the flint to cut and sharpen a wooden pole to make a spear.

If we define man as those hominids using speech, a complex, sound-based idea-communication system, having the ability to doubly solve the tool-making problem, and possessing an open, "V" shaped tooth-row and dental arch; it is quite likely that not many of these factors were characteristic of <u>Ramapithecus</u>, the earliest known hominid. Therefore <u>Ramapithecus</u> was not a man, but an ape-like hominid. Very likely <u>Ramapithecus</u>, made and used some tools, possibly slightly modified twigs, branches, leaves, unmodified stones, as do modern apes. It is very unlikely that <u>Ramapithecus</u> used sharpened rocks to cut tree limbs or sticks for use as tools. Furthermore, how well <u>Ramapithecus</u> could communicate orally, and to what extent is not known. <u>Ramapithecus</u> lacked the well-developed simian shelf found on the mandibles of modern great apes. Absence of the shelf would have facilitiated but not indicated the presence of a wide-ranging vocalization ability by lack of interference of the bony shelf with the tongue and some of the muscles used in talking. The possibility of using speech was present, but the probability of its presence was low. <u>Ramapithecus</u> seemingly lacked the qualifications needed to be called human or man, but was definitely hominid.

Behavioral definitions of man or definitions based on mental capability are not readily applicable to fossils. Vernon Reynolds (in "The Apes") has discussed how living great apes possess artistic aestheticism, creativity, imagination in play-acting, as well as sympathy and concern for injured or sick human companions. Therefore it seems likely that well-defined mental, social, and behavioral boundaries may not have existed between fossil hominids and fossil apes, or among fossil and Recent hominids.

This brings us back to the dental arch as the most readily and easily applied criterion for hominid identification. Combined with the dental arch of Ramapithecus are other hominid features, such as small canine teeth, simply constructed bicuspid molars, lack of a diastem in the tooth row, and a low degree of prognathism or forward projection of the muzzle. Hominids can best be defined on a morphologic basis, as can any other animal or plant species.

Some anthropologists and paleontologists have used the criterion of cranial capacity to characterize the genus Homo. They consider those homids with cranial capacities exceeding 750 cubic centimeters to belong to Homo, and those with lesser capacities to belong to different genera. This criterion is untenable as individuals within a given population may have a normal range of variation of 200 cc or more, and in addition, females, are generally smaller, lighterweight, and have correspondingly smaller cranial capacities. This could result in the family population of an extinct species being classified in a different genus, than that of the male members of the same population.

Although cranial capacity is a readily measurable criterion, it should be used with caution, for as some scientists have said, "brains are like wallets, the contents are more important than the size."

Man may be defined as a hominid with an extensive vocalizing ability that is used to communicate, along with abstract concepts of tool-making, presumed better reasoning powers, the use of fire, and development of a more or less permanent dwelling location. Probably the term "man" should be applied only to the genus Homo, containing two known species, Homo erectus and Homo sapiens.

The term "human" should be reserved for Homo sapiens, including Neanderthal man; as some of those hominids developed art to a high degree and invented the concept of an after-life in a frantic scramble to escape a sure and certain death, the existence of which, only they of all the animals seem to be aware. It should be kept in mind that some early Homo sapiens were probably less advanced and may be best classed as subhuman. Furthermore, Homo sapiens has been able to develop physiologic and cultural adaptations capable of sustaining primate life in cold temperate and arctic environments, areas previously ecologically closed to other primates and hominids with less developed cultures. Even though we apply the term "human" to Homo sapiens, the species is seemingly little more, if not actually less, humane than other hominids, and anthropocentric definitions of the term human based on man's "innate goodness", possession of a soul, or similar presumptions should be rejected.

Territorialism and Society

Robert Ardrey ("African Genesis" and "The Territorial Imperative") has ably discussed the importance of an animal's occupation and defense of a territory. Normally this territory is selected and defended by a male, and females are seemingly attracted only to propertied males when reproductively inclined. Males lacking a territory usually fail to mate and reproduce.

Territory defense (frequently a larger area than that needed for a minimal food supply) occurs in invertebrates, fish, reptiles, birds, and mammals, and territorialism within mammals may be divided into five kinds. The most advanced kind of territorialism is probably that of the "arena species" as practiced by some artiodactyls such as the kob (Kobus sp.), an African bovid. In "arena species" only a few dozen males, out of a population of hundreds, occupy the stamping ground, and maintain their individual territories in that area by actively fighting. Females reproduce only with males occupying a stamping ground plot, and preferably with those occupying what is considered to be the best plot.

Two other kinds of territorial animals belong to societies that aggressively defend their areas from other groups of their own species. The simpler society, as practiced by many tree-dwelling monkeys, consists of small family-sized groups, or groups of a few families, that avidly defend and demonstrate along the borders of their territory to protect it against all trespassers of their own species. Rarely is violence needed in this defense, instead demonstrations, threats, and screamed challenges seem to suffice. A larger and more complex social group is that exemplified by ground-dwelling monkeys, such as baboons. Although they stake out territories and will defend them, they largely seek to avoid their neighbors and do not demonstrate along the territorial borders. The baboon society is run by aggressive, tyrannical leaders who may head troops of as many as 500 members. Their social order is kept intact by fear and tyranny. The combination of a strictly structured society, primate intelligence, and aggressiveness has made the baboon a successful ground-living primate. Baboon society is most like the societies of man, apparently the most successful ground-dwelling monkey and the most successful ground-dwelling hominid have developed basically parallel societies and behavior patterns. The living great apes (gorilla and chimpanzee) that dwell mostly on the ground have less well-organized societies and are not as numerically or territorically successful as men or baboons. Apparently man's present behavior pattern is mostly genetic, and was acquired during and after the ramapithecine stage, as our ancestors adapted to life on the ground and formulated the kind of territorial-holding society most successful in that environment for primates.

Chimpanzee bands, as do those of gorillas, range over loosely defined and largely undefended territories, generally in numerically small groups. Usually the groups are not aggressively antagonistic toward others of the same species, and the bands are largely incapable of concerted action. Their societies are largely inwardly benevolent, and their non-aggressive natures are undoubtedly contributing to their numerical decline and eventual extinction. According to Ardrey, the degree of success of an animal species is directly dependent upon active territorial defense, antagonistic behavior toward outsiders of the same species, and ability to cooperate within the group.

There is another society that Ardrey has called a society of inward antagonism, wherein aggression is directed toward members of ones' own group and territorial defense is at best poor. Such societies, according to Ardrey, are exemplified by the bowerbirds of New Guinea and Australia and some human societies. Individuals in those human societies lack trust, friendship, and loyalty, but according to Ardrey, may produce geniuses.

Defense of territory may have led to private property and warfare, as practiced by man.

Fossil Hominids

The oldest known primate generally recognized as an hominid is a very ape-like creature called Ramapithecus that lived in the Miocene and early Pliocene, about 10 million years ago. The first recognition of Ramapithecus as a distinct man-like genus was by Dr. G. Ed Lewis during the 1930's from a specimen found in sediments of the Siwalik Hills of India. The specimen, a fragmentary upper jaw, was described by Dr. Lewis as a new and very man-like genus of primate.

In 1962 Dr. Louis Leakey discovered in late Miocene sediments of Kenya a partial palate of a Ramapithecus-like hominid which he named "Kenyapithecus" wickeri. Since then a few other ramapithecine jaw fragments have been recently (1965) identified from among the bone fragments contained in collections gathered prior to 1960 from Europe and China.

The body bones and most of the skull of Ramapithecus are unknown, so that the animals' height, weight, further skeletal resemblances to man, cranial capacity, and facial features are unknown. Dr. Elwyn Simons has speculated that:

> "On the basis of the size of its teeth and mandibular fragments, we know that
> the cranium of Ramapithecus was about the size of that of an adult female
> pygmy chimpanzee. If, relative to apes, its head was large compared to its
> body size (as was the case with Australopithecus and later hominids), then
> this earliest hominid would have been rather smaller than has generally been
> realized .... perhaps only three or four feet tall if standing erect."

Apparently Ramapithecus inhabited a region of swampy tropical forests with interspersed dryer grasslands. The animal bones found fossilized in the same beds as Ramapithecus include those of forest-dwelling forms such as giraffes, pigs, and some small carnivores. The presence of fossil palm trees and crocodile bones indicate a swampy forest, and bones of gazelles and an aardvark indicate that grasslands were nearby, and the entire assemblage suggests a tropical climate.

Ramapithecus may well have had a level of social organization and a behavior-pattern resembling that of numerically small bands of monkeys. This would have consisted of individual bands of animals wandering about within their well-defined territories, regions avidly defended against other individuals of the same species. The bands may have nested in trees overnight, then abandoned the nests before the next night. Travel would have been both terrestrial and arboreal. Dr. Elwyn Simons suggested that Ramapithecus may have been a graminivorous (grass and seed-eating) primate, because flattened, large teeth suited for grinding are present in the known jaws. If this were so, Ramapithecus would have spent a large number of hours daily out on the savannahs feeding, and returned to the forests to nest at night. This would have been the beginning of the development of a terrestrial group of hominids that culminated with the evolution of man.

Australopithecus

The second stage of hominid evolution is typified by the australopithecines (Australopithecus = southern ape), small, simian-appearing, man-like species (Figure 60) that lived during the late Pliocene and early through mid-Pleistocene, from possibly as long as six million years ago until as late as a half million years ago. Seemingly some australopithecines were still living after Homo erectus, the next stage of hominid evolution appeared. Apparently it is not unusual to have some temporal overlap of species in hominid evolution, as a more primitive form may survive after the initial appearance of the next stage.

A fully grown australopithecine of the A. africanus group would have been about four feet tall, weighed between 80 and 100 pounds, had an upright posture and a body with a man-like skeleton, and a relatively small (from our point of view) brain ranging in volume from about 450 to a little more than 600 cc. The lower jaws were relatively large and consisted of massive dentary bones bearing large teeth.

The first discovered australopithecine remains were found in 1925 in southern Africa, and several other crushed and fragmentary skulls and some body bones were found shortly thereafter in cave deposits of the same region. Unfortunately nearly each specimen was assigned a new and separate generic name, without regard for the supposed generic characteristics possibly being caused by sexual dimorphism or age induced differences.

More recently, Dr. L. S. B. Leakey has made an important series of discoveries of fossil men from Olduvai Gorge in Tanzania, the remains are those of australopithecines that he has named Zinjanthropus and pre-Zinjanthropus man or "Homo habilis". Although most authorities regard "Homo habilis" to be a member of Australopithecus africanus, and probably on the line of evolution toward Homo, Dr. Leakey believes "Homo habilis" to be a genetically separate and morphologically distinct species of fossil man directly on the line of evolution toward Homo sapiens. This implies that the australopithecines were an evolutionary dead-end and did not give rise to Homo sapiens. Dr. Leakey's opinion however, is accepted only by a minority of the students of fossil men.

Other poorly known and fragmentary hominid remains, named Meganthropus, that have been found in Java, the Jordan Valley, and northern Africa may also be those of australopithecines. They consist of jaw fragments and it is difficult to distinguish jaws of Australopithecus from those of Homo erectus, a later species of man. Therefore Meganthropus may actually be fragments of Homo erectus and not australopithecines. It is also possible that Meganthropus could include both Homo erectus and australopithecine remains.

Some specialists who have studied the available australopithecine remains classify all the previously named genera and species into one genus with two species; Australopithecus africanus, a late Pliocene and early Pleistocene, small-bodied and lightweight species that could have a given rise to Homo, and Australopithecus robustus, a late Pliocene through mid-Pleistocene, larger-bodied species that did not give rise to Homo, or any other known descendants.

Examination of the African cave sites indicates the australopithecines (Australopithecus africanus) may have lived in caves at least some of the time, probably used bones as tools, hunted and ate baboons, antelope, and crayfish, and broke open skulls of their own species, possibly to obtain brains for eating. This could have been a postmortem ceremonial rite normally accorded the dead, a cannibalistic disposal of corpses, a bit of hunger inspired murder, or the result of bad manners and ill tempers. In Olduvai Gorge, Dr. Leakey has found pebble tools, or eoliths, of the Oldowan culture associated with australopithecine remains indicating that australopithecines may have made and used those tools. Stone tool making seems to have begun between three and four million years ago. No bits of charcoal or cooking fire pits have been found in the cave sites or Olduvai Gorge sites, presumably these primitive men lacked the use of fire and may have eaten raw meat, as well as raw seeds and plants. Some specialists think that Australopithecus robustus was largely; if not completely a vegetarian, whereas, A. africanus was largely a carnivore.

The australopithecines, in spite of their propensity for skull cracking must have been capable of a good deal of cooperative effort if they hunted baboons regularly and successfully. Baboons travel in troops of many individuals and the large dominant males vigorously defend the troop against onslaughts of predators. Baboons are capable of killing unarmed men and have been known to attack and kill leopards in defense of their troops.

An alternative hypothesis is that the South African caves were dens of hyaenas that hunted baboons and australopithecines and left the bones of their victims in the caves.

The South African australopithecines lived in a slightly arid and warm region, not in tropical rain-forests similar to those inhabited today by the great apes. Apparently the australopithecines lived in a more open grassland environment than did Ramapithecus, and had probably evolved rapidly by being selected for tool production, repeated use of the same natural shelters as dwelling areas, and cooperative food-gathering or hunting efforts with food sharing among the "family" group.

The australopithecine bones from Africa have been found associated with fossilized remains of baboons, antelope, pigs, rhinoceros, leopard, giraffes, horses, porcupines, hyaenas, tortoises, vultures, and jackals, a fauna that must have lived in a dry tropical area much like the present-day grasslands of the Serengeti Plains. The hippopotami and crayfish undoubtedly lived in nearby rivers or lakes.

Very likely hominids began to rely mainly on hunting as a source of food only after men moved into temperate or subarctic climate zones where food-gathering was an impractical means of providing year around subsistence.

During or shortly after the australopithecine stage, hominids may have abandoned the ape-like pattern of never staying two successive nights in the same nesting area. This may have resulted from hunting bands tending to stay near the scenes of large kills until the meat was all consumed. This tendency may have been naturally selected for, as more efficient utilization of the available food supply would permit survival during times when the food supply was insufficient.

Storing baboon or other carcasses gathered, in excess of the amount needed for immediate use as food, during successful hunts could have led to the use of caves or dens as the first permanent pantries and residences of hominids. The greatest chance of successful survival would then have accompanied those hominid groups able to make use of cooperative hunting techniques and the most advanced food utilizing and hoarding developments.

Homo erectus

The third stage of hominid evolution is represented by Homo erectus (Plate 25, Figure A, formerly known as Pithecanthropus erectus from Java and Sinanthropus pekinensis from China). Studies of the morphology of the numerous skulls found in Java and China indicated that the two hominid groups were closely related genetically and did not differ to an extent greater than the range of variability displayed by the living human subspecies. Because of these similarities, the Chinese and Javanese species were taxonomically merged into a single species. Furthermore, the known body bones of Homo erectus are nearly identical to those of living men so the species has been reassigned to our genus. Homo erectus stood 5'8" to 5'11", had limb bones nearly identical to those of Homo sapiens, but differed in being chinless and smaller-brained with a range of cranial capacity from 830 to 1,300 cc., in having a very heavily developed torus, or brow ridge, and a low sloping forehead.

Homo erectus probably lived from 700,000 to 200,000 years ago, and age determinations using the potassium-argon radioactive decay sequence have shown some Homo erectus remains from Africa to be 500,000 years old. During this stage of hominid evolution, Abbevillian Culture (Plate 27, Figure H), the use of fire began, along with the manufacture of crude hand axes and scrapers, and at least the northern-most members lived in caves and built fires for warmth

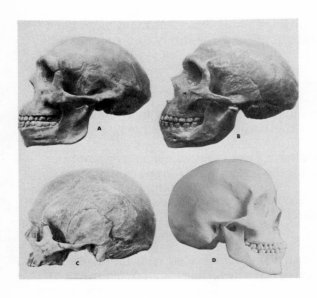

Plate 25. Skulls of Homo.

    A.) Homo erectus, composite cast of the skull of the Chinese form. Saint Louis Museum of Science and Natural History. B.) Homo sapiens, cast of the skull of Neanderthal man. Saint Louis Museum of Science and Natural History. C.) Homo sapiens, Paleoamerindian-like skull from North America (Illinois) characterized by a heavy brow ridge, long skull, wisdom teeth, and a protruding occiput. Southern Illinois University, Edwardsville. D.) Homo sapiens, skull of modern Caucasian, with a weakly developed brow ridge. The brow ridge (or torus) is less heavily developed on female skulls. Saint Louis Museum of Science and Natural History.

and cooking. Possibly the Chinese H. erectus practiced cannibalism, as most of the skulls found in the caves near Peiping seem to have been broken open so that the brains could have been eaten. It is possible that Homo erectus could have constructed some form of dwellings or shelters and did not have to depend on caves for protection from the weather in cool regions. Caves were probably used simply where caverns were present and convenient.

Bones of Homo erectus were first sought and found in 1891 by a Dutch army surgeon, Dr. Eugene Dubois, from alluvial sediments along the Solo River, near the town of Trinil in central Java. Dr. Dubois had requested assignment to Java specifically to search for fossil men and had the fantastic good luck to find a skull cap, a molar, and a femur, all within a small area and from the same stratigraphic horizon, so that the remains probably came from the same individual. Even though other expeditions searched for more bones in 1906, none were found until 1936-1939 when the geologist von Koenigswald found a series of specimens.

Similar hominid remains were found in cave deposits within Choukoutien Hill, about 25 miles southwest of Peiping, beginning with the discovery of two human-like molar teeth in 1921. A third molar tooth was found in 1927 and Dr. Davidson Black designated it as a new genus and species of fossil man, Sinanthropus pekinensis. Two years later, in 1929, a skull-cap was found, and a second skull-cap was discovered shortly after. These discoveries led to a systematic excavation and exploration of the cave deposits being financed by the Rockefeller Foundation of New York and by 1939, the fragmentary remains of about 38 sinanthropines had been discovered. Unfortunately these specimens were lost during the second World War. Although they had been crated for shipment to the United States, they disappeared enroute, and were probably destroyed in China by the invading Japanese army.

In 1963 Dr. L. S. B. Leakey discovered a skull-cap of Homo erectus in Olduvai Gorge, Tanzania, that was associated with Chellean (Abbevillian) tools. The skull-cap was determined to be 490,000 years old by the potassium-argon age dating method. This important discovery demonstrated that Homo erectus was not an exclusively Asiatic species and that some fragmentary Homo erectus-like remains previously reported from northern Africa may be those of Homo erectus.

The mandible from the sandpit dug in alluvial sediments along the Neckar River in Germany and known as Heidelberg Man, may also be a relict of Homo erectus, partly because of an age determination of 400,000 years and association with a "Chellean" fauna. This correlates well with age of Dr. Leakey's African specimen, and the presence of Chellean (Abbevillian) implements in Europe. The fauna associated with Heidelberg Man is of early Pleistocene age, and contains many bones of animals typical of the Pliocene. This, along with the occurrence of similar faunas (horses, rhinoceros, and elephants, Elephas antiquus) in southern France and Italy indicates the presence of a warm-temperate climate in Germany at that time. Heidelberg man could have lived in a warm-temperate European climate or one similar to that of today by means of the fire-using Chellean culture.

The Java form of Homo erectus (from the Trinil beds) was associated with fossil bones of Elephas antiquus, Rhinoceros sp., Hippopotamus sp., deer (Cervus sp.), cattle Bos and Bubalus sp.), pigs (Sus sp.), and a bear (Ursus sp.), indicative of a fauna that lived in a tropical, well-watered, and largely forested area.

The Peiping subspecies of Homo erectus was found associated with a fauna that was neither tropical, nor did it inhabit a cold climate. Probably it dwelled in a climate much like the present-day one of that area. The animal remains associated with the hominid bones consist of seven kinds of cats (including saber-toothed cats), horses, camels, buffalo, elephants, rhinoceros, deer, sheep, and antelopes, a fauna that lived in a cool, largely grasslands environment.

In northern Africa H. erectus remains (at Ternifine) have been found in association with bones of zebras, giraffes, antelopes, elephants, rhinoceroses, carnivores (including saber-toothed cats) and wart-hogs. This fauna very likely inhabited a warm (subtropical?), grasslands region, that was probably semi-arid.

Early Homo sapiens

The fourth and most recent stage of hominid evolution is that of Homo sapiens, within which are included all the living groups of modern man and his morphologically similar, large-brained, thin skull-boned precursors, including Neanderthal man. It is not possible to determine easily whether some fossil skulls belong to Homo erectus or Homo sapiens, as the two species are linked by evolutionarily intermediate forms that are not clearly typical members of either species.

Seemingly, the first three stages of hominid evolution were confined to the tropical and subtropical regions of the Old World. Fossil remains of hominids are either absent or extremely rare in the northern regions that are usually characterized by cool climates, indicating that hominids were largely restricted to tropical regions. This genetic adjustment of early hominids to warm climates and the lack of land bridges in those regions kept nearly all late Cenozoic primates from reaching the New World. The gradual development of an extensive cool-temperate climate zone in the late Cenozoic, culminated in the Pleistocene subarctic climate zone that formed an effective barrier to primate distribution. The cold climate region was impassible to hominids that were not genetically adapted to cold, and who lacked suitable clothing as well as fuel to make fires in wood-lacking subarctic regions.

The latest known Homo erectus remains from northern Africa are associated with Acheulean artifacts (usually considered to have been made by H. sapiens) and H. erectus may have originated this culture that their descendants continued, or their remains could have been introduced into sediments bearing artifacts manufactured by Homo sapiens. It is possible that Homo erectus survived in some regions into the time range of Homo sapiens, so that the temporal ranges of the species overlapped, and at least locally they lived in the same areas.

The known specimens of early Homo sapiens are largely fragmentary skulls and include, among others, the Swanscombe skull from England, the Steinheim skull from Germany, the Fontechevade skulls from France, and the Quinzano bone from Italy. Some of the bones are possibly from sediments of the second interglacial stage, and definitely some of the bones came from sediments of the third interglacial stage. The Steinheim skull was associated with warm climate-dwelling animals, Elephas antiquus (elephant), Dicerorhinus merckii (rhino); and the Swanscombe skull was found associated with a similar warm climate fauna, E. antiquus, Dicerorhinus megarhinus and the Irish elk. Members of another, and possibly more generalized Homo sapiens group continued to evolve simultaneously as a largely geographically isolated and genetically distinct population in warmer regions.

Homo sapiens evolved at least three times into subspecific groups (Neanderthalers, Caucasoids, and Mongoloids) adapted physically, and culturally, to live in cool-temperate or arctic climates.

Homo sapiens normally ranges in height from five to six feet, has a normal cranial capacity range of 1,100 cc to 1,700 cc with a mean of 1,350 cc. Most late Wisconsinan and all post-Wisconsinan subspecies of Homo sapiens possess well-developed, projecting chins and prominent, nearly vertical foreheads. Furthermore the skull bones of the more recent forms of Homo sapiens tend to be thinner than those of pre-Wisconsinan members of Homo sapiens.

Unfortunately the facial profiles of most of the earliest known skulls referred to Homo sapiens are unknown. Those skulls are mostly fragmentary occipital or parietal bones. Although a recently (1971) discovered skull, found in a cave at Tautavel in France, has a well-preserved face, and may be 200,000 years old. The skull is characterized by heavily developed brow ridges, a flattened forehead, and a relatively small braincase. Apparently the specimen is a skull that is intermediate between Homo erectus and Homo sapiens and when studied should yield some significant details regarding the development of Homo sapiens.

The oldest known skulls considered to be Homo sapiens are from sediments of the third (Eem) interglacial stage, and the species must have evolved by 100,000 years ago. Remains tentatively identified as H. sapiens have been found in sediments deposited during the second (Holstein) interglacial stage. Many of the skulls from the second (Holstein) interglacial stage and possibly earlier sediments cannot be adequately classified as to whether they are early Homo sapiens or late Homo erectus, and some of the skulls are from sediments of unknown ages or sediments that cannot be correlated definitely with a glacial or interglacial stage. If the skulls from the second (Holstein) interglacial stage are those of Homo sapiens, the species may have evolved as long ago as 500,000 years.

The oldest known remains are those of generalized forms of Homo sapiens and consist of relatively thin parietal and occipital bones, with cranial capacities ranging from 1,100 to 1,350 cc, and are associated with artifacts of the Acheulean culture and (in Europe) with warm-climate interglacial faunas. The Acheulean culture was characterized by thinner and better-fashioned hand axes (Plate 27, Figure G) than those made during the Chellean. Furthermore other tools such as scrapers, cleavers, and at least one wooden spear with a fire-hardened tip have been found in Acheulean sites.

Neanderthal Man

An intermediate stage of evolution from primitive <u>Homo sapiens</u> into Neanderthalers is probably represented by the Saccopastore skulls from Italy, the Mount Carmel skeletons from Israel, and the Ehringsdorf skull from Germany. In general, those skulls possess thick brow ridges (torus) trending in development toward those of the Neanderthalers, however, other features characteristic of generalized, primitive forms of <u>Homo sapiens</u> are present. The skulls are presumed to be of late third (Eem) interglacial to early Würm glacial ages. The oldest known <u>Homo sapiens</u> and primitive Neanderthalers lived in warm to cool-temperate climates. An interesting premise is that the so-called "Neanderthalers" from Java (Solo Man) and Rhodesia (Rhodesian Man) are not actually Neanderthalers, but are primitive <u>Homo sapiens</u> or advanced forms of <u>Homo erectus</u>. In view of the predilection of Neanderthalers for cold climates, this explanation seems highly probable. Furthermore, the Neanderthal-resembling Australoids (aboriginal Australians) may be a relict population that has descended from Solo Man-like ancestors.

Typical Neanderthalers (Plate 25, Figure B) may have evolved about 100,000 years ago, and were characterized by being short (five feet), stocky, possessing prominent brow ridges, were chinless, and flat-headed with a cranial capacity of 1,300 to 1,600 cc. Their remains have been found associated with Mousterian artifacts only and they lived in caves along the glacial ice front in association with cold climate-dwelling animals such as cave bears, woolly mammoths, woolly rhinoceros, reindeer, Bison, and the Aurochs. Presumbaly geographic separation of the Neanderthalers from the more southern dwelling forms of Homo sapiens led to development of morphologic distinctiveness through adaptive genetic changes. The relatively short-limbs and bulky torso of Neanderthal man is most serviceable in a cold climate, as such adaptations help conserve body heat. Modern Eskimos inhabit an environment similar to the one Neanderthal man lived in, and Eskimos have evolved a similar body form.

Although Neanderthalers used to be considered to have been brutish-appearing cave men that lacked civilized mores, they developed a progressive culture, by inventing metates for cracking and grinding seeds, stone spear points, and the beginnings of religion. The invention of religion is indicated by their burial of the dead with artifacts, a wasteful practice unless the Neanderthalers believed in an afterlife wherein the dead would make use of the articles. Belief in an after life is the central theme of most religions. The development of religion gave rise to the world's oldest profession, that of the shaman or practitioner of religion and healing. Prostitution is a more recent profession, that developed after a need for it was created by the shamans. Furthermore, Neanderthalers erected altar-like structures with skulls of cave bears as seemingly enshrined items. If one considers the difficulties involved in evicting reluctant bears from choice caves, it is no wonder that the Neanderthalers had a religious-like respect for them.

No European or Near Eastern Neanderthal men survived beyond 34,000 ± B.P., seemingly they were evicted or exterminated by a new form of cold-climate dwelling man.

Cro-Magnon Man

The Cro-Magnons were a tall (about six feet), large-brained (up to 1,700 cc) group of cave-dwellers able to live in a cold climate. They left bones and drawings of a cold to cool climate steppe-dwelling fauna (horse, aurochs, deer, ibex, and woolly mammoth) in their caves. Cro-Magnons' bones are remarkably like those of modern Europeans, and physical anthropologists recognize a definite Cro-Magnon skull type among some of the modern western and northern European, some north African and aboriginal Canary Island populations. This is based on the presence of geographically restricted population groups that are characterized by square faces, long heads (Figure 61), with deep-set eyes well under the orbital arch, and a flattened occipital region, as well as some other features. The Guanchos (native Canary Islanders) seem to retain more structural affinities with the Cro-Magnons than does any other living population.

In view of this, it is very likely that the first-known Cro-Magnons closely resembled modern Europeans and had lightly pigmented skins and light-colored eyes that are usually interpreted to be adaptations to a climate with hazy or weak sunlight.

The Cro-Magnons appeared in Europe about 34,000 B.P., brought the Aurignacian Culture with them and abruptly terminated the tenure of the Mousterian Culture and Neanderthal man. Possibly the conflict between Cro-Magnons and Neanderthalers has survived as the source of some of our folk and children's tales dealing with trolls, mean dwarfs, and unpleasant, forest-dwelling, little men. These tales could well have been retold for generations through prehistory in some of the geographically confined remnants of the Cro-Magnon populations.

The Aurignacian Culture fostered development of the arts, including magnificent cave paintings, and carvings and sculptures, especially of rather obese women, were made in bone and ivory. The first bows and arrows, known only from paintings found in Spanish caves, were brought to Europe during the latter portion of the Aurignacian by a population from northern Africa, the Capsians, who possibly were Cro-Magnons.

The Solutrean Culture

The dominance of the Aurignacian Culture ended about 18,000 B.P., with the appearance of the Solutrean Culture that had developed in an unknown area, and then spread rapidly over Europe and northern Africa.

During and prior to this stage of human development, the greatest advances in man's physical and cultural evolution were not occurring in cold northern regions. Rather they took place in the warm tropical and subtropical areas that had been inhabited by primates since the Cretaceous. As more advanced hominid groups and cultures evolved, they radiated outward from the main region of hominid evolution and supplanted the earlier evolved and previously arrived populations.

The Solutrean Culture abruptly appeared about 18,000 B.P., and the bearers of the culture are unknown as to physical type. They spread rapidly over an extensive area, and their cultural relics overlie Aurignacian artifacts in Europe and Mousterian relics, that were not made by Neanderthalers, in Africa. The Solutreans made thin, finely-crafted, pressure-flaked, willow or laurel leaf-shaped spear points and smaller projectile points probably intended for use on either arrows or darts. The Solutrean Culture disappeared after 17,000 B.P. as rapidly as it had spread, and was replaced by a culture similar to that of the Aurignacian, but characterized by better manufactured blades, and more highly developed art.

The Magdalenian Culture

Artifacts of the Magdalenian Culture include needles, fishhooks, harpoons, spear-throwers (atlatl), and polychrome cave paintings. Magdalenian tools are much like those made by modern Eskimos, though it is very unlikely that Eskimos introduced this culture to Europe. The resemblance is more likely the result of cultural adaptation to life in a similar climate. Eskimos had not yet differentiated as a distinct group 17,000 years ago, and the geographic range of Mongoloids was considerably more restricted then, than at the present time. In fact, some authorities are of the opinion that the Mongoloid subspecies did not begin to evolve until 15,000 B.P.

The climate of Magdalenian time has been determined from a study of fossil pollen and mammals. There was a gradation from arctic tundra in early Magdalenian time into a pine and birch forest of a cold-temperate climate, as time elapsed and some of the animals associated with Magdalenian artifacts include reindeer, woolly mammoths, horses, bison, and bears.

The Magdalenian Culture either evolved into subsequent Mesolithic cultures or was displaced shortly after 10,000 B.P., as the major ice sheets began to melt and a more equitable climate slowly returned to Europe. Although the oldest known domestication of animals (sheep and goats) occurred from 9,000 to 11,000 B.P. in the Near East, animal herding societies may have developed independently in cool northern areas where hunters followed seasonally migrating herds such as reindeer, sheep, or bison-like species. The only year-around source of food for men in arctic and cool temperate regions would have been meat. Therefore only hunting or herding societies could live in such areas, before the invention of farming. This probably led to bands of hunters following (and owning hunting territory rights as well as the herd animals) individual herds of migratory game. The migration patterns could have been either the summer-highland to winter-lowland migration like that of the American elk, or one wherein the summer is spent in the north, followed by a southward migration during the winter, similar to those of the reindeer and American bison. Capture and taming of young or injured members of the herds would have led to domestication of some herd animals and eventually establishment of a non-migratory domestic stock.

The migratory herding pattern largely declined as a way of life following the post-Weichsel warming up of Europe and appearance of the Mseolithic industries. The first known agricultural societies began to develop nearly simultaneously in three centers, China, Mexico, and the Near East about 9,000 B.P. and spread outward by cultural diffusion from the regions of origin. By 6,000 B.P. agriculture diffusing from the Near East reached the Baltic Sea region, and began to spread throughout western Europe. Agriculture began in Mexico, independently of the Old World, and diffused throughout the Americas.

The initial domestication of plants seems to have developed in regions with warm or nearly subtropical climates. Probably some of the largely non-hunting and non-migratory food-gathering societies living in regions with warm climates began to increase local food yield by planting seeds, either accidentally or intentionally, and developed agriculture, thus relieving a major portion of man's time from the constant search for food.

The Near Eastern agricultural society was developed by Caucasoids, however the southeastern Asian agricultural society was very likely developed by Mongoloids. It is not certain which area developed agriculture first, and whether or not there was any cultural exchange between the two areas. Presumably agriculture in Mexico was an independent invention, and seems to have been developed at the same time as that of the Asian societies. Quite likely Caucasoids, or Caucasoid-like Amerindians began agriculture in Mexico.

Additional development of agricultural products took place in several "non-centers" of innovation, a "non-center" being a region in which "farming" of a limited number of plants took place, and not development of an agricultural economy. Such "non-centers" developed in South America, Africa, and southeastern Asia.

It is interesting that man's main, original efforts at agriculture developed by domestication of grasses, corn in Mexico, rice in China, and wheat, as well as other grasses, in the Near East.

ANIMAL DISTRIBUTION

Matthew's Climate and Evolution

In 1915 W. D. Matthew published his book "Climate and Evolution" in the New York Academy of Sciences Transactions. Matthew attempted to explain the geographically unequal distribution of animals, particularly vertebrates, as resulting from biological evolution occurring mainly within the northern hemisphere with a resultant radial dispersal pattern away from the northern continents. Matthew believed that the most successful animals evolved in the inhospitable northern climates, and these supposedly more hardy species then spread southward and displaced the earlier evolved animals that were not able to evolve into competitive forms.

P. J. Darlington has questioned the mechanism (climate) and center of radiation (northern cool-temperate region) cited by Matthew. Darlington considers that although animal dispersal is a complex problem, the dominant groups of plants and animals have evolved in the larger land areas (Eurasia, e.g.), and in more favorable climates, and then dispersed outward with a continual replacement of species, and in part, an accumulation of relict species in the cool to cold temperate regions of the southern hemisphere. A partial confirmation of this is that the number of species of any animal group is greatest in the tropics and on larger land masses.

The number of species inhabiting an island is seemingly directly proportional to the area of the island. Darlington's concept of the effect of selection in unfavorable climates is that only climate-tolerant forms would evolve, whereas selection in more favorable climates, where organisms are more numerous and varied, would result in generally superior forms that could compete on a more than favorable basis with previously evolved species.

The pattern of animal distribution is one wherein animals such as bears (Figure 65), sheep, goats, deer, and bison live on the main portion of the Eurasian-North American land masses. More primitive animal groups are found in southern Africa, South America, Australia, on islands and other areas where they are geographically isolated from more highly evolved species. Evolution took place more rapidly on the larger (Eurasian-North American) land masses and the consequently more advanced evolutionary products of these areas radiated outward from their area of origin in successive waves. Furthermore, evolution of basic vertebrate stocks on those continents (South America, Australia, and Antarctica) isolated by continental drift proceeded at slower rates, with some lines trending in aberrant directions. The sum of such evolution resulted in morphologically similar, but not ecologically competitive or genetically equal animal groups.

Examples of Matthew's Distribution Pattern

Living lungfish are grouped into three genera and include Lepidosiren found in the Gran Chaco of South America, Protopterus of the Congo region of Africa, and Ceratodus from the interior of Australia. Lungfish are closely allied to primitive land vertebrates and to the crossopterygian fishes that gave rise to the first tetrapods. During the latter part of the Paleozoic Era and during the Mesozoic Era lungfish were distributed throughout the northern hemisphere. Fossil lungfish dental arrays are abundant in the rock strata of North America and Europe. This is an excellent example of an animal with a former nearly cosmopolitan distribution becoming confined with the passage of time to a remnant distribution in the southern hemisphere.

The Rhynchocephalia are a group of primitive, lizard-like reptiles, whose only living representative, Sphenodon, lives in New Zealand. Some fossil rhynchocephalians, such as Champsosaurus, whose remains are found in uppermost Cretaceous and lower Cenozoic rocks, lived in the northern hemisphere.

Figure 62. Didelphis marsupialis,
the Virginia opossum,
one of the three South
American mammals
(and the only mar-
supial) to successfully
migrate into the north-
ern hemisphere and
live north of Mexico.
Saint Louis Zoo.

Figure 63. A "side-necked" or pleurodire turtle, in
which the neck folds sideways into the
shell. Living "side-necked" turtles are
found only in the southern hemisphere.
Saint Louis Zoo.

Turtles are classified into two main taxonomic groups, "pleurodire" or side-necked turtles (Figure 63), and "cryptodire" or straight-necked turtles (Figure 64). These terms refer to the manner in which the turtles retract their heads within their shells. Cryptodire turtles are mainly a northern hemisphere group and live today on at least a portion of each continent except Australia and Antarctica. Cryptodire turtle remains are not found as far back in the fossil record as pleurodire turtle bones and are the "latest word" in turtle evolution. The old-er group of turtles, the pleurodires, are found living today only in South America, Africa, and Australia. Fossil pleurodire turtle remains are abundant in some of the Cretaceous rocks of North America, and pleurodire turtles were formerly widely distributed throughout the northern hemisphere.

Giant tortoises have a similar history, they were formerly widely distributed over North America and other large land masses during the Pliocene and Pleistocene Epochs. Today giant tortoises are found living only on the Andaman Islands in the Indian Ocean, Madagascar (the Malagasy Republic), the Galapagos Islands in the Pacific Ocean, Australia, and the Patagonia region of South America.

The most primitive living vertebrates generally considered to be mammals are the egg-laying spiny anteaters or echidnas of New Guinea, Australia, and Tasmania, and the duck-billed platypus (Plate 19, Figure C) of Australia and Tasmania. Fossil mammal and mammal-like reptile bones closely resembling those of the living egg-laying mammals have been found in early Mesozoic rocks of the northern hemisphere.

Marsupials formerly were widely distributed during the latter portion of the Mesozoic Era in a similar pattern to that of Mesozoic mammal-like reptiles. During early Cenozoic time the geographic range of marsupials became restricted to South America and Australia. Both those continents were isolated from northern land masses, because of crustal movements caused by continental drift, throughout the remainder of the Tertiary, and the isolated continents formed a haven for marsupials which became extinct in the northern continents as the more highly evolved placental mammals became dominant and replaced them. Late in the Cenozoic Era, South America was reunited with North America by the formation of Central America and the Cordilleran Mountain Chain. Northern hemisphere dwelling animals migrated onto the southern continent, displacing much of the indigenous fauna, and today over 50% of the fauna of South America is descended from former northern area-dwelling species. Conversely, only three mammalian genera derived from South America live today north of Mexico, the armadillo, opossum (Figure 62), and porcupine. No species from South America have entered and become established on the Eurasian land mass. Other South American mammal

Figure 64. Cryptodire turtle (aquatic) with its head partially withdrawn into its shell. The head is retracted straight backward. Saint Louis Zoo.

species were not able to compete with northern animals on their home ground and become established in the United States and Canada, although several other species that are now extinct tried unsuccessfully to colonize America north of Mexico. Another species, the nutria, recently introduced by man, may become a successful colonist of the United States.

Many other animals have a history of a former nearly cosmopolitan distribution and a later, restricted (southern) distribution. Additional examples include lions and wild horses that live today in Africa, zebras, and possibly south-central Asia. Fossil horses have been found in Europe, Asia, and North America. Tigers probably originated as a northern species but have successfully invaded southern Asia through India. Rhinoceros live in southern Africa and southeastern Asia. Fossil rhinos (Plate 20, Figure E) have been found in the United States, Europe, and Asia. Elephants have a similar distribution pattern and history, as do camels (llamas), and the hippopotamus. Africa is also the homeland of some bovids, antelope, and related forms that do not occur elsewhere.

Dr. Alfred S. Romer in the first edition of his book Man and the Vertebrates (1941) applied Matthew's distribution concept to man. Man is at

Figure 65. Ursus arctos, the Kodiak bear, a large subspecies of the brown bears, a northern hemispheric animal group. Saint Louis Zoo. ern hemispheric animal group. Saint Louis Zoo.

best an animal, and should therefore follow the basic rules of animal distribution; or at least in the geologic past man should have.

The premise is, that if we examine the pre-Columbian distribution of man (Figures 66, 67) and compare the distribution pattern with the animal distribution patterns in Matthew's study, we should be able to at least partially develop an evolutionary sequence for the living subspecies of man.

Our discussion of primate evolution indicates that fossil hominids arose and evolved in tropical regions of the Old World, especially in Africa and southern Asia, and largely remained there through all the pre-Homo sapiens stages of hominid evolution. In this respect primates fail to fit the typical mammalian evolution and distribution pattern as determined by Matthew, and although the tropical center of most hominid evolution is as yet unknown, it could have been either Africa or southern Asia and thus fits Darlington's concept of the vertebrate distribution pattern. Seemingly men, beginning with Homo, and perhaps only because of a better known fossil record, began to radiate away from the tropics, and move north into the European and Asian land masses. The early evolution and radiation center of man was one of tropical origins and not one of northern hemispheric origins. The northern hemisphere became a center of human evolution only after the making and use of fire and clothing was discovered. This was followed by the development, within Homo sapiens, of several cold climate-dwelling varieties of man, first of whom were the Neanderthalers, who were displaced by the Cro-Magnon Caucasoids, who were subsequently largely succeeded by Mongoloids (Figure 68). During the latter period of hominid evolution in the north, other groups of men continued to evolve, with gene pools largely insulated from "contamination", because of geographic separation in the southern continents of the Old World, while extirpations and natural selection of other human groups went on in the north.

According to the ideas of Matthew and Romer, the more primitive or earlier evolved subspecies of man should have occurred (long before 1500 A.D.) as geographically isolated remnant populations in the southern hemisphere, or in relatively inaccessible islands and inhospitable regions such as deserts or densely vegetated swampy areas.

A differing point of view is espoused by some scientists, especially Dr. Carlton S. Coon (The Origin of Races, 1969), who maintain that the subspecies of man developed within Homo erectus, and the living subspecies are older than the species (H. sapiens). That is, the daughter species (Homo sapiens) retained subspecific characteristics that evolved within the species H. erectus.

Dr. Coon believes that the five modern subspecies (he uses the term races) evolved in four partially isolated regions, so that there was no Caucasoid-Mongoloid contact, but Caucasoid-Australoid, Australoid-Mongoloid, and Caucasoid-Capoid-Negroid contacts could and did occur. Briefly, Dr. Coon's visualization of the evolution of man begins with the appearance of Australopithecus in Africa, and its migration eastward across the tropical regions of the Old World. Homo erectus then evolved from the australopithecines, probably in southeastern Asia, migrated outward and differentiated into subspecies. The pithecanthropines evolved through Solo man, Wadjak man (with some mongoloid genes added?) into the living Australoids, who also include the Negritos, and the Papuan-Melanesian groups. The sinanthropines, already characterized by shovel-shaped incisor teeth, evolved into the living Mongoloids, and Heidelberg man (European H. erectus) evolved into Neanderthalers and then the Caucasoids. The Capoids (Bushmen-Hottentots) evolved from a subspecies of H. erectus in northern Africa, with the Singa skull being intermediate in development. The development of the Congoid (African Negro) subspecies, according to Dr. Coon, is "the weakest warp in the racial fabric", and is supposed to have evolved from Homo erectus, through Rhodesian man into an old population that was driven into dense forests and then became dwarfed, the modern Pygmies. Interbreeding between Capoids, Caucasoids (Capsians) and Pygmies is supposed to have given rise to the modern Negroes, at least before 6,000 B.P. Because of the former geographically wide distribution of Caucasians and the seeming late origin of the Mongoloids, this concept of hominid evolution is not generally accepted by most students of fossil men, although such a long-term development of subspecies could well have occurred at least in part (Bushmen and

Australoids may have been separately derived from <u>Homo erectus</u>), and some recent studies seem to have shown similar parallel development of species and subspecies from an ancestor in common in some rodents.

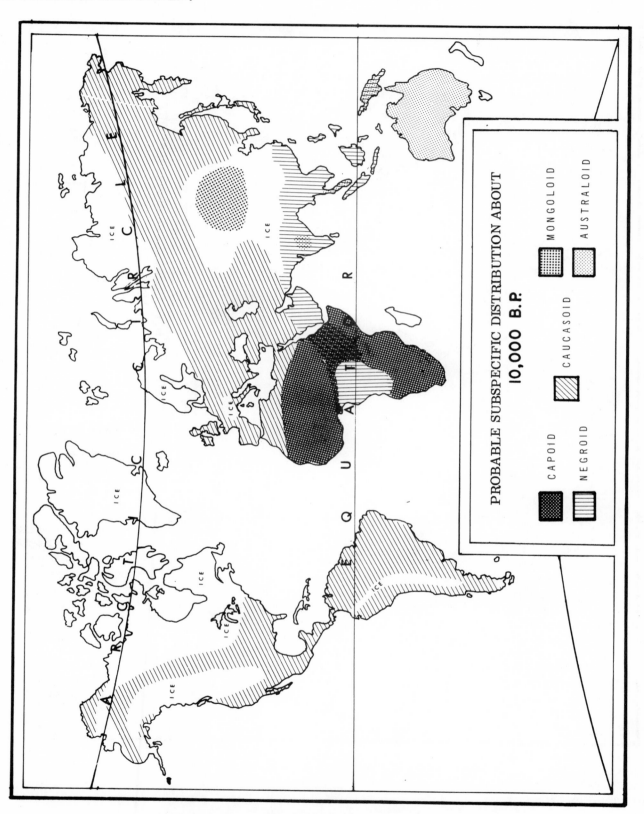

Figure 66.   Distribution of man about 10,000 B.P.

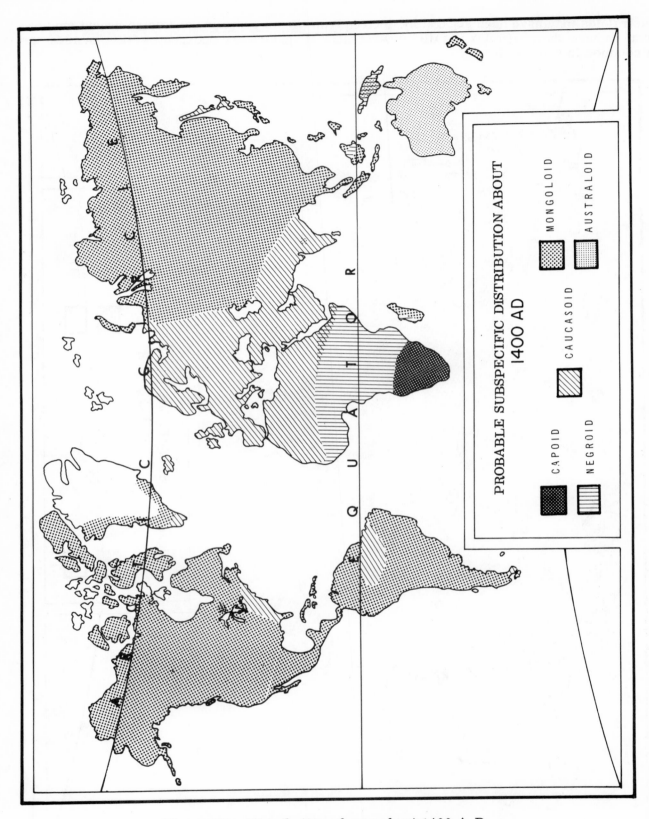

Figure 67. Distribution of man about 1400 A.D.

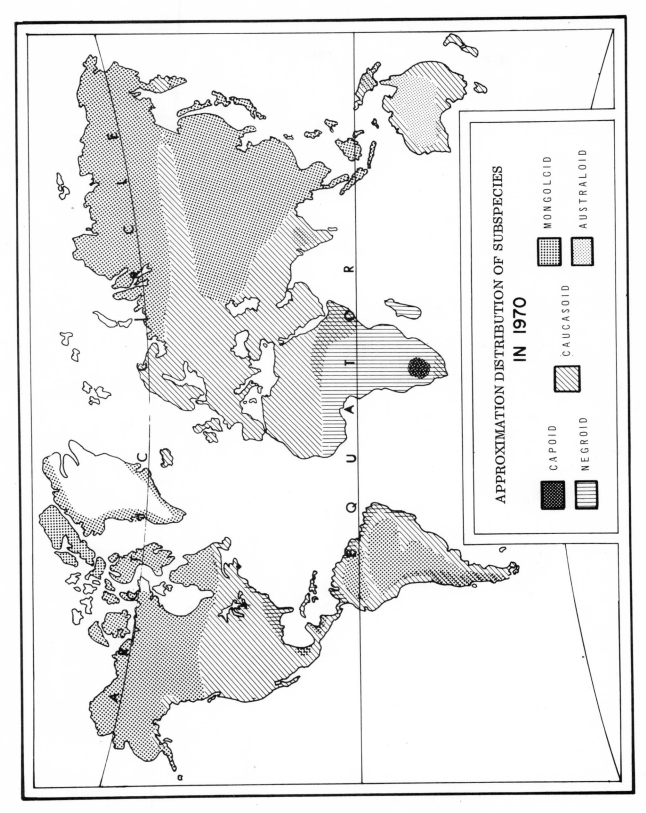

Figure 68. Distribution of man, 1970 A.D.

Chapter XIV

THE SUBSPECIES OF MAN

The Living Subspecies of Man

Modern men are generally classified into from three to five main subspecies, Caucasoid, Mongoloid and Negroid, with Capoid and Australoid being added as distinct subspecies by some specialists. These five principle subspecies can be subdivided into lesser groupings although some of those groups cannot be certainly identified as to subspecific affinities, and may be distinct subspecies. Our knowledge of Homo sapiens variability is not yet complete enough to enable us to define and formally name subspecies.

The five main groups of man are considered herein to be subspecies, as that taxonomic unit is generally determined by morphology and geographic isolation, and not on a genetic basis. The great mobility of modern man is probably causing the disintegration (although perhaps incompletely and slowly) of the major subspecies, and new population groups are in the process of formation by interbreeding among the older subspecies.

Australoids

Australian aborigines are characterized morphologically by prominent brow ridges, sloping foreheads, deep-set eyes, long skulls, broad noses, brown eyes, near black to light-brown, non-glossy skin, and wavy, dark-brown hair, although blond hair (possibly caused by sun-bleaching) occurs among some central Australian tribesmen. The presence of wavy hair, prominent brow ridges and more body hair aids one to distinguish Australoids morphologically from Negroids.

Some authorities believe the Australoids are closely related to the stock of Homo sapiens from which the Caucasian subspecies arose, because both groups grow bald and turn gray at a relatively young age. The Australoids also have a Caucasoid-like beard and body-hair distri-bution, as well as a Caucasoid-like muscularity or body build. The primitive aspects of Australoid skulls include the following characteristics, early Homo sapiens-like heavy brow ridges, deep set eyes, sloping foreheads, and concave temples. These primitive character-istics indicate that Australoid ancestory was derived from men closer to the stem or origin of our species than any other living group, and they probably gave rise to most of the other living subspecies.

The material aspects of Australoid culture were also primitive in that bows, pottery, metal, herding, and agriculture were unknown in Australia before the arrival of Europeans.

There was a former wider than the present-day distribution of Australoids, as Austra-loid-like tribal groups, or strong genetic traces of Australoids have been found in peoples presently living in New Guinea, Indonesia, India, Ceylon, southern Arabia, and portions of mainland areas of southeastern Asia. This distribution pattern could be a marginal remnant of a formerly very widespread and geologically ancient group of Homo sapiens, that has subsequently been exterminated or assimilated over most of its original geographic range by subsequently evolved groups of Homo sapiens and their more progressive cultures.

Capoids (African Bushmen)

Bushmen are characterized in possessing long-bellied muscles with short tendons that may permit them to excell in endurance and chasing wounded game, extreme development of fatty buttocks, or steatopygia, especially among the women, dark-yellowish skins, flattened noses, extremely kinked "peppercorn" hair, moderate beard growth, a lack of body hair and development of a mongoloid-like eyelid fold. The Hottentots are closely related genetically and in physical appearance to the Bushmen, and together both groups may consist of about

120,000 living individuals. Traces of Bushman-like and Hottentot-like individuals, or numerically small populations of such people, are found in Libya and Morocco in northern Africa, where they live in a rather isolated fashion, either culturally or occupationally, among more recently arrived populations of Arabs, Berbers, or Tuaregs. Also Bushman art work of great antiquity has been found in the Sahara Desert, but fossil remains or living individuals of Capoid descent or their identifiable artifacts have not been found outside Africa. This would indicate that Bushmen are a geologically old group, and occupied most if not all Africa in the past, and have been subsequently displaced by the more recent evolution or arrival and geographic expansion of Negroids in central Africa, and the arrival of Caucasoids in northern and southern Africa. The genetic origin of the Bushmen is not known. Authorities are not certain whether the Bushmen gave rise to the Hottentots, and subsequently to the Negroids, or if the Hottentots are the result of Bushmen-Negroid interbreeding. If the Negroids evolved in central Africa, the first alternative would seem more logical, in that Negroids would have developed as a specialized subspecies, dwelling in humid tropical areas of dense rain-forests. It is probable that Bushmen are not descended from any other living subspecies and may (as Dr. Carlton Coon has suggested) have descended from Homo erectus independently of the Australoids, in northern Africa.

Today only 25,000 to 50,000 Bushmen are still living and they reside mainly in the Kalahari Desert. In historic time, before 1600, Bushmen occupied nearly the whole of southern Africa. They were displaced by means of a bipartite invasion; the Dutch landed on the southern coast and migrated north, and the Zulus migrated south from central Africa. Thus it would seem there is no valid territorial claim to South Africa through right of prior occupation by Negroids. The real claim belongs rightly to neither the Dutch nor the Negroids, but to the now nearly extinct Bushman who was the original inhabitant.

Negroids, Tropical Climate Dwelling Men

Negroids are characterized morphologically by long skulls with protruding occiputs, wide flattened noses, kinky hair, black eyes with flecks of pigment in the sclera, relatively small and closely set ears, thick everted lips, large teeth, short bunchy muscles with long tendons, lordosis of the spine, apocrine (sweat) glands that secrete the enzyme acetylcholinesterase and impart a characteristic racial odor, very dark glossy skins, and a minor amount of body or facial hair. The enzyme acetylcholinesterase is present in all living human beings and has many pharmacol functions including that it causes muscle fibers to relax after contractions occur, however it is excreted in sweat only by Negroids. Furthermore Negroids lack the ability of full use or development of the platysma, the expression-creating facial muscle, and Negroids tend to be lithe, flexible, and their muscles excell in short, rapid bursts of muscle-induced speed, but generally lack endurance for sustained athletic efforts.

Central Africa is the present-day home of most of the Negroids, and may be the region in which the group evolved from Bushmanoid or Hottentot-like ancestors. Although Negroids could have originated in southeastern Asia (the oldest known Negroid skull, 40,000 B.P., is from Borneo) and evolved from an Australoid ancestor, and migrated to Africa where subsequent evolution occurred. To date, no Negroid bones of Pleistocene age are known from Africa. Evolution of Negroids was a continuation of natural selection and evolution of man in the original primate homeland, the tropics, while other trends of human evolution were originating farther north in Europe and Asia. Pygmies, Coastal tribes, and Nilotic Negroes are among the varieties within this group. The differences between Pygmies and Nilotics are great, as the Nilotic Negroes tend to be tall, thin-lipped, narrow-nosed and are adapted for life in a warm, slightly dry climate. Pygmies are typically short, thick-lipped, wide-nosed, and adapted for life in a tropical rain-forest environment. African Negroes differ serologically from Asian Negroid populations, and presumably are more highly evolved or specialized for life in tropical regions, and it is possible that African and Asiatic Negroids are descended from different groups. The Australoids could have given rise to only the Asiatic group and Bushmen could have given rise to only the African group. Nevertheless there could have been some genetic exchange between the two Negroid groups.

Presumably Negroids migrated from the region of their origin and their geographic range formerly extended from Africa across Arabia, India and along the southern margin of Asia and out into Melanesia and possibly beyond onto other Pacific Islands. Chinese archaeologists have recently uncovered evidence that southern China (and probably most of southern Asia) was largely inhabited by small Negroids until 2,000 years ago. Thus Negroids occupied most of the tropical climate regions of the Old World beginning with an as yet undetermined period of the Wisconsinan Stage and up until 2,000 years ago. Since then Negroids have been largely replaced as the dominant population in southeastern Asia by Mongoloids, and in India and Arabia by Caucasoids. Negroid groups still living in Asia and the Indo-Pacific area include the Papuans in New Guinea, Melanesians on the eastern Pacific Islands, and Negritos (Pygmies) in the interior portions of the Philippines, the Malay Peninsula, and New Guinea. Other largely genetic traces of formerly more numerous Negroid groups have been found in some tribal groups of India and Arabia.

A former geographically widespread distribution of Negroids that confined or displaced Bushman and Australoids, seems to have occurred. Possibly the early migrations of Negroids northward (in Africa) to the Sahara and westward (or eastward) across southern Asia, displaced other subspecies of Homo sapiens that had previously occupied portions of those continents.

Caucasoids, Cold Climate Dwelling Men

Caucasoids are characterized by either long or broad skulls (Figure 61), skin color ranging from pale through brownish to almost black, narrow noses, straight to wavy hair ranging in color from blonde to black, blue to dark-brown eyes, thin lips, usually well-developed beards and body hair among the males, with a tendency toward balding of males and hair-graying at a relatively young age. The muscles of Caucasoids tend to be long-bellied and have short tendons, and function best at athletic endurance feats. Apocrine (sweat) glands are present, but no acetylcholinesterase is secreted, and there is a characteristic racial odor differing from that of the Negroids.

The Caucasoids are rather variegated, as are the other human subspecies and can be divided into several population groups, e.g., Mediterraneans, Nordics (including Slavs), and Alpines.

Evidence for a geographically wide late Pleistocene distribution of long-headed Caucasoids includes the discovery of long-headed skulls with heavy brow ridges, wisdom teeth and lacking shovel-shaped incisor teeth, in Arizona, Santa Rosa Island and Calaveras County in California, and caves in Brazil. These skulls are the remains of a physical type whose presence in the Americas pre-dates the largely broad-headed, wisdom-tooth lacking, and shovel-shaped incisor teeth possessing Mongoloid Amerindian groups of today. Some living, long-headed, Amerindians are found in the rather inhospitable environments of the Amazon Basin and Tierra del Fuego regions of South America. Possibly some of the tribes of the eastern United States were long-headed Caucasoids or were at least partially descended from them. Early genetic contamination by anxious Europeans with little regard for later genetic studies has clouded the original evidence. Other forms of evidence, such as early paintings made by European artists, and skulls obtained from Amerindian burial sites tend to support the idea that some of the eastern tribes were of Caucasoid ancestory and appearance.

If the earliest populations of the Americas were Caucasoid, then the westward migration of the Polynesians from South America would be plausible as they could have been derived from a remnant population of the early American Caucasoids. Thor Heyerdahl in his book, "Kon Tiki", discussed and sought to document such an hypothesis. Legends of bearded men in sail-rigged ships and bearded statues from Central America, South America, and Easter Island form a small part of Heyerdahl's evidence.

Other Caucasoid-like, isolated, remnant populations include the Ainus of Japan. Today they live only on Hokkaido, the northernmost island of Japan. In the historic past they proba-bly occupied the entire Japanese archipelago. Indications of this are that some place names, such as Fujiyama, are of Ainu origin, and the written history of Japan records a long conflict between Mongoloid Japanese and the Ainus.

The Indian subcontinent has historically been insulated from oriental population infiltration and conquest by the Himalaya mountains and Burmese jungles, and has consequently become an Asiatic haven or asylum for some Caucasoid and Australoid populations. Other Asiatic-dwelling Caucasoid groups include some of the more isolated and culturally primitive hill tribes of Indonesia and the Malay Peninsula.

Europe and northern Africa are the historic homeland of the majority of the Caucasoid race. There is a stratified, remnant distribution of the earlier evolved Caucasoid subgroups in Europe; Mediterraneans seem to form an outer fringe across southern Europe from Spain to the Black Sea, and across northern Africa. Other small groups of black-haired, blue-eyed, Mediterranean-appearing peoples are found living today in Wales and Scotland. They seem to have been displaced by the later-occurring Nordic population increase that subsequently filled most of Europe. The Slavs are a Nordic offshoot and seem to be the latest development of Caucasoid evolution and geographic expansion.

C. S. Coon, in "The Living Races of Man", estimated that Caucasoids were the numerically dominant human population as of 1965.

Predominantly Caucasoid	1,757,000,000	55.7%
Predominantly Mongoloid	1,171,000,000	37.1%
Predominantly Negroid	216,000,000	6.8%
Australoid[1]	13,000,000	0.4%
Capoid[2]	126,000	0.004%
	3,157,126,000	100.004%

Mongoloids, An Improved Cold-Climate Subspecies

Mongoloids are the last group of mankind to evolve, they probably developed from a small population of Caucasoid-like people, that were geographically isolated in a cold region of central or south-central Asia during the latter portion of the last glacial stage. This evolution presumably took place within the last 15,000 to 30,000 years. Mongoloids are the highest development of cold-climate dwelling man as they constitute the latest product of that line of evolution, and could conceivably replace Caucasoids, Ainus, and some Australoids that live in cold or cool regions. Because of the prevailing cold-climate in their place of origin, Mongoloids developed some morphologic specializations for life in cold areas, such as sinus-protecting cheek pads, epicanthic eyelid folds (protection against cold and snow-blindness), and more "efficient" metabolisms. The Mongoloids lack of beard growth probably was advantageous in the extreme cold of central Asia, as beards tend to accumulate ice that forms from moisture condensed out of exhaled breath.

Mongoloids are characterized morphologically by skin color that ranges from pale-yellowish to reddish-brown, brown eyes, hair that is straight, coarse and black, sparse growth of beard and body hair, baldness is rare, and hair graying is delayed until advanced old age. Forward projecting and shovel-shaped or concave-backed incisor teeth, prominent and protruding cheek bones, thin lips, flattened faces (in most), and long-bellied muscles that lack "speed" are also typical. Furthermore Mongoloids have no apocrine (sweat) glands, do not secrete acetylcholinesterase, and therefore lack a dinstictive racial odor.

As a general rule, where Mongoloids are present in southeastern Asia they occupy the more desirable coastal areas whereas aboriginal Caucasoids, Australoids or Negroids are confined to the mountainous interior regions.

---

[1] Dr. Coon includes Negritos and Melanesians in this group.
[2] Bushmen and Hottentots combined.

The Mongoloid infiltration of North America, with the subsequent displacement of most of the long-headed Caucasoids, is an excellent example of the territorial expansion of a sub-species with population absorption and replacement. Defense of a "home-territory" by an animal group nearly always results in defeat or retreat of the invaders. The "home team," even when inferior in numbers or size usually wins. Man is the only animal that consistently violates his neighbors' home territory and can do so with a high degree of success, either killing or driving off the original occupants. Such "warfare" has been observed only once in the other primates, rhesus monkeys, and was described by Carpenter, based on his studies of wild but confined populations in Puerto Rico.

In early historic time, Caucasoids and Ainus occupied much of Siberia, Japan, and western Asia, and were forced out in Recent (post 5000 B.P.) time by the Mongoloid territorial expansion. At about the same time Mongoloids began to enter southeastern Asia, a still continuing process. The Mongoloid migration toward the west is well-documented in historical records of the incursions of the Huns, the "Hordes" of Tamerlane, Ghengis Khan, and Kublai Khan. Human distribution occurs in a manner similar to the distribution methods and patterns of other animals and is not solely the result of military invasions. A single battle, war, or conquest is not enough to distribute one subspecies of man and replace or markedly restrict the distribution of another group. Distribution pattern changes are slowly occurring processes and are not always accomplished through violent means. Some of the more successful human distribution sequences seem to have been largely peaceful infiltrations, or non-violent, slow immigrations of a new population into an already populated area.

The "Golden Hordes" were neither slow nor peaceful. They were primarily military operations, and only incidentally resulted in genetic and cultural distribution. The "Hordes" entered Europe across the steppes of southern Russia, far south of the dense coniferous forests of the Moscow region. They defeated western armies at nearly every encounter. The Mongols had developed efficient cavalry tactics, Greco-Roman military tactics had been long forgotten by Europeans, who relied on heavy armor and fought inefficiently as individuals. The Mongols usually managed to pick their own battlefield and entice the westerners into a web of certain defeat.

The invasions did not result in a permanent occupation by Mongoloids and replacement of the indigenous population, but the Mongoloids left lasting traces in genes and languages, and locally, tribes such as the Kalmuks remained in the west after the main body of the "Hordes" had left. The invasions were a means of success as far as animal distribution is concerned. Each successive invasion penetrated farther into Europe, eventually as far as Austria. Mongoloid genes and cultural influences are apparent in eastern Europe today, and many Slavs have prominent cheek bones indicative of partial Mongoloid ancestry.

The Probable Reasons for Human Variability

The idea of "racial superiority" has often been connected with interpretations of the obvious morphologic and cultural differences among the groups of living men. Many men have tried to identify a more advanced culture, or "cultural superiority" with a particular sub-species. The inference is that only the human group with an advanced culture could have developed it, and only that group is capable of further advancing the culture, therefore that group is racially, genetically, and mentally superior. I believe the false logic involved here needs no pointed demolition.

Actually, each human group is morphologically superior in its own way, in the environment of its origin, to the other human subspecies. No one human group is demonstrably superior or inferior, in an across the board manner to any other group of humans.

Mongoloids are tolerant of a wide temperature range, but as a group possess several adaptations for life in the cold-climate of their region of origin. The epicanthic eyefolds help protect eyeballs from cold, and fatty cheek pads similarly help protect the facial sinuses. The relatively short limbs and thick bodies of the northern-most Mongoloid populations help conserve body heat and the increased flow of metabolic blood to the hands and cheeks of arctic or subarctic dwelling Mongoloids aids to prevent freezing of those body areas while exposed to extreme cold. Furthermore only Mongoloids have been able to develop a tolerance for life at high altitudes above 12,000 feet, in regions such as Tibet and the Andes. This tolerance has been attained by development of larger hearts, a greater lung capacity, and a greater volume of blood that is richer in hemoglobin and red corpuscle content. At similar high altitudes Caucasians may fail to reproduce, abort, or die in infancy, and Negroids may die because of the presence of sickle-shaped red blood cells, that aid in resisting malaria but fail to carry enough oxygen for life above 12,000 feet.

Negroids are adapted for life in an area of humid tropical heat, but not the extreme dry heat of the desert. Physiologic studies have shown that in tropical regions Negroids lose less salt in perspiration, and are therefore less susceptible to heat stroke than Caucasoids. Negroids also possess sickle-cells, that is mutated blood cells that aid in resisting malaria, a major reason for Negroid survival in tropical areas where other human groups sicken and die. The extreme flexibility, litheness, and rapid muscular reactions of the Negro are an advantage in traveling or pursuing game through dense rain-forest jungles. Other adaptations to life in a region of humid heat include short, wide noses, a woolly, skull-protecting hair mat that does not hang down over the neck and shoulders, and less body fat. Some of the Negroids' adaptations are disadvantageous in areas away from equatorial regions, as a dark or nearly black skin color absorbs forty percent more solar heat in the desert and may cause sun-stroke. Furthermore about 40 degrees latitude, dark skins block the entrance of enough ultraviolet light to prevent rickets. The lack of body fat combined with relatively long, slender limbs and extremities leads to excessive loss of body heat, that is advantageous in hot areas, but in cold-climates may result in frostbite.

The apocrine glands of Negroids and Caucasoids, and the resultant body odors, may have originally served to ward off carnivores by unappetizing aromas. This would have been of great selective advantage to poorly armed early Homo sapiens. In that respect, it is interesting to note that Mongoloids lack similar odors and evolved after man's protective weapons and shelters made such genetically controlled protective devices needless.

Caucasoids are physiologically adapted to drier climates that have at least one cool season. Their beak-like noses are an adaptive feature to help warm and moisten air before it reaches the cold and dryness sensitive lung region. Lightly pigmented skins are more prevalent in northern areas in that they aid to absorb ultraviolet radiation above 40 degrees latitude, although browner colors may occur below that parallel. Long muscles, endowed with high endurance, would have been an advantage in hunting and traveling across dry steppes, deserts, and the cool, less densely-forested regions of the north. Blue eyes are more sensitive to the blue and violet end of the visible light spectrum, and may be advantageous in seeing distant objects in hazy, poorly lit regions.

The rather obvious morphologic, physiologic, and athletic differences found in the different subspecies of men do not disappear and are not minimized by a misguided, "liberal" attempt to pretend that they do not exist, or that the only difference is skin color. Such an attitude could lead only to frustrations, and a lack of pride in one's own subspecies, their evolution, inherent abilities, and accomplishments.

The Significance of Non-Adaptive Characteristics

The human subspecies can be characterized by two distinct (but not readily separable) sets of factors, 1. adaptive features, and 2. non-adaptive factors.

The adaptive characteristics were evolved or selected, so a population group could more readily live and reproduce in a given climate, or geographic region, and resist the diseases endemic to that area. Such adaptive factors may rapidly change and nearly identical characteristics may occur in non-related peoples, because of introduction of new or old diseases in an area or because of long-term changes in climate. Therefore adaptive changes can not be considered to be constant and ever-present characteristics that one can use to distinguish a particular subspecies and to identify closely related populations. Among the adaptive characteristics are hair form, body-fat distribution, blood factors that aid in resisting diseases, sweat gland distribution, nose-shape, salt content of sweat, body height and bulk, eye color, and skin color.

Convergence of adaptive characteristics includes independent development of the anti-malarial sickle-cell trait among some Caucasoids (but from a different mutation and gene than that of the Negroids), presence of dark skin color among Caucasoids in India and Ethiopia, the tall, lean body-build of steppe and desert-dwelling peoples, and the short, stocky body form of cold climate-dwelling men. An independent mutation (but probably not adaptive) resulted in the development of kinky, Negroid-like hair in some Scandinavians. The introduction of smallpox to North America has been presumed to have radically altered the blood group distribution pattern of the living northern plains Amerindians from (probably formerly) O to A.

There are limits to the development of convergent features, as the South African Boers, of Dutch descent, are unlikely to independently develop into a Capoid-appearing race. Although they may leave many descendants with some Capoid genes, e.g. the Rehobother Bastarden. The term, incidentally, is not considered by the Rehobothers to be insulting, and is used by them as their own group name.

Non-adaptive characteristics have presumably developed independently of selection influenced by environment, and should be rather constant within a population and very likely could (with much further investigation) be used to accurately determine subspecific origins and relationships. Some non-adaptive characteristics that may prove to be useful are percentage of individuals in the populations with dry (versus sticky) earwax, ability to taste PTC, finger-print patterns, and possibly colorblindness, and some blood factors such as Diego, Duffy, and haptoglobins.

Exactly what factors are significant and what are not is difficult to tell. Furthermore, inherited blood traits are many and complex. There are at least 15 blood group systems, such as ABO, P, MN, and RH; RH alone has 28 known alleles; furthermore there are many rare antigens that occur with high frequencies in some populations; about 100 known hemoglobins (e.g., A, E, S), and variants of at least 15 red cell enzymes, one of which (G6PD) has 30 alleles, as well as inherited deficiencies of 12 red cell enzymes and many serum protein systems (e.g., haptoglobins, transferrins, and albumins). This gives a complex amount of information (unfortunately incomplete) that is difficult to assimilate and evaluate objectively. By selecting a few traits (both adaptive and non-adaptive) nearly any point of view regarding racial and subspecific relationships and former gene flow can be "scientifically" established. By attempting to use the entire body of known information, one would include some undoubtedly misleading data and quite likely be defeated by the sheer bulk of available, and frustratingly incomplete data.

Supposedly Non-adaptive Genetic Characteristics

	Austra-loids	Negroids	Bushman	Cauca-soids	Ainus	Mongoloids	Amerindian
Dry Earwax	? low	.07 (in U.S.)	?	.17	.37	.67-.98	.02 ? (Mayans only)
Tasters	50-67%	59-74%	?	60-83%	95%	83-100%	83-100%
Loops	to 46%	to 73%	to 68%	to 76%	to 70%	to 64%	to 61%
Whorls	to 73%	to 40%	to 21%	to 42%	to 35%	to 55%	to 57%
Arches	0-1%	3-12%	13-16%	0-9%	2-7%	1-5%	2-8%
Diego	0	0	0	0	0	0-3%	0-35%
Duffy	100	0-6	8	37-82	?	90-100	22-99
Haptoglobins	46-63	40-87	29	9-44	?	23-50	32-73
Colorblind-ness	low	low	low	high	?	high	low
Transferrin TFDI	high	high	?	low	low	low	low
Enzyme AK^2 allele	low	low	low	high	?	low	low
G6PD	low	high	high	low	low ?	(Japan) low	low

The chart of supposedly non-adaptive characteristics indicates a close Mongoloid-Amerindian relationship (based on tasters, fingerprints, Diego factors and G6PD), a close Negroid-Bushman relationship (based on fingerprints, especially arches, G6PD and the Duffy blood factor). Australoids show a relationship to Negroids in percentage of tasters, transferrin TFDI, dry earwax, and haptoglobins. Australoids, Negroids, Caucasoids, Ainus and some Amerindians (Mayans) have a low percentage of dry earwax in common. Caucasoid and Mongoloid similarities include high incidence of colorblindness, haptoglobin percentages, low incidence of arches, a high percentage of tasters, a low G6PD and a low transferrin TFDI content of their blood. The Ainus combine Caucasoid and Mongoloid traits, but are probably more nearly Caucasoid. Caucasoid and Amerindian similarities include low incidence of dry earwax, high percentage of tasters, low incidence of arches, similarity of Duffy factor percentages, low G6PD and low transferrin TFDI percentages.

These conclusions have been drawn from a few factors, selected from among a great many, and seem to establish a gene flow and relationship pattern consistent with the distribution pattern of man as discussed in Chapter 13. However, my selection and even interpretation of the factors is subjective, and is definitely not the final (or even correct) interpretation.

The former gene flow (and development of the subspecies) may be diagrammatized as follows:

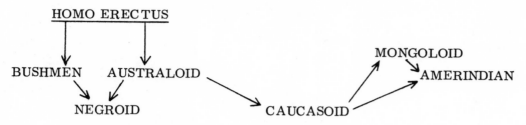

This implies that the Australoids are the main stem of Homo sapiens and gave rise directly to the Negroid (at least in part) and Caucasoid subspecies, and indirectly to the Mongoloids and Amerindians. The Bushmen seemingly represent a distinct, but parallel development of Homo sapiens, that may have given rise to Negroids (at least partially) and may have evolved independently from Homo erectus.

Chapter XV

EARLY MAN IN AMERICA

The First Arrivals

The first men to reach North America arrived during the latter portion of the Wisconsinan glaciation. They wandered into Alaska across the then dry Bering Straits from Siberia. Recent discoveries indicate that the Arctic Ocean may have been ice-free at that time, and that ice-free corridors existed through central Alaska to the Yukon and then possibly south along the eastern edge of the Rocky Mountains across Canada into the United States.

Thus immigrants from Asia could have traveled from cold, but largely unglaciated Siberia, across dry land into Alaska as they wandered randomly in pursuit of game. Undoubtedly the wanderers were unaware of their discovery of a "new" continent. They were merely tribal groups seeking new hunting areas.

In all likelihood this migration took place before 30,000 B.P., and just how long before 30,000 B.P. the initial crossing occurred is hotly debated by archaeologists. Early man could have arrived in North America as long as 100,000 years ago, as some archeologists have identified mid-Pleistocene hand-axes or choppers and scrapers (Plate 27, Figure A) on river terraces, that contain fossil elephant bones, along the Little Colorado River in Arizona. Similar hand-ax cultures have been described from Wyoming, Texas, and New Mexico. Great antiquity for the ax cultures is indicated by a lack of pottery and projectile points, and occurrence of the axes and scrapers on old river terrace sediments with a geologically determined ages of more than 100,000 years. Many archaeologists consider the axes and scrapers to be products of a much later culture, and regard them as only discarded rock-cores from a flake industry. The discarded cores became surficially associated with old river terrace sediments, and so far choppers or scrapers have not been found in place within the sediments.

Supposed eoliths have been found in an alluvial fan in the Mohave Desert, north of Barstow, California. The artifacts are crudely fashioned pieces of chalcedony that some scientists interpret as being pebble tools more than 40,000 years old, although many other scientists think they are not man made.

Other early man sites, such as those on Santa Rosa Island off the coast of California are more convincing. The charred bones of a dwarf mammoth from Santa Rosa Island have been determined to be about 28,000 years old by the carbon 14 method of age dating. This mammoth was quite likely killed and cooked by man, as the flesh of a mammoth burned in a natural grass or brush fire would be roasted and charred, but not deeply enough to char the bones. Man-gnawed bones thrown into a cooking fire would char readily.

The Tule Springs site north of Las Vegas, Nevada, consists of some fire pits with associated artifacts, and the fire pits have been determined to be 24,000 years old. However, not all archaeologists are convinced of the sites authenticity, and that the flaked tools were really associated with the allegedly man-made fire sites.

The earliest known skulls found in the Americas are similar in that they are long-headed with heavy brow ridges, had flat, slab-like sides, keeled crania, and bun-shaped bases or occipital regions. Wisdom teeth were present and shovel-shaped incisor teeth were not. Skulls of this general pattern have been found on Santa Rosa Island (Plate 26, Figures A, B, C, D, E, F), Calaveras County in California, near Midland, Texas, from caves in Brazil, and elsewhere (Plate 25, Figure C). Essentially, these are Caucasoid-like skulls, and indicate a widespread late Pleistocene geographic range for that dry and cold-climate dwelling subspecies prior to Mongoloid territorial range expansion in very late and post Pleistocene time.

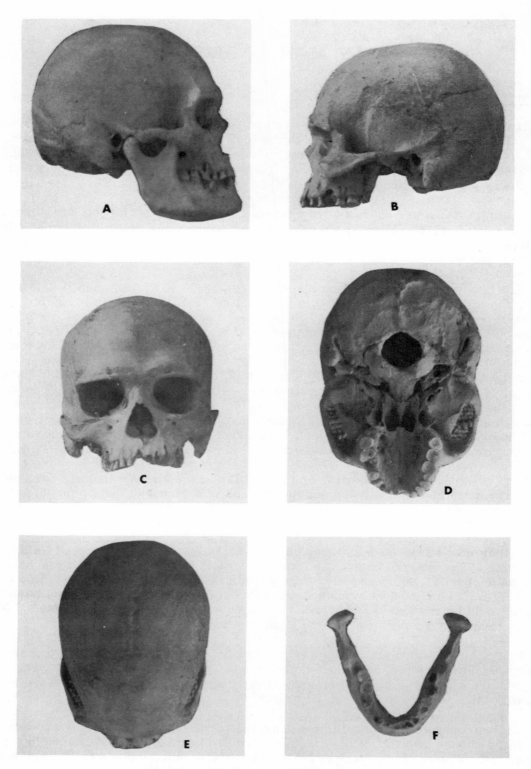

Plate 26. Paleoamerindian skull.

A.) Right side of an archaic-type Amerindian skull from Santa Rosa Island, off the coast of California. B.) Left side showing heavy torus. C.) Frontal view showing squared orbits. D.) Ventral view showing elongate skull. E.) Dorsal view showing long-headedness. F.) Mandible of same skull. Courtesy of Robert T. Davison.

Plate 27. Artifacts.

A.) Scraper from Pleistocene terrace gravels along the Little Colorado River in Arizona.
B.) Clovis (Llano) projectile point. C.) Sandia (Type 2) projectile point, from Sandia Cave,
New Mexico. D.) Pre-Columbian copper celt from the middlewestern United States.
E.) Argillite spear point from the Trenton gravels, New Jersey. F.) Folsom projectile point
from the Lindenmeier Site, New Mexico. G.) Hand ax, from the Acheulean Culture (early
Homo sapiens) of eastern Africa (Olorgesailie). H.) Chopping tool from the Patjitanian Culture
(Homo erectus?) of Java. Southern Illinois University, Edwardsville.

No Neanderthal-like skulls are
known from the Americas and it seems
likely that group of men never reached
the New World, unless the supposed
hand ax cultures were products of their
industry. Even if the hand ax cultures
are of the antiquity suspected, they
could have been made by a Caucasoid-
like member of <u>Homo sapiens</u>, possibly
similar to the former occupants of the
previously discovered fossil skulls
from California and Brazil.

Undoubted Pleistocene Sites

Some human bones, such as the
skull of Vero Beach Man from Florida
and the pelvis of Natchez Man
(Figure 69) from Mississippi have been
found associated with bones of extinct
elephants and other cold-climate
Pleistocene animals, and are undoubtedly more than 11,000 years old; few
fossil elephants' remains have been
found in sediments younger than 11,000
B.P. in North America.

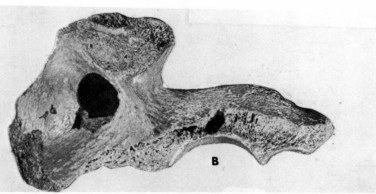

Figure 69. A,B.) The pelvis of Natchez man
from Pleistocene river terrace
sediments along the Mississippi
River. The round hole was cut to
remove a bone sample for fluo-
rine content analysis. Courtesy
of the Department of Geology,
Academy of Natural Sciences of
Philadelphia.

The earliest human remains so
far discovered in the New World
consist of a male skeleton found by
sewer workers in the 1930's in
Los Angeles, California. Recent radiocarbon age determinations indicate that
those bones may be 24,000 years old

The Laguna skull, found at Laguna
Beach, California, in 1933, was also
recently determined by the radiocarbon
method to be 15,200 years old. Both
these remains are remarkably old, and
indicate a need for much further investigation into the antiquity of man in the New World.

The skull of a 30 year-old woman, associated with bones of now extinct species of horses,
antelope, and bison, was discovered near Midland, Texas in 1953. Carbon 14 radiometric dates
imply that she lived sometime between 18,000 and 10,000 B.P. The skull was from sediments
overlain by a stratum containing Folsom artifacts.

Charred human bones of about nine individuals from the state of Washington (Marmes
Ranch) have been dated from 13,000 to 11,500 years ago by the carbon 14 method. A bone projectile point and bone needles were found at the same site.

The oldest known human remains (12,600 B.P.) from South America consist of a mandible,
that had wisdom teeth, from Guitarrero Cave in northern Peru.

A well-defined sequence of late Pleistocene projectile point cultures associated with
extinct elephants and bison in the western United States begins with the Llano Culture or Clovis
points (Plate 27, Figure B), the oldest projectile-point culture recognized thus far in North
America. The Llano Culture lasted from at least 13,000 B.P. until 11,000 B.P., and Llano
men were geographically widely ranging hunters of mammoths, bison, and even tundra-dwelling

musk oxen. His weapons were spears tipped with elongate, fluted, pressure-flaked and partially ground-edged stone points, and the spears could have been either hand thrown, or launched with a wooden spear thrower or atlatl (Figure 70). The spears would have been effective for use in killing thin-skinned animals at close range, but were hardly guaranteed dispatchers of elephants.

Figure 70. Atlatl or spear thrower.

Near the end of the tenure of the Llano Culture, a group of Solutrean-like spear points, characterized by off-center tangs, were manufactured by people living in and near Sandia Cave, New Mexico (Plate 27, Figure C). Similar lop-sided tanged points have been found in many younger sites, and it is very likely that none of these American points are really Solutrean because the Solutrean Culture of Europe lasted from 18,000 to 17,000 B.P. and abruptly disappeared 6,000 years before the Sandia Culture came into existence, so there is a wide geographic gap as well as an untenably long temporal gap separating the two cultures. The seeming re-invention of this type point led to the manufacture and later discovery of similar points from the late Pleistocene and Archaic Trenton Gravel Cultures of New Jersey and elsewhere, and indicates that off-centered tangs were independently invented at different times in various places.

The Llano and Sandia Cultures were succeeded by the geographically widespread Folsom Culture (Plate 27, Figure F) lasting from 11,000 until 9,000 B.P. that was characterized by manufacture of short, finely pressure-flaked and fluted projective points, that were probably mounted on shafts and the spears were probably launched with spear throwers. Seemingly, bows had not yet been introduced or independently invented in the Americas, even though bows were known to have been used in Europe at least 7,000 years before. This is evidence of slow diffusion of ideas and lack of cultural exchange and human contacts between the Old and New Worlds for several thousand years during the final stages of the Wisconsinan glaciation. Probably the first bows were used in the Americas about 3,500 B.P.

Elephants were rarely killed by Folsom man, as elephants (especially the grasslands dwelling mammoths) were quite likely scarce and nearly extinct by 11,000 years ago, and most Folsom kill-sites contain the bones of extinct species of large-horned bison.

The next geographically widely distributed culture was the Plano Culture that lasted from 9,000 to 7,000 B.P., and was characterized by production of several types of tools among which were long, narrow, diagonally-flaked projectile points shaped like willow leaves. The points are called Eden (or Yuma), were presumably spear tips, and are of excellent workmanship, equal to the best European Neolithic stone flaking. Other points including those known as Plainview and Scotts Bluff were also made at that time.

After the Plano Culture the next sequence was the Archaic (Plate 27, Figure E), a more complex culture that was more advanced and versatile. The Archaic stage temporaly overlapped older and younger cultural stages and generally extended from 10,000 B.P. until 3,000 B.P., but locally lasted until Europeans arrived in North America. The Archaic stage was succeeded by more advanced and more localized cultures (Plate 27, Figure D), until the Woodland Culture largely replaced many of them.

Trans-Oceanic Contacts

For many years the subject of post-Pleistocene and pre-Columbian transoceanic contacts between Old World peoples and North American populations has been a highly controversial one.

In 1962 and 1965 a well-documented trans-Pacific contact was described by B. J. Meggers, C. Evans and E. Estrada. Mid-Jomon style pottery presumably introduced from Japan was discovered on the coast of Ecuador. The first known pottery from anywhere in the world is

Early Jomon pottery from Japan made between 9,500 and 7,700 B.P. The oldest known New World pottery is the "Mid-Jomon-like" pottery made between 4,000 and 5,000 B.P. and found in Ecuador. It is rather unlikely that Americans would have suddenly invented well-made pottery, without a series of crude pottery products produced during experimentation and early production. The contact was not one of Mongoloid Amerindians with Mongoloid Japanese, but probably Caucasoid-like Amerindians and differing but broad-headed ? and (Caucasoid? or Ainu-like) Japanese. The mummies of early Amerindians from Peru have a high frequency of blonde and red hair, and some paintings from Central and South America show fair-skinned peoples with light-colored hair being defeated by Mongoloid appearing Amerindians.

The Japanese prehistorian Nishimura has described the similarities of early Japanese rafts to those of South America. Similar rafts could have readily sailed or drifted from Japan to the Americas on prevailing currents. Thor Heyerdahl's epic voyage across the Pacific on the raft <u>Kon Tiki</u> demonstrated the seaworthiness of such craft (Figure 74). It is interesting that American Indians were keeping some shipwrecked Japanese sailors as slaves at the time the first Europeans reached the northwestern regions of Canada and the United States.

Meggers and Evans, subsequent to their original discovery, announced further archaeologic evidence of a colonization of a portion of the South American coast by oriental fisherman about 2300 B.P. Furthermore, some archeologists seem to recognize a suspected Chinese influence on early South and Central American art forms. Apparently the art influence is thought to resemble that of the Shang Dynasty of China (circa 4,000 B.P.), but first appears in the Americas about 3,000 B.P.

Another probable early contact is recorded in Chinese written history, as a junk was alleged to have sailed eastward across the Pacific Ocean in 499 A.D. and contacted a large land mass, and then sailed southward along a coast whose physical description as given by the explorers is similar to that of the United States and Mexico. Descriptions of plants, including cactus-like plants, that were unknown then in Asia were given in the account.

Prior to the arrival of the junk, migrating Mongoloids had entered North America (possibly before 4,000 B.P.) by way of the Bering Straits in large numbers. This was at least the second major immigration from Asia, and consisted of men whose broad, round skulls had no prominent brow ridges, no wisdom teeth (dental formula of $\frac{2-1-2-2}{2-1-2-2}$), and possessed shovel-shaped incisor teeth. The adaptive significance of shovel-shaped incisor teeth is obscure. The reduction of the number of molar teeth is a result of reducing the size and massiveness of the dentary bones in evolving from strongly muscled, heavily jaw-boned, seed and meat-eating, but fire-lacking ancestors. The advent of cooked, and easily chewed foods made massive teeth, strong jaws and large chewing muscles far less necessary for survival.

Figure 71. Monks' Mound, the largest pre-Columbian pyramidal earth work in North America. The structure covers 13 acres and is located near Collinsville, Illinois.

One, or possibly more, Mongoloid population immigrations gave rise to such Amerindian groups as the Algonquins and Athabascans, who largely displaced the earlier arrived Caucasoid Amerindians, so that Caucasoid Amerindian remnants were confined to regions isolated by mountainous barriers, as the eastern United States was isolated by the Appalachian Mountains, or the less desirable regions for habitation, such as the Amazon jungles, Tierra del Fuego, and other distant or less than choice regions. Perhaps the first Mongoloid Amerindians introduced the bow, and thus had an initially significant cultural advantage for use in displacing the Caucasoids. A later major Mongoloid incursion occurred shortly before 2,000 B.P., and consisted of the Aleuts and Eskimos, who differ from the major Mongoloid morphologic pattern by possessing long instead of broad heads.

The first well-documented trans-Atlantic contacts were those of the Viking leaders Leif Erikson (Leiv Eiriksson) and Thorfinn Karlsefni, shortly after 1,000 A.D., and resulted in construction of at least one temporary village, at L'Anse-Aux-Meadows in Newfoundland. Recently a map has been identified as having been drawn in the mid-15th century and the map apparently accurately depicts a portion of eastern North America. Other alleged trans-Atlantic contacts include those of the Irish St. Brendan about 570 A.D., a Breton in the late 1400's, Portugese fishermen and mariners in the 1300-1400's and those of classical times, but those contacts, if they occurred, had little genetic or cultural effect as the main pre-Columbian influence on the Americas was Asiatic in origin.

Possibly pre-Columbian European contacts with North America initially introduced some European diseases such as smallpox to eastern North America and caused the decimation of northeastern American populations reported by Indians to the first permanent European settlers. Even if such trans-Atlantic contacts had occurred they could readily have been largely forgotten and unrecorded if the contacts had been temporally short and sporadic. Even the nearly 500 year long Norse occupation of Greenland (1,000 A.D. to about 1,500 A.D.) was nearly forgotten, the colonists disappeared and their fate is unknown.

Figure 72. Central American pyramid with step-like sides and a temple located on the flat top.

Evidence of classical European contacts with America consists of legends of Greek and Roman origin and an extremely Roman (second century A.D.) appearing pottery bust from Mexico, other bearded figurines (Figure 73), as well as Central American legends of robed and bearded strangers in ships with sails. Furthermore Roman coins from the second century A.D. have been found on Iceland, an indication that classical sailors got at least half-way.

Other evidence of pre-Columbian contacts include the transoceanic distribution patterns of cotton, sweet potatoes, coconut palms, Lagenaria gourds, and an identical species of fresh water reed known, for example, from Lake Titicaca in South America and Easter (Ascension) Island.

Lagenaria siceraria gourds were grown for food in Europe, for use as bottles in India and southeastern Asia as well as in Central and South America. Many botanists believe the gourds were originally domesticated in India, and their seeds and culinary uses of the gourds were introduced to the New World before 4,000 B.P.

Cotton has been cultivated for more than 4,500 years in both Peru and India. American and Old World cotton plants differ in chromosome content, for Old World wild cotton has only thirteen small chromosomes, and American domestic cotton has thirteen small chromosomes and thirteen large chromosomes for a total of twenty-six. American wild cotton has only thirteen large chromosomes. Many botanists believe American domestic cotton resulted from

Figure 73. Bearded figurines and busts from Central America.

crossing Old World wild cotton with the wild American species, causing a doubling of the chromosome number known as tetraploidy. If this is so, someone must have brought cotton seeds from Asia, the only plausible source at the time, to South America and interbred the American and Old World cotton species more than 4,500 years ago.

Sweet potatoes were grown before 1,500 A.D. in a region extending from South America to Easter Island, north to Hawaii, and across Polynesia to New Zealand. Polynesians referred to sweet potatoes by variations of the word kumara, a South American Indian name for the plant. There is little doubt that sweet potatoes were carried westward from America across the Pacific by Amerindians and Polynesians. Thor Heyerdahl gave added emphasis to South American-Pacific island contacts by discovering pre-Columbian Peruvian pottery on one of the Galapagos Islands.

The fresh water reeds that grow in Lake Titicaca are cut and then tied into bundles, and then the bundles are lashed together to make small, serviceable boats. The same species of reed has been found growing in fresh water on Easter Island more than 2,000 miles away, and seeds or plants must have been transported there from South America by pre-Columbian seafarers.

Coconuts may have been carried and planted by pre-Columbian transoceanic seafarers. However, coconuts float well in water and will take root and grow in salty soil, so that the present distribution of coconut palms could be at least partially the result of distribution of floating nuts by oceanic currents.

The trans-Pacific eastward-trending transoceanic contacts that resulted in vegetable and plant transplanting took place more than 4,000 years ago, and all could have occurred about the time Mid-Jomon pottery manufacturers arrived in Ecuador. It is quite possible that Mid-Jomon men from Japan brought cotton and Lagenaria gourds to South America from Asia at the time they introduced pottery making.

The Mid-Jomon trans-Pacific contact (between 5,000 and 4,000 B.P.) took place near the end of the Hypsithermal or "Thermal Maximum", a short period of time with temperatures warmer than those of the present-day and a sea level that was slightly higher than the modern sea level. The large continental ice sheets had melted before the "Thermal Maximum", and the milder climate would have provided an excellent opportunity for man to indulge his urge to explore, and to to exchange genes and distribute culture.

Westward-trending contacts across the Pacific Ocean probably did not occur until long after 4,000 B.P., and were undoubtedly coincidental with the migration of Polynesians across the Pacific, probably from South America. That these contacts were

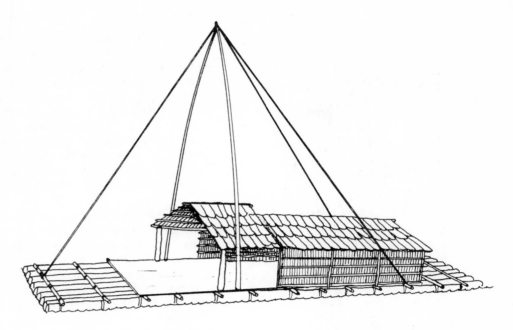

Figure 74. A balsa raft, the type used by pre-Columbian sailors along the west coast of South America. Thor Heyerdahl's Kon Tiki was a replica of such a raft.

sporadic and did not result in importation of an entire culture is shown by such examples as the unique or prior New World inventions of the mathematical concept of zero, the distinctive Aztec (Nahuatl), Mayan, and the recently identified Inca forms of writing, cultivation of unique crops in the New World such as corn, potatoes, tobacco, and rubber, through a hoe-centered, non-plow using form of agriculture. Manioc, normally a poisonous plant, was rendered edible and became a dietary staple through use of the acid-removing manioc press.

Development of perspective in art (about 1,000 A.D., at Bonampak in Mexico) preceeded that in Europe by several hundred years, although it had been previously developed by the Romans and subsequently forgotten.

Some objects in common to both the Old and New Worlds, such as bullroarers and spear throwers could have been brought across the Bering Straits by immigrants. Other objects such as panpipes and the techniques involved in making copper bells by the lost-wax process of bronze casting, could have been introduced by either Chinese or Japanese colonists, or much less likely by trans-Polynesian diffusion. Concepts such as the use of fertilizer were probably independent inventions. The bearded statues from Central and South America were mostly (but not all?) accurate representations of bearded Caucasoid Amerindians. The majority of American pre-Columbian art is stylized and the faces that are depicted are not bearded. Seeming similarities, such as pyramids, probably were not the result of cultural transfer, but were parallel developments as the Egyptian pyramids were smooth-sided, sharply peaked and mainly mausoleums, whereas the Central American stonework pyramids (Figure 72), and the related North American earth mound pyramids (Figure 71), were chiefly flat-topped, step-sided supports for temples, and interment of bodies within the pyramid was either secondary or absent.

The cultural similarities between Polynesia and South America are quite likely the result of rather frequent human contact, after the year 1,000, by ship and diffusion of ideas. The similarities include a decimal counting system, a mnemonic device called the quipu (Figure 75), stepped digging sticks for planting, polygonal locked-joint stonework, stretched earlobes, and bearded statues, as well as boats built from reeds.

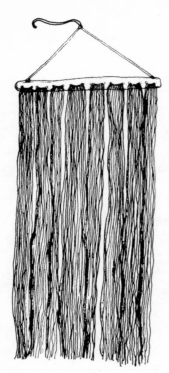

Figure 75. Quipu, a mnemonic
device used by the
Incas.

Summary

Human contacts across the Pacific Ocean
consisted of early (30,000 B.P. through 2,000 B.P.)
migrations across the Bering Straits from Siberia,
with sporadic but important trans-Pacific sailing
contacts that resulted in some colonizations beginning
in 4,500 B.P. There was a lack of culturally or genetically influential European contacts with America
until after 1,000 A.D., therefore the greatest Old
World cultural influences upon pre-Columbian human
history in the Americas were of Asiatic origin.

Polynesia was culturally influenced and populated by men (very likely from western South America, and possibly also the Pacific northwest region of
North America) so that people and ideas tended to
flow westward across the Pacific from America after
the year 1000. The American cultural factors become fewer toward the west and largely disappear
before reaching Melanesia and Micronesia, so that
there was little interchange or contact, if any, with
southeastern Asia.

Chapter XVI

HUMAN BEHAVIOR

The Balance Tipped

The Mongoloid territorial expansion from Asia toward Europe and within the Americas was stopped when Caucasoids became technologically dominant and began to conquer and occupy areas formerly inhabited by Orientals. This reversal of the subspecific distribution pattern trend seems to have been made possible by several developments. First, in Europe, the study of of science and philosophy became separate; this enabled the empirical methods of modern science science to develop and to replace most of the mythically based facts and somewhat doubtful logic of many medieval scholars. Second, a tendency toward the separation of religion and the state freed scientists from oppressive legal confinement and persecution and permitted the expansion of scientific theories into areas that had been considered heretical, even though the theories had no immediate economic application. Third, the discovery of the New World added to the development of science as people from overpopulated areas, where their consumption of food and living space exceeded their material production, emigrated from Europe to the Americas where they began to produce an excess of mineral and agricultural wealth that was made available to them and to Europe, so that a larger leisure class with time to expend in pursuit of knowledge and further technologic development came into being. This led to the creation of more wealth, id est, greater exploitation of mineral deposits and an accompanying increase in the level of technologic development.

The first firearms were invented by Europeans about 1,300 A.D., and were small, inaccurate, pole-mounted "hand-cannon" that were no more effective than other weapons already in existence. However, fear created by the noise, smoke, and mystery associated with the devilish aspects of projectiles speeding out of sulfurous clouds of gas undoubtedly helped compensate for lack of accuracy. Later, larger, more accurate, and faster-to-load firearms were made and integrated with concordant military and naval tactics. This enabled Europeans gradually to relieve the largely Mongoloid Amerindians of the burden of ownership of the New World and to colonize much of Asia. But even as late as 1776, the issue smoothbore military muskets were inaccurate and slow to load, the most accurate weapons were those with rifled bores and they were mostly even slower to load and were not generally used as military weapons. Benjamin Franklin recognized the shortcomings of standard military firearms and pointed out that infantry armed with long bows would have an increased rate of fire with greater range and accuracy than was possible with the standard smoothbore military muskets. Franklin's suggestion was ignored because a musket-using infantryman could be trained in a few weeks, whereas development of a skilled archer requires years of practice.

In view of this, it seems remarkable that the European colonists were not driven off the North American continent by bow-using Amerindians. Several factors may account for the Amerindians failure to accomplish this, for the Amerindians largely benefitted by trading with the first colonists, the Amerindians disliked to attack palisaded forts protected by cannon, and the Amerindians lacked a large, unified, social or governmental body capable of getting large numbers of people to put forth the effort necessary.

The governmental groups that did exist, such as the Iroquois Nation (a confederation of six powerful tribes), were kept at bay by being suspended between conflicting British and French interests and promises, until smallpox, internal political problems, and participation in minor wars destroyed their unity. They delayed, then parleyed and appeased too long, and were overrun.

Orientals failed to separate the disciplines of science, philosophy, and religion; and consequently they did not develop an advanced technology. Only since the 1850's, have Orientals, Japan being first, begun avidly to adopt western scientific ideas and engineering methods. Japan rapidly developed an efficient modern technology, and at first modern weapons, such as Colt's revolvers constituted a larger part of the absorption than did European customs or nonmilitary consumer goods. By 1904 Japan had developed into an efficient military power and defeated Tsarist Russia in a war. Orientals are undoubtedly capable of developing and advancing a modern technology without "borrowing" from another culture.

The pans of the balance may now be beginning to become level. The development of a well-organized, industrialized Asiatic coalition with effective leadership would be a serious threat to Caucasoid dominance and existence, even though such international Asiatic cooperation is unlikely. In the past the Caucasoids' main advantage has been the possession and use of superior weaponry developed by a more advanced technology. If use of this advantage is neglected, it could result in a series of military withdrawals and defeats that may largely destroy the armies of the western world.

The Present Status of Human Relationships

Man is grouped into a number of nationalistic population groups in economic competition with each other. Many of these groups consist of a single subspecies (or a subdivision of one), on this basis the competition can be "racist". The most violent phase of this economic competition is war. As Dr. George F. Carter has remarked, great contrasts in cultural development become the reason, or excuse, for destruction when differing subspecies come into contact. Compounding the factor of economic competition is the tendency of each group of mankind to increase in numbers without limit, as there is little voluntary control of human population size growth. An excessively large population causes further economic problems if the rate of economic growth is slower than the population growth rate and if the available land area is insufficient to supply mineral wealth and agricultural products needed to support the increased population. People with little or nothing to lose may gain by war, and by following a despotic leader.

Stated simply, the main intent of war seems to be extermination of an enemy population. Is war really more moral, if only a uniform-wearing military force is annihilated? Or if only 10,000 or 100,000 deaths result, instead of several million? Is it more immoral to destroy the food producers and the weapons producers that support an enemy army instead only the individuals in the army?

Total war or the complete destruction of an enemy population has a long history. A few well-known examples of the practice of genocide include that mentioned in the Old Testament, in which the Hebrews were allegedly instructed to enter the land of Canaan, kill every man, woman and child, and to populate the area with their own kind. The Mongols exterminated the entire population of some cities if they deemed them to be cowards, or brave enough to constitute a future threat. The English killed nearly the entire aboriginal population of Tasmania in order to make farming feasible. The Dutch in South Africa killed or extirpated the Bushmen because they interfered with cattle raising. Was American use of atomic weapons on Japanese cities worse than the intensive fire bombing of Tokyo? or London? or Berlin? In all the cited examples of bombing of cities the death and destruction totals are approximately of the same order of magnitude. The only major variables are the numbers of aircraft constituting the destructive force, and the period of time involved in the actual destruction. But do these factors really make death and destruction less moral or more fearful? There is no doubt in my mind that man will eventually use atomic weapons again in aggression or defense of territory. It is only a matter of time, circumstances, and the availability of atomic weapons to nations with irresponsible leaders whose primordial instincts may be dominant.

This then is the normal relationship of one group of men to another group of men. Our past has been summed up briefly, and in so doing we have integrated portions of paleontology, animal distribution, and human history. The result is a summation that may, unfortunately, be all too accurate. Our future as predicted from an examination of our past behavior indicates that we shall continue to follow behavior patterns that are already established.

Does Man Change Mentally?

Are human relationships dependent upon eons-old instincts and in an unchanging state, such as that we have just discussed? Or is man evolving with respect to an improvement in group behavior patterns?

Fossil men, such as the Neanderthalers and Cro-Magnons had cranial capacities equal to or larger than the average of those for modern men. But brain size is not necessarily linked to intelligence, nor is intelligence linked with humanitarianism. Therefore we can apparently make no valid deductions here.

Modern liberal philosophy does not differ markedly from that of Plato and other Greek or Near Eastern liberal philosophers. Have we made any significant advances in mental ability or social morality during the last 3,000 years?

Roger J. Williams in discussing human understanding and the development of an individual's behavior pattern, has aptly pointed out that the prevailing point of view, that an individual's behavior pattern is determined by environment is only a partial truth. Although Williams concedes that this "environmental determinism", as Aldous Huxley has termed it, has some effect, he considers genetic effects and unknown factors that cause differential organ and brain tissue growth even in genetically identical (twins) individuals to have a greater effect.

Furthermore Williams relates "the more deep-seated characters--form, yield, intelligence, speed, fertility, strength, development of parts, etc., to quote well-known geneticists --is obscure and cannot be tied in with single genes or with any number of specified genes."

Apparently human behavior patterns are neither entirely genetic nor entirely environmental. So perhaps neither education nor natural selection are the only important factors in human mental development, but rather some unknown cause that exercises control over organ formation and cellular growth during the gestation period of an individual must be included. Human mental ability and mental evolution may well be the result of evolutionary trends begun in prehuman and possibly preprimate ancestors, with limiting (and directive) factors that are unknown, but modified by genetic and educative processes. Therefore man's behavior patterns can best be explained and understood through study and understanding of prehuman mental processes, behavior, and distribution patterns.

It seems likely that man's family-life pattern was derived from the basic primate features of availability of year around sexual relations, lack of arena-species type of competition for sex, and development of slow-growing young that require a considerable amount of education. Although man, as do gorillas, chimps, and most monkeys, leads a family-type life, the family members of those groups tend to be somewhat less than monogamous. Human males are usually considered to be more overtly aggressive sexually (although this may be questioned by observers of female dress and prostitution), in the other primate groups females are more aggressive in sexual matters, and issue invitations to males.

The dominant role of the male human probably arose as females were relegated to the care and feeding of slow-growing (and probably numerous) young. Thus only males had time for leadership, territorial defense, and exploration of their territories for food sources. The females tended to be "stay-at-homes", that is they remained clustered near a food source with their young as the males ranged more widely and either searched for new food sources or defended their territory. The family group probably, as is true of most primates, was of a "harem-like" organization. The less than successful tendency toward a monogamous family life in man may be an outgrowth of private property, that is, individual possessions, with personal real estate being a parallel development. Accumulation of personal wealth (tools, clothing) and formation of a material culture would most readily occur on an individual basis, where such possessions would not willingly be shared.

Nationalism (and "racism") are likely the modern-day overt expression of group territorialism as practiced by most living monkey and lemur groups. The inability to defend one's
territory, or even legal prohibition of personal and territorial defense by modern man has
probably contributed a high degree of boredom. Confinement of man to crowded cities, in
which normal territorialism, and personal identity can not be properly expressed may be an
abnormal and mentally deleterious state for man. This confinement and boredom could have
resulted (as in caged, and bored apes and monkeys) to an overly high interest in sex, and to
male aggressiveness in human sexuality, with development of sexually-caused jealousy.

Man still retains some allegedly prehuman behavioral characteristics, such as head-
shaking (for yes or no), fingernail-biting (when anxious), hair-patting, chin-rubbing and head-
scratching while in thought or an indecisive state of mind. Hand-rubbing and body-brushing
(to remove food or other particles) are also in common with men and other primates. Some
primates (macaques) have been observed to wring their hands, after seeing worms or snakes,
much in the fashion of an anxious or worried human.

Dr. William Shockley has recently questioned the validity of the theory that improvement
of environment for the less affluent members of a population will result in an automatic
improvement in poverty-stricken individuals with high failure records. Dr. Shockley stated,
"Many of the large improvident families with social problems simply have deficiencies in those
parts of the brain which enable a person to plan and carry out plans. And I also suggest that
this characteristic, especially if found in both parents, can be passed from one generation to
another." Whether these negative characteristics are passed on by the genetic makeup of the
individuals, the environmental factors, or the unknown factors which cause identical twins to
develop differently is still undetermined. Considering that one cannot separate an individual
from his environment or control the environment to any extent may cause this to remain an
unanswered question. Dr. Shockley discussed a San Francisco youth who had been hired to
throw acid in the face of a storekeeper. The boy was one of seventeen illegitimate children
borne by a woman with an IQ of 55. Dr. Shockley further stated, "I believe that if a study
were made and we found out that the acid-throwing teenager represented a hereditary class
which is now doubling its members in less than half the time of the rest of the population, we
would soon start looking for solutions. Why? Because it would clearly be a matter of life and
death for our nation." Furthermore Dr. Shockley feels that the people of the United States will
fail to face the issue because of "a deep psychological reason, I think, people hate to feel that
they are subject to the same laws of nature as 'things' or 'animals'. It is unnerving to them.
Furthermore, it runs counter to so much of our social doctrine, the belief that the poor are
victims of hard luck and poor environment, and that all that can be changed by giving them a
helping hand."

Charles Galton Darwin in "The Next Million Years" states that man is evolving mentally,
but that man is still a beast and has not completed his mental evolution. Darwin believed that
it would require a million years for man to evolve into a perfect social animal, and develop a
utopian society. Until that time, Darwin concluded, we shall continue to have capitalistic
competition, wars, and an overpopulated earth with some undernourished or starving people.

Can we really wait a million years for man to evolve mentally? Is man capable of
evolving into Darwin's hypothetical "perfect social animal"? Man seems to be the only beast
capable of formulating and carrying out his own destruction, and he has made tremendous
progress in that capability during the last fifty years. Can civilized man survive beyond the
next hundred years?

The Prospects

Today statesmen dream of peaceful coexistence among the existing nations. But is this
possible if one considers the historic trends of human behavior and present international
politics? Within recent years, there have been many liberal changes within national governments. There has been a trend toward socialization with help for the less fortunate members
of society. This program is not really new, as internally communistic and socialistic groups

are abundant, but not universally present or even completely humanitarian, in non-technologic or primitive societies. We are not being innovative or becoming more moralistic, but only returning to old customs and turning away from the violent competition that characterizes individuals acting within the larger (national) social units. This intraspecific, ingroup competition seems to characterize man and probably evolved from the animal pecking order or the rule of primate troops by the dominant males, in which the alpha individuals (most aggressive) rule over a hierarchy that extends down to the omega (most subjugated) individuals. Man has made such competition more extreme as he can hoard goods far in excess of that required for his own personal use, while other men nearby may starve or freeze. But such competition is less vicious today than it was during the 19th century in England, as described by Charles Dickens, although it still exists and may always continue to do so.

Violent outgroup (international) competition still exists with little or no change, and modern national governments have not been able to develop a panacea to end international strife.

Woher Nun Weisser Mann?

The greatest needs of mankind seem to be, first, the eradication of remnant territorialism, nationalism or "racism"; second, population-size control, and control of population quality by selective sterilization as well; third, an end to self-destructive, natural resource-consuming wars; fourth, an end to depersonalization and loss of individuality. As Roger J. Williams said, "It should not be our aim to produce a citizenry who will receive the same training, enjoy the same amusements, read the same books, and go to the same church." Dr. Williams aptly pointed out that individuals, even "identical" twins, are not identical with respect to internal organ development and mental ability. Fifth, we need the establishment of an effective, active, and functioning world government, with the power and ability to reasonably control international politics.

These requirements are not only far beyond the capabilities of any existing government; they are unpopular concepts, and would be rejected at least in part by most people, and may go counter to our most basic primate instincts.

Plato in the "Republic" wrote "I said: Until philosophers are kings, or the kings and princes of this world have the spirit and power of philosophy, and those commoner natures who pursue either to the exclusion of the other are compelled to stand aside, cities will never have rest from their evils, --no, nor the human race, as I believe, --and then only will this our State have a possibility of life and behold the light of day."

The Philosopher King

Could a "philosopher king" institute such reforms as we have discussed? Alexander of Macedon could possibly have been such a ruler, if he had lived longer, and had not been so impressed with his own alleged divinity. Philosophers are usually impotent politically. Human leaders (alpha individuals) are unusually potent in the direction of self-importance, aggrandization, and reelection.

The Ruling Elite

Groups of men are less corruptible than individuals, but can record just as many failures. Some nations have attempted rule by an intellectual elite, and it has not been more successful than other kinds of government. Some forms of government may depend upon an "innate goodness" in man, as in Rousseau's "noble savage," that probably does not exist.

Where Does The Fault Lie?

The potentially great leaders seem to be largely powerless, politically ineffective, philosophers or religious leaders. Perhaps we tend to be attracted to and support the wrong people as political leaders. Is this a conditioned response, the fault of poorly oriented educational processes? An heritage from our lower primate ancestry and acceptance only of violent dominance for leadership of our troop, as in the other most successful ground-living primates, the baboons?

The greatest leaders, in the sense of wielding power and being recorded in history, seemingly are dominant in the sense of personality and may be paranoidal, militarists, or revolutionaries, that do not necessarily advance the good of the species, or subspecies, or even that of their own followers, however such group activity may perform strongly in the process of natural selection.

Perhaps man's ability with self-control is still insufficient and population groups are much too numerous, have spread over too great geographic areas, and men have too many conflicting interests, and can not divorce themselves from the basic pattern of primate behavior.

The final resolution of the problem lies in the hands and minds of others. I have tried to outline what I believe to be the basic causes of human group behavior and one should keep in mind that treatment of symptoms may temporarily relieve the pain, but does not cure the disease. Quite frankly, we seem to know more about the interior of the sun than we do about man's behavior, its origins, and control.

THE FUTURE OF MAN

Neocatastrophism

The probable future of Homo sapiens is bipartite (a) in that man is the only animal social-ly organized enough to exert a measure of control over his fate, and (b) nature may exert cata-strophic controls that man can not cope with, and these natural controls may operate at disas-trously destructive levels in the near future.

The destruction of one human subspecies, or a human culture, or even the entire popu-lation of a continent, is not necessarily the end of Homo sapiens. Complete and instantaneous destruction of the entire species in the near future is unlikely, but it is very possible that one or more, affluent, highly industrialized societies could disappear. In general those populations with a more primitive cultural development could best survive most of the impending natural or man-caused catastrophes.

Population

Among the problems over which man could exercise some control is the excessive and rapid increase of human population during the last 8,000 years.

World Population Growth (Estimated)

8,000 B.P.	$\frac{1}{2}$ million
4,000 B.P.	5 million
1,600 A.D.	450 million
1,900 A.D.	1,600 million
1,970 A.D.	3,500 million
2,000 A.D.	6,500 million

The population growth chart records the rapid increase of the Earth's human population during the last 8,000 years, a rate that seemingly could become asymptotic. This could only be sustained if enough land and other natural resources were available to permit an ever-increasing food production rate. Unfortunately the necessary natural resources, such as fossil fuels, metals, and chemical fertilizers are available only in limited quantities. A continued high population growth rate will lead to severe and ever-increasing shortages of those mineral substances needed to support a modern industrialized civilization. Therefore, it is imperative that man voluntarily control his numbers, or undergo, as Dr. Charles Park, Jr. in "Affluence in Jeopardy" has forewarned, a loss of our affluent industrialized society.

Leadership

Another problem stemming from prehuman behavior patterns that man may be capable of controlling (although this may be impossible!) is the elimination of nationalistic or "racist" attitudes derived from remnant territorialism, economic warfare on an international basis, and actual wars that result from nationalistic attitudes and economic policies. There seems to be little hope of this, as long as man continues to select, or permit the rise of dominant "alpha-group" leaders, or leaders interested only in power, that they will obtain by any means possi-ble.

Technology

If man is incapable of selecting or following humane leadership, and exorcising national-istic attitudes, perhaps technology could be controlled, and the manufacture and use of highly destructive weapons could be effectively banned. Would this be really feasible, especially if all nations did not choose to be signatories, and there are no secrets or difficult processes involved in the manufacture of atomic fission weapons?

Any nation with technicians capable of setting up atomic power plants to produce electricity, can be assumed capable of manufacturing nuclear weapons. The risk involved here is an obvious one, similar to prohibiting possession of weapons by an honest, law abiding population, thus leaving only the unlawfully inclined armed, because any machine shop could produce useable fully automatic weapons. Priming and propellent components for functional ammunition may be manufactured from photographic film and matches.

Pollution

The elimination or control of atmospheric, soil, and water pollution is of vital concern in the industrialized nations. It seems that industrial society has created a series of pollution problems that could cause a slow decline of our civilization.

Air pollution is largely caused by combustion of fossil fuels (oil, coal, and natural gas), and could be partially alleviated by wider use of electricity generated in plants powered by atomic energy. But such plants create their own pollution problems, for they leak radiation, and create radioactive waste materials far in excess of the original input of radioactive substances. Disposal of the waste products, in a pollution-proof manner, has not yet been satisfactorily solved. So we may trade one cause of air pollution for another variety of pollution.

Soil pollution, caused by excessive use of chemicals in farming, and the resultant effects of water runoff carrying the insecticides and chemical fertilizers into nearby surface waters is a well-known matter of national concern. Poisoned water yields poisoned food to man, birds, and other fish-eating predators. The long range effects can only be guessed at, but could result in the physical weakening of the majority of the individuals of a population, or even accumulation of genetic changes within species.

The outlook is, again, less than hopeful, however, geographically isolated primitive societies should be able to survive the pollution crisis relatively unscathed.

Mineral Resources

Nature has some limitations man can not exceed, and catastrophies over which man still has no effective control. If man's activities or consumption rates exceed those natural limitations, a large number of humans may perish.

For example, our industrial society depends upon abundant, cheap energy sources (fossil fuels), inexpensive structural material (steel at $.06 or $.07 per pound), and plentiful supplies of about 100 other mineral substances. These industrial minerals must occur in large, mineable accumulations, so that the energy invested in wresting them from the Earth's crust does not exceed their worth on the human scale of valuation. All these minerals are found in limited amounts distributed over small areas, and only locally do they occur in large enough quantities to be economically obtainable for industrial use.

Our reserves of many of these 100 mineral substances have been declining because of high production rates in recent years. In 1946 the United States' reserves of natural gas were equivalent to 32 times our yearly useage rate, but in 1965 our reserves were equivalent to only 19 times our yearly useage rate. Our proved reserves of liquid petroleum are probably equivalent to a ten year supply. Silver, mercury, tin, manganese, gold, chromium, cobalt, nickel, titanium, and other metals vital to modern industry are in such short supply in natural deposits in the United States that we either import all or most of what we consume. Many of those metals are rising rapidly in price, as a result of limited mine production and high demand on the world market. All the people of the world can not be supported in a highly affluent state.

There are not enough industrial minerals, fossil fuels, and ores to supply the entire population of the Earth.

Of all the mineral resources required by an industrial society, only a few, coal, iron, and aluminum seem to occur worldwide in such abundance that there is no immediately impending shortage.

Exhaustion of a large portion of our mineral wealth, or even a scarcity of a few items, could slow or stop economic expansion and technological advances. Extension of a North American standard of living to an ever-increasing world population would result in a much lower standard of living in the United States, and eventually an even lower standard on a worldwide basis than that existing now in India or central Africa.

Hopefully, this might mean construction of fewer destructive military devices, but that only means it will take longer to exterminate the same number of people. The same old goal, just slower methods.

Carbon Dioxide

Glenn T. Seaborg has cautioned that we are adding six billion tons of carbon dioxide per year to the atmosphere as the result of combustion of fossil fuels. This should cause an increase of the Earth's atmospheric temperature, for the sun's heat is absorbed by the atmosphere directly from sunlight and as reflected from the Earth, only by water vapor, carbon dioxide, dust, and smoke particles in the air. This is known as the "greenhouse effect", and is analogous to a greenhouse because once the heat has entered the atmosphere and been absorbed it is trapped inside and cannot be radiated outward again. If a general increase of the Earth's atmospheric temperature occurs, we may expect a marked rise in sea level of at least 100 and perhaps more than 200 feet, as the remaining glacial ice melts.

However, most of the carbon dioxide released into the atmosphere, about 75%, is extracted by and dissolved into the oceans. As the carbon dioxide content of the oceans increases, it becomes reduced by incorporation of carbon dioxide into calcium carbonate during the manufacture of limey shells by marine animals, or by precipitation of lime muds on the sea floor. Thus the carbon dioxide content of the atmosphere will be kept low, preventing an extreme development of the greenhouse effect. Literally billions of tons of limestone (calcium carbonate) have been precipitated on the sea floor in the geologic past, and this process will continue as long as calcium and carbon dioxide are available in the sea. This could have another far reaching consequence, as tremendous quantities of limestone are being deposited in deep sea areas today, where they may never become reincorporated into land areas, or continental crustal blocks. In effect, this robs the land of lime, and extracts carbon from the land and atmosphere, placing it where it cannot be made readily available again by weathering processes. This constant loss of carbon dioxide could eventually reduce the amount of atmospheric carbon, hence the amount of carbon available for use by plants and other life forms. Abundant life could not exist in a carbon-short world. But this is a slow process, and should take millions of years to have far reaching effects, and will be delayed as long as volcanic activity continues to add more carbon dioxide to the atmosphere.

Rise of Sea Level

During approximately the past three million years the Earth has undergone at least four major glaciations, that cyclically alternated with warmer than present periods. The development of geographically extensive glaciers (approximately 30% of North America covered at the maximum) has probably not yet ended, and we are probably still within a time of cyclic glaciations.

During the glacial maxima, sea level dropped as much as 350 feet below the present-day sea level, because of the large amount of water removed from the oceans and contained in

10,000 foot-thick continental ice sheets. The lowering of sea level created land connections of Alaska with Siberia, and Great Britain with France and the Benelux countries, and exposed portions of the continental shelf sea floor as land in other areas over the world.

The interglacial stages were mostly characterized by a warmer climate than that now extant and disappearance of most or all of the continental ice sheets and glaciers and a rise of sea level far above the present-day sea level. Most authorities agree that if the ice sheets of Greenland and Antarctica, and the smaller glaciers located elsewhere were to melt, sea level would rise at least 100 feet. This is based on the presence of a well-developed, interglacial beach at an altitude of 100 feet, extending along the Atlantic Coastal Plain from Sandy Hook, in New Jersey, to Georgia. A few geologists believe sea level would rise higher, possibly as much as 270 feet.

A rise of sea level of 100 feet or more would inundate the entire Atlantic Coastal Plain, destroy all major port facilities, and at least partially drown the cities of Boston, Providence, New York, Philadelphia, Baltimore, and Washington. The entire state of Florida would be submerged.

In 1956, I read (for then) a highly speculative article in a Russian magazine, discussing how Siberia could be made more pleasantly inhabitable for men by orbiting a large satellite, consisting of a nuclear device with a controlled fusion rate so that it would radiate heat. This device would orbit lowest over the polar regions, and greatly accelerate polar ice melting, creating a more equitable Siberian climate and a disastrous rise of sea level for most of the rest of the world. Apparently only the controlled fusion device, an artificial sun, remains to be invented.

Ice Sheets

Even if polar and glacial ice melting is not accelerated, it may all eventually melt, although this could take hundreds or thousands of years to occur naturally. On the other hand, occurrence of a colder climate would cause further growth of present glaciers, and if the climate were to remain cold long enough, the formation of large continental ice sheets. Most modern valley glaciers (Plate 23, Figure B) advance at a rate of only a few yards during a year, but some valley glaciers have moved as fast as five miles a year, when snow is plentiful and temperatures are cool. If the required lowering of temperature were nearly instantaneous and if the precipitation rate were high enough, a continental glacier could form that might be able to move as fast as five miles per year and could expand 500 miles outward in all directions from its source area during only 100 years. This certainly is fast enough to disrupt the many northern hemisphere centers of civilization, although such a rate of glacial formation and advance is extremely unlikely.

The Magnetic Field

The Earth is surrounded by a magnetic field that extends as an invisible force field out into space from one magnetic pole to the other. This magnetic field attracts cosmic rays and confines them within the Van Allen Belts, and prevents most extra-terrestrial radiation from reaching the Earth's surface. If a large amount of cosmic radiation were to reach the Earth's surface for a long period of time, it might be lethal for many terrestrial and shallow-water life forms. Many species could become extinct, and others might survive with mutated genes.

Studies of the Earth's magnetic field and the remnant magnetism of rocks are conducted by geophysicists. Igneous magmas, and lavas as they issue from volcanoes may contain sus pended crystals of magnetite that respond to the Earth's magnetic field as do compass needles. Geophysicists obtain fragments of solidified lava flows, determine the orientation of the magnetic polarity of the lavas' magnetite grains, and thus the directions of the north and south magnetic poles at the time the lavas hardened and froze the grains permanently in position. Studies of rock magnetism indicate that the north and south magnetic poles have reversed positions in the geologic past, and that reversals of polarity seem to occur on a 700,000 year major cycle, with smaller, shorter cycles interspersed. The sequence is far from being completely worked out, but seemingly before the magnetic poles reverse, the magnetic field weakens, and then disappears before it reappears with a new polarity. This leaves the Earth open to an influx of cosmic radiation of at least twice the present rate of infall. The exact rate of infall and the extent of harmful genetic changes is debated by geophysicists.

Recently, geophysicists have detected that the Earth's magnetic field has gradually weak ed over the past 2,000 years, and presumably may undergo another disappearance and reversal. Man may possibly become extinct if this occurs. Perhaps the extensive extinctions discovered in the paleontologic record were, at least in part, caused by sudden influxes of cosmic radiation. It is significant that some life, and probably most representatives of the majority of life forms then present, have survived each reversal of polarity, and many paleontologists consider the Earth's passage through zero geomagnetism to have little effect on the world's fauna and flora.

Meteorite Impacts

Meteorites are rare in that few people have ever seen one fall, and then recovered the specimen. So far as I know, written history records few human injuries or deaths (the deaths were those of Siberian reindeer herdsmen during the Tunguska impact of 1908) caused by collision of man with meteorites or other extra-terrestrial bodies. Most meteors enter the Earth's atmosphere as small particles, and ablate before reaching the Earth's surface. The few larger specimens that reach the surface have plenty of unpopulated areas in which to land, as 71% of the Earth's surface is covered by ocean, and much of the Earth's land surface is largely un-inhabited.

Within the past 70 years, two large meteoritic impacts or explosions have occurred on the Earth's land surface. In 1947 near Sikhote Alin in Siberia, a large meteorite disintegrated in the air and its fragments made more than 100 craters in the earth, and in 1908 near the Tunguska River in Siberia, impact of what may have been a comet caused a tremendous explosion that killed all life out to 18 miles and felled trees to a radius of 30 miles.

Many large (from 5,000 B.P. to several hundred million years old) meteorite craters have been identified in recent years by the presence of coesite and tektites. The latter are apparently splashed out and fused particles of sedimentary rocks formed by explosions of large meteorites. North America has at last 27 large meteorite explosion craters ranging from 4,000 feet to more than 2 miles in diameter. Other large craters are recognized in Europe and Africa range from one to as many as 26 miles in diameter. Recently Soviet geologists have identified the Popigai Basin as a meteorite explosion crater nearly 50 miles in diameter and with a present day depth of 1,500 feet. The crater is located along the Popigai River in the Krasnoyarsk region of Siberia. Apparently the collision of large meteorites with the Earth's surface is a never ending, although sporadic occurrence. The Moon's surface is covered by similar craters.

Figure 76. Composite photograph of Meteor (Barringer) Crater in Northern Arizona.

Figure 77. A mushroom-shaped cloud rising over a city could result from either the explosion of a large meteorite or use of atomic weapons.

Dr. Robert S. Dietz discussed the formation of the 26 mile-wide presumed meteorite crater that is known as the Vredefort Ring in the Transvaal region of South Africa. Dr. Dietz estimated that the blast effect of the one mile in diameter meteorite that allegedly formed the crater was equivalent to a 1.5 million megaton explosion. Compared with this, the slightly more than 4,000 foot in diameter Barringer Crater (Figure 76) in northern Arizona only required the equivalent of a five megaton explosion.

Although the explosion of a meteorite large enough to create a Vredefort ring-sized crater would probably annihilate most life within a more than 100 mile radius, it would not have a permanently adverse effect on the human species.

But consider the possible result of the fortuitous explosion of a large meteorite on a major northern hemisphere city, with the accompanying tremendous blast, widespread destruction, and formation of a mushroom-shaped dust cloud. Would deliberation and reason prevail, or would panic-inspired button pushing result? If the latter occurred, one large meteorite could result in eradication of much of our civilization (Figure 77).

Minor Problems

There are some scientific "scare-stories" that are too remote with respect to time to worry about. Such things as the sun running low on hydrogen and becoming a nova; or the Earth slowing down from tidal friction and always having the same side facing the sun; or the crust of the Earth thickening, so that volcanic activity would give off large quantities of water, cause an increase in the volume of the sea and flood the continents.

Other problems include the replacement of mammals and man by arthropods, especially insects, in selective competition for a limited food supply, or the extinction of man because of what has been called "racial senesence", the supposedly unexplainable dying out of a genetic line after a few million years of existence.

Summary

The future of man is in jeopardy, largely because of his own shortsighted policies that lead to nationalism, overpopulation, exhaustion of mineral resources, and the problems resulting from his highly technologic industry, environmental pollution and highly destructive weapons. Man's future is largely in his own somewhat less than competent hands.